Chemistry for GCSE

E. N. RAMSDEN

BSc, PhD, DPhil

Third Edition

SIMON & SCHUSTER
EDUCATION

© 1986 E.N. Ramsden

First published 1986
Reprinted with corrections 1987
Reprinted 1987 (twice)
Second edition 1989
Reprinted in 1990, 1992, 1993 (twice)
Third edition 1994

Published by Simon & Schuster Education
Campus 400
Maylands Avenue
Hemel Hempstead
Herts HP2 7EZ

A catalogue record of this book is available
from the British Library.

  ISBN 0 7501 0680 8 (school)
  ISBN 0 7501 0681 6 (trade)

Illustrated by Angela Lumley, Anne Langford,
Lorraine White, Jane Bottomley and
Trevor Mason

Typeset in 11 on 13 pt Melior

Printed in Great Britain by
T.J. Press (Padstow) Ltd, Padstow, Cornwall.

Contents

More advanced material required for higher grades.

More advanced material required for higher grades.

More advanced material required for higher grades.

More advanced material required for higher grades.

Preface

The first edition of this text was published in 1986 to cover the GCSE Chemistry syllabuses which were first examined in 1988. The second edition included additional sketches of careers in chemistry and also questions from the 1988 examinations. The third edition has been extended to cover the new National Curriculum syllabuses in Chemistry.

The book covers the *GCSE Science: Chemistry* syllabuses that were published in 1993 in conformity with the National Curriculum Key Stage 4 requirements. These syllabuses, which will be examined from 1995 onwards, have been published by the following examining groups:

Midland Examining Group, MEG
Northern Examinations and Assessment Board, NEAB, jointly with
Welsh Joint Education Committee, WJEC
Northern Ireland Schools Examinations and Assessment Council, NISEAC
Southern Examining Group, SEG
University of London Examinations and Assessment Council, ULEAC

The syllabuses in *Science: Chemistry* provide a GCSE level in Chemistry as a separate subject and also provide the Chemistry component of National Curriculum Science: Double Award and Science: Single Award. The different syllabuses have the same core of material that is required for the Chemistry component of Double-Award Science. The following table indicates where the programmes of study for Science Attainment Target 3 can be found.

Where to find Science Attainment Target 3 programmes of study

The elements of the programmes of study in Attainment Target 3 of the National Curriculum in Science at Key Stage 4 are listed with the chapter and section under which they can be found in *Chemistry for GCSE*, for example, a reference to 14.5 means Chapter 14, Section 5.

Elements of programmes of study	Location in *Chemistry for GCSE*
(i) The properties, classification and structure of materials	
Selected elements and their compounds	3, 7, 8, 9, 11, 13, 14, 15, 16, 18, 19, 22
Metals and non-metals	3.1–3.7
The Periodic Table: groups, periods, electronic structure	4.5–4.6
Reactivity series of metals	11.5
Neutralisation	7.1–7.4
Materials – properties, structure, uses of:	
metals	11, 19.5
ceramics	13.13, 19.5
glasses	13.10, 19.5
plastics, fibres	19.4, 19.5
concrete	13.1, 19.5
cellular materials and composites	19.5
Separating the components of mixtures	2.1–2.8
Emulsions, foams, gels, solutions	1.5, 9.19

Where to find Science: Chemistry extension topics

The different examining groups have to some extent chosen different extension topics. These topics are required for GCSE Science: Chemistry but not for GCSE Science: Double Award or Single Award. In the following table, the topics are identified by a phrase taken from the syllabus of an examining group. The location in *Chemistry for GCSE* is given by the chapter number and section number under which the topic can be found. The examining group reference gives the initial of the Group (see the key) and the number of the unit or topic or strand in the examining group's syllabus.

Key

I(3.9n) = NISEAC (new Statement of Attainment)
L(v) = ULEAC (extension strand number)
M(C6) = MEG (unit number)
MS(Cv) = MEG, Salters (new strand)
N(vi) = Nuffield (extension strand)
N/W (3.7.1) = NEAB/WJEC (topic number)
S(21) = SEG (unit number)

Extension topic	Examining group references	Location in *Chemistry for GCSE*
Alcohols: oxidation, dehydration, esterification	M(C6), N(vi), S(22)	19.6
Alloy steels	L(v), N/W (3.7.1), S(19)	11.10
Ammonia, manufacture	L(v)	15.3
Analytical chemistry	I(3.8, 3.9), L(v, vi), M(C7), N(v), S(19,20)	17
Biodegradable plastics; recycling of plastics	L(vi), M(C6), S(17)	19.4, 19.5
Bond energy values	M(C7)	20.8
Carbohydrates	MS(Cvi), N(vi), S(22)	22.2
Carboxylic acids	N(vi)	19.7
Chemical calculations extended	M(C7)	12
Chemical equilibrium	L(v), M(C7)	13.2
Chlorine as a bleach	N/W (3.6.1)	16.8
Chlorine as an oxidising agent	L(v), N(v), N/W (3.6.1)	16.6–16.8
Cigarette smoke	L(vi)	19.10
Collecting gases, methods	L(vi)	13.9
Colloids	MS(Cvi), N(vi, vii)	9.19
Concentrated nitric acid	S(16)	15.5
Concentrated sulphuric acid	L(v), N(v), N/W (3.7.1), S(20)	14.7
Concentration of solution	I(3.10j), L(vi), M(C7), N/W (3.6.1)	12.11
Drinking alcohol	L(v)	19.6
Dry cells: comparison	M(C7)	5.11
Drying gases, methods	L(vi)	13.9
Enzymes	MS(Cvi), N(vi)	22.4
Equilibrium	L(v), M(C7)	1.6, 13.2
Equilibrium and acids and bases	N/W (3.6.1)	7.6
Equilibrium and the Contact process	I(3.8m), L(v), N/W (3.7.1)	14.6
Equilibrium and the Haber process	I(3.9m), L(v), N/W (3.7.1), S(16)	15.3
Equilibrium and thermal dissociation	S(18)	13.2
Esters: solvents, fats and oils, saponification	N(vi)	19.8
Ethanol manufacture from ethene	L(v), M(C6), N/W (3.5.1), S(22)	19.6
Extraction of lead from galena	M(C6)	11.9
Extraction of magnesium from sea water	M(C6), N(v)	11.9

Extraction of metal related to position in reactivity series	I(3.9n)	11.9
Extraction of tin from cassiterite or tinstone	M(C6)	11.9
Extraction of zinc from zinc blende	M(C6), N(vii)	11.9
Fats and oils, saturated, unsaturated	L(v), MS(Cvi), N(vi)	22.3
Fats: saponification, hydrogenation	L(v), MS(Cvi), N(vi), S(22)	22.3
Fermentation in baking	L(v), N(vi), N/W (3.5.1), S(22)	19.6
Fermentation in ethanol manufacture	L(v), N(vi), N/W (3.5.1), S(22)	19.6
Flame colour	I(3.8p), L(vi), M(C7), N(v)	17.1
Food additives	N(vi)	22.5
Heat of reaction	L(vi), M(C7), MS(Cv)	20.7
Mendeleev's work on the Periodic Table	I(1.8c)	11.6
Molecular formula from empirical formula	I(3.9l), M(C7), N(vi)	12.9
Nitric acid, manufacture	I(3.9m), N(v), S(16)	15.5
NPK fertilisers	L(vi), N/W (3.6.1, 3.7.1), N(v)	15.3, 15.4
Organic chemistry extended	I(3.8t, 3.9q)	19, 22
Oxidation and reduction	N(v), N/W (3.7.1)	9.18
Oxidation–reduction and gain or loss of electrons	L(v), M(C6), N(v, vi), S(19)	16.7
Protein structure	N(vi)	22.4
Proteins: amino acids, peptides	M(C6), N(vi), S(22)	22.4
Recycling metals	S(17)	11.11
Recycling plastics	L(vi), M(C6), S(17)	19.4
Shapes of covalent molecules	M(C7)	6.4
Simple chemical cells	M(C7)	5.11
Soil pH	N(v)	7.1
Solubility curves	I(3.9i)	1.5
Solubility of some oxides, hydroxides and salts	L(v)	7.10
Structure of metals	M(C6)	11.1–11.3, 19.5
Substitution reactions of alkanes	S(21)	18.3
Sulphur dioxide as a bleach	S(20)	14.3
Sulphur dioxide as a reducing agent	S(20), N(vi)	14.3
Sulphuric acid, manufacture	L(v), M(C6), N(v), N/W (3.7.1)	14.6
Test for an alkene	L(vi), N(vi), N/W (3.7.1), S(21)	19.3
Testing for gases	I(3.8q), L(v, vi), S(20)	17.3
Tests for ions in solution	I(3.8 o,r,s; 3.9p), L(vi), M(C7), N(v), S(19)	17.2
Tests for oxidising and reducing agents	L(vi), N/W (3.6.1), S(20)	16.9
Tests for sulphur dioxide	L(vi), S(20)	14.3
Transition metals	M(C6), S(19)	11.6
Volumes of gases reacting	L(vi)	12.10
Volumetric analysis	I(3. 10k), L(vi), M(C7), N(vi), N/W (3.6.1)	12.11

Students need to familiarise themselves with the content of the syllabus they are following. To give some guidance, the text uses asterisks to denote extension material required for Chemistry as a separate subject by some (but not all) examining groups, and topics designated by the examining groups as level 9–10.

The approach of Chemistry for GCSE

This text emphasises the social, economic, technological and environmental aspects of chemistry. Each topic is introduced in a social context. Throughout, the practical applications and social implications of the subject are interwoven with the theory.

Some of the topics of economic importance which are included are the contribution of fertilisers to the world's food supply, the energy crisis and the need for careful use of the Earth's resources. The importance of chemical technology is apparent in the coverage of metals, crystals, liquid crystals, plastics and other topics. The text spotlights some of the medical benefits of chemistry, such as anaesthetics, antiseptics and painkillers. Some instances of the impact of the chemical industry on society are described in the accounts of the pollution and purification of water, the pollution and purification of air and the effects on the landscape of mining and quarrying. The idea that science is a rewarding human activity is fostered by giving credit for their discoveries to people like Alfred Nobel, Marie Curie, Roy Plunkett and other present-day scientists. Scientific method is illustrated in the accounts of the development of the fertiliser industry, the analysis of the effect of fluoride ion on tooth decay and the discovery of radioactivity. Some case histories of the solving of scientific and technical problems, such as the manufacture of plate glass and 'gasohol', are included.

Where possible, information is presented in the form of charts and diagrams. At intervals in the text, margin summaries focus the reader's attention on salient points. At the end of each short topic, there is a brief 'Just Testing' section to allow readers to reinforce their grasp of that topic before they proceed to the next. The exercises at the ends of the chapters give readers a chance to apply the knowledge they have gained to different situations and to problem solving.

The author assumes that readers will be following a course of practical work. The experiments to which the text refers can be found in the companion book, *Practical Chemistry for GCSE*, which contains pages for photocopying and is supported by an *Assessment Guide to Practical Chemistry for GCSE*. Further questions can be found in *Questions on Chemistry for GCSE*.

E. N. Ramsden, 1994

Acknowledgements

I am grateful to Mr G. H. Davies, Mr D. Haslam and Mr M. Vokins for their helpful comments and suggestions. I thank Ms Laura Hale for the original drawings on which the cartoons are based and Mr Keith Waters for taking many of the photographs. Organisations which have kindly supplied photographs and given permission for their use are:

1.1 Peter Gould; 1.2 James Bell/Science Photo Library; 1.9 British Museum of Natural History; 1.11 Dr H. H. Sutherland; 1.12a–d K. Waters; 2.1 Hulton Deutsch Collection; 2.5 ICI plc; 2.7 Robert Harding Picture Library; 2.11a Peter Gould; 2.11b The British Petroleum Company Ltd; 3.2 The British Petroleum Company Ltd; 3.3 The British Petroleum Company Ltd; 3.7 Ferranti; 3.8a The Gold Information Office; 3.8b The Gold Information Office; 3.9 NASA; 4.3 John Mills Photography Ltd; 4.10 Cookson Industrial Materials Ltd; 4.11 Geoscience Features Picture Library; 4.14a&b AEA Technology; 4.14c Alyeska Pipeline Service Company; 4.15a AEA Technology; 4.15b Cookson Industrial Materials Ltd; 4.15c AEA Technology; 4.17 Imperial War Museum; 5.1 W. Canning Materials Ltd; 5.2 W. Canning Materials Ltd; 5.8 PMC (Sheffield) Ltd; 5.11 ICI plc; 5.13 Philip Parkhouse; 5.14, 5.16, 5.18 Peter Gould; 6.21b, 6.22b, 6.23b, 6.24a&b E. N. Ramsden; 7.1 Peter Gould; 7.3 K. Waters; 7.4 Philip Parkhouse; 7.6 Hulton Deutsch Collection; 8.1 Popperfoto; 8.4 James Holmes/Science Photo Library; 8.5 Barnaby's Picture Library; 8.6 J. Hazzard; 8.7 NASA; 8.8 Thames Water; 8.9 K. Waters; 8.11 New Scientist; 8.12 Peter Crawshaw; 8.22 Greenpeace; 8.23 HMSO; 8.24 Hulton Deutsch Collection; 8.26 V. Miles/The Environmental Picture Library; 8.34a R. Thompson/FLPA Ltd; 8.34b M. Nimmo/FLPA Ltd; 8.34c Pekka Parvia/Science Photo Library; 9.1, 9.2 Oxfam; 9.3 J. Allan Cash Photo Library; 9.4 Associated Press; 9.7 Cambridge University Collection of Air Photographs; 9.10 Institute of Geological Sciences; 9.11 K. Waters; 9.14 Permutit Co; 9.17 Oxford Scientific Films; 9.18 Simon Fraser/Science Photo Library; 9.19 Shell Photographs; 9.20 Van den Burghs & Jurgens Ltd; 10.3 Marc Deville/Science Photo Library; 10.15 John Meehan/Science Photo Library; 10.16 Robert Harding Picture Library; 10.19 Martin Bond/Science Photo Library; 10.22 Geoscience Features Picture Library; 10.24 David Parker/Science Photo Library; 10.26 Sinclair Stammers/Science Photo Library; 10.30 Simon Fraser/Science Photo Library; 10.32 Sinclair Stammers/Science Photo Library; 11.2 Philip Parkhouse; 11.3 British Airports Authority; 11.21 K. Waters; 11.22 Australian Information Service; 11.25 British Steel Corporation; 11.27 Capper Pass; 11.28 Pacemaker Press International Ltd; 11.30 The Mary Rose Trust Ltd; 11.34 Robert Harding Picture Library; 11.35 Audi Press Office; 11.36 DJB Engineering Ltd; 11.37 Nigel Dickinson/The Environmental Picture Library; 13.1 Humber Bridge Board; 13.7 Farmers Weekly; 13.11 Pepsi-Cola; 13.17 J. Allan Cash Photo Library; 13.20 Chubb Fire Security Ltd; 13.25 Pilkington Group; 13.26 Barnaby's Picture Library; 13.28 NASA/Science Photo Library; 14.2 The Goodyear Tyre & Rubber Company (Great Britain) Ltd; 14.3 DJB Engineering Ltd; 14.8 K. Waters; 14.9 Hulton Deutsch Collection; 14.10 New Zealand Forest Products Ltd; 14.13 Fisons plc; 15.1 Professor D. A. Jones, University of Hull; 15.4 Nigel Cattlin/Holt Studios International; 15.5, 15.7 ICI plc; 15.9 Peter Gould; 15.10 Jeyes Ltd; 15.14 Central Electricity Generating Board; 15.18 K. Waters; 16.1 K. Waters; 16.2 Barnaby's Picture Library; 16.4 ICI plc; 16.11 E. N. Ramsden; 16.15 K. Waters; 18.1 Prof. David Hall/Science Photo Library; 18.2 Martin Bond/Science Photo Library; 18.3 Tommaso Guicciardini/Science Photo Library; 18.5a,b&c K. Waters; 18.7 Shell Photographs; 18.8 The British Petroleum Company Ltd; 18.9 Esso Petroleum Company Ltd; 19.2, 19.4, 19.5 K. Waters; 19.7 Yachting Monthly; 19.10 Allsport; 19.12 Imogen Young/Format Partners; 19.13 K. Waters; 19.15 Lion Laboratories plc; 19.17 Brazilian Institute of Sugar and Alcohols; 19.18 K. Waters; 20.3 Miller Homes; 20.4 The Wind Energy Group; 20.5, 20.6 Allsport; 22.1a, 22.4a&b, 22.5, 22.6, 22.9, 22.10, 22.11, 22.12, 22.13 E. N. Ramsden.

In addition, the following illustrations have been redrawn with permission:
Figure 11.1 is taken from *AA Book of the Car*, The Reader's Digest Association Limited, London/The Automobile Association.
Figure 13.5 is redrawn by permission of Blue Circle Industries plc – taken from *New Scientist*, 15 March 1984.
Figure 18.13 is adapted from *Energy* by J. Ramage, published by Oxford University Press 1983.
The graphs on p. 392 are adapted from B. Selinger, *Chemistry in the Marketplace*, by permission of Brace, Harcourt, Jovanovich.

Every effort has been made to contact copyright holders of material reproduced in this book. Any omission will be rectified in subsequent reprints if notice is given to the publishers.

I thank the staff of Simon & Schuster Education for the care which has gone into the editing, illustration and production of the book, and my family for their encouragement.

E. N. Ramsden, 1994

CHAPTER 1 _Solids, liquids and gases_

1.1 Liquid crystals

Liquid crystals are an unusual kind of matter. These substances look like liquids, but seen through a microscope they show strange patterns (Fig. 1.2). They flow like liquids, but in other ways they behave like crystals.

You will have seen how widely liquid crystals are used in digital watches and calculators. The letters 'LCD' stand for 'liquid crystal display'. You have probably seen them in use as room thermometers. This is because liquid crystals change colour as their temperature changes. Doctors use them as thermometers to help in cancer diagnosis. The temperature of a cancer is higher than that of the surrounding tissue because more blood circulates in the tumour area. Liquid crystals can show up the cancer as a 'hot spot'. The doctor paints the patient with a film of liquid crystal. Different liquid crystals have different colour ranges. For this use, the doctor might choose one that is red at normal body temperature and blue at a higher temperature. Then a cancer would show up as a blue 'hot spot' on a red background. This technique is used to detect cancer of the face, throat or breast, where the suspect area is easy to paint.

Liquid crystals are an unusual **state of matter**. You can read about the chief states of matter in Section 1.2.

SUMMARY NOTE

Liquid crystals are an unusual state of matter. They change colour with temperature. They are used in thermometers and in LCDs.

Fig. 1.1 An LCD display on a thermometer

Fig. 1.2 Liquid crystals seen through a microscope

1.2 The states of matter

Water, air, minerals, trees and animals are all **matter**. Anything that occupies space and has mass is matter. There are different kinds of matter: **solid**, **liquid** and **gas**. These are referred to as the **states of matter**. You are familiar with water in all three states: solid **ice**, liquid **water** and gaseous **water vapour**. Table 1.1 summarises the differences between the three states of matter. They are given **state symbols**: solid (s), liquid (l) and gas (g).

Table 1.1 States of matter

State	Description	
Solid (s)	Has a definite mass. Has a definite volume. The shape is usually difficult to change.	
Liquid (l)	Has a definite mass. Has a definite volume. Changes its shape to fit the container.	
Gas (g)	Has a definite mass. Changes its size and shape to fit the size and shape of its container.	

P57

1.3 Change of state

Matter can change state (see Experiment 1.1). Some changes of state are summarised below.

Sometimes, the word **vapour** is used to describe a gas. A liquid evaporates to form a vapour. All vapours are gases. A gas is called a vapour when it is cool enough to be liquefied by compression.

Vapour $\xrightarrow{\text{Either cool or compress without cooling}}$ Liquid

2

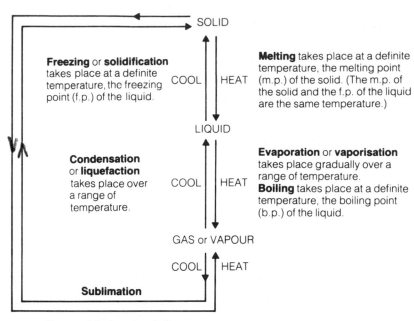

Some solids do not melt: they change directly into a vapour when heated. The vapour solidifies on cooling. This behaviour is **sublimation**.

Solid carbon dioxide and iodine sublime.

The hotter a liquid is, the more quickly it evaporates. Eventually, it becomes hot enough for bubbles of vapour to appear inside the liquid. When this happens, the liquid is boiling. The temperature at which this happens is the **boiling point** of the liquid (see Chapter 2).

Physical and chemical changes

All the changes discussed so far are **physical changes**. The substance heated or cooled changes its state only. It does not change into a different substance. Physical changes are easily reversed. Many of the changes we shall be studying are **chemical changes**. When a substance changes into a new substance, a chemical change or **chemical reaction** has happened (see Experiments 3.1–3.4). Chemical changes are difficult to reverse.

JUST TESTING 1

1 Copy this scheme. Fill in the names of the processes represented by arrows. Some of the processes have two names.

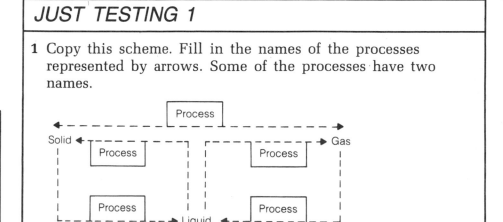

1.4 Particles

Scientists believe that matter is made up of tiny **particles**. The way in which solids, liquids and gases behave can be explained with the help of this theory. It is called the **particle theory of matter**.

Change of state explained by the particle theory

Vaporisation. The vaporisation of liquids can be explained. Figure 1.3 shows what happens when a drop of the brown liquid, bromine, is put into a gas jar. You can explain what happens if you assume that bromine consists of tiny particles. Given all the space in the gas jar to occupy, particles leave the liquid state and move about until they are spread throughout the gas jar.

Solid, liquid and gaseous states. We can explain the relationship between the solid, liquid and gaseous states of matter.

In a solid, the particles are arranged in a regular three-dimensional pattern. They cannot move out of position. The only movement they can make is to vibrate.

If a solid is heated, the particles gain energy. They vibrate more and more until they break away from their regular arrangement. When this happens, the solid has turned into a liquid: it has melted.

A liquid has no fixed shape because the particles are free to move. If a liquid is heated further, the particles gain still more energy. Some of them will break free from the body of the liquid: they will become a gas.

A gas occupies a very much larger volume than the liquid which vaporised to make it. One litre of water forms 1200 litres of water vapour. The particles are very much further apart in a gas than in a liquid, and are free to move.

Particles in motion: the kinetic theory

p52 The **kinetic theory of gases** tells us that gases consist of particles which are always moving. (*Kinetic* comes from the Greek word for *moving*.) Most of a gas is space, and the particles shoot through the space at high speed. Occasionally they collide with other particles or with the walls of the container.

The kinetic theory can explain the connection between the pressure and the volume of a fixed mass of gas:

- Increase the pressure → the volume decreases (Fig. 1.5a)
- Decrease the pressure → the volume increases (Fig. 1.5b)

Gases are much more compressible than other forms of matter. Since a gas consists largely of space, the particles occupying the space can move closer together. Gases exert pressure because their particles are colliding with the walls of the container. If the volume of the gas is decreased, the particles will hit the walls more often, and the pressure will increase.

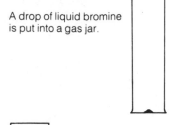

A drop of liquid bromine is put into a gas jar.

Two minutes later, the jar is full of bromine vapour.

Fig. 1.3 Liquid bromine vaporising

solid

solid heated.

Liquid

Gas

Fig. 1.4 The arrangement of particles in a solid, a liquid and a gas

SUMMARY NOTE

The particle theory of matter is the theory that matter is made up of tiny particles. The theory explains the differences between the solid, liquid and gaseous states, and how matter can change state.

4

(a)

One cylinder of a four-stroke car engine

2 The volume of the mixture of petrol vapour and air decreases. The pressure increases.

1 During the compression stroke, the piston moves up the cylinder.

(b)

A cylinder of gas under pressure

When the valve is opened, the pressure decreases.

The gas expands out of the cylinder.

(c)

If you heat the bottle, the air inside cannot expand, and its pressure therefore increases. Eventually, it pushes the cork out.

(d)

The lump of bread dough contains air and carbon dioxide.

When the dough is heated in an oven, the volume of gas increases and the bread 'rises'.

Fig. 1.5   The connection between pressure, volume and temperature

The kinetic theory can also explain how the pressure and the volume of a fixed mass of gas change with temperature:

- Increase the temperature → the pressure increases (Fig. 1.5c) (while keeping the volume constant)
- Increase the temperature → the volume increases: the gas (while keeping the pressure constant) expands (Fig. 1.5d)

If the temperature of a gas increases, the particles will have more energy, move faster and collide more often with the walls of the container. If the gas cannot expand, the pressure will increase. If the pressure is kept constant while the temperature is raised, the gas will expand.

Evidence for the kinetic theory

Diffusion. What evidence have we that the particles of a gas are moving? The **diffusion** of gases can be explained. Diffusion is the way gases spread out to occupy all the space available to them. Figure 1.6 shows what happens when a jar of the dense green gas, chlorine, is put underneath a jar of air. If gases consist of small particles which are always on the move, it is easy to see how diffusion can occur. Moving particles of air and chlorine can spread themselves between the two gas jars.

Dense gases, such as carbon dioxide, diffuse more slowly than

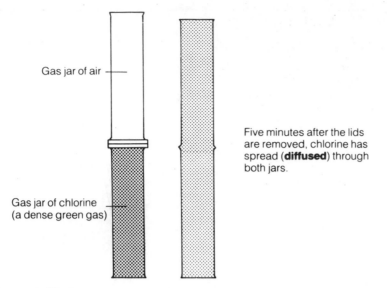

Gas jar of air

Gas jar of chlorine
(a dense green gas)

Five minutes after the lids
are removed, chlorine has
spread (**diffused**) through
both jars.

Fig. 1.6   Gaseous diffusion

SUMMARY NOTE

The kinetic theory of gases
says that the particles in a gas
are always in motion. The
theory explains the
compressibility of gases. It
explains gas pressure and why
gas pressure increases with
temperature. It can also
explain gaseous diffusion.

The particles in a liquid
move too. Brownian motion is
evidence of this.

gases with a low density, such as hydrogen. This is because
dense gases have heavy particles, which move more slowly than
light particles. Figure 1.7 shows an experiment to compare the
speeds of diffusion of the gases ammonia and hydrogen chloride.

Cotton wool and concentrated
ammonia solution. The gas
ammonia escapes.

Cotton wool and concentrated
hydrochloric acid. The gas
hydrogen chloride escapes.

When ammonia and hydrogen chloride
meet, the white solid ammonium chloride
forms. In a 1 metre tube, the solid
deposit begins to form 60 cm from the
ammonia end of the tube. (How many
times faster than hydrogen chloride
does ammonia diffuse?)

Fig. 1.7   An experiment to compare the rates of diffusion of hydrogen chloride and
ammonia

Brownian motion. What evidence have we that the particles of a
liquid are moving? A botanist called Robert Brown saw
something mysterious in 1785. He was looking through a
microscope at grains of pollen floating on water. He saw that
they were constantly moving about (Fig. 1.8a). We now call this
movement **Brownian motion**. We can explain it by the particle
theory (Fig. 1.8b).

(a) A view through a microscope of the path
taken by a grain of pollen floating in water

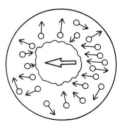

(b) A magnification of (a) (not to scale). Water
particles, which are invisible under a microscope,
strike the pollen grain from every direction. If at
any instant more water particles collide with the
right-hand side than with the left-hand side, as
shown here, the pollen grain will move from right
to left.

Fig. 1.8   Brownian motion

Career sketch: Laboratory assistant 1

Bob works in industry. His job is to make a complete analysis of
the firm's products. He must make sure that the analysis of each
product matches that on the label. His laboratory is well
equipped with instruments to use for titration, chromatography,
radiochemistry and other methods of analysis. Bob left school
after GCSE.

1.5 Pure substances and mixtures

You have seen how matter can be subdivided (**classified**) into different states. Another way of classifying matter is to divide it into pure substances and mixtures.

Pure substances

A **pure** substance is a **single** substance. No other substance is present in a pure substance. Pure X is 100% X. Impure X contains another substance or substances as well as X.

We sometimes use the word *pure* in a different sense. We talk about 'pure' water, 'pure' air or 'pure' food. If a health official describes water as 'pure', he or she means that the water is safe to drink. In this sense, *pure* means *containing no substance which is harmful to health*. 'Pure' drinking water does in fact contain many substances dissolved in it (see Chapter 12). Chemists use the word 'pure' to mean 'consisting of one substance only'. If a chemist describes water as *pure*, he or she means that the water *contains no other substance*.

Crystals. Many pure solids are **crystalline**. A **crystal** is a piece of solid which has a regular shape and smooth faces which reflect the light (Fig. 1.9). Most crystalline material is made up of many small crystals. It may therefore not appear to be crystalline until you look at it under a microscope.

Solids which do not consist of crystals are **amorphous** (without shape).

Speaking of crystals. These beautiful forms of matter are useful too. Quartz crystals vibrate when an electric current is applied.

Fig. 1.9 Crystals of quartz

The rate of vibration is absolutely constant. A quartz crystal (silicon(IV) oxide) is used to keep a radio transmitter on a fixed frequency. This is why you always find your favourite programme at the same spot on the tuner. A quartz crystal controls the timing of the liquid crystal display in your quartz watch.

When light falls on a crystal of a substance called selenium, electricity is generated. In a photographer's light meter, the amount of light falling on a crystal of selenium determines the amount of electric current generated. This shows as a deflection of the needle in the light meter.

In satellites there are solar cells consisting of thousands of silicon crystals. These crystals also convert light energy into

Fig. 1.10 Crystal magic

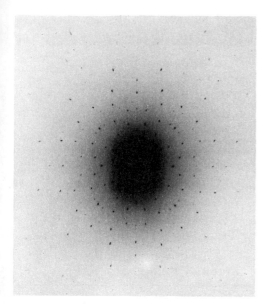

Fig. 1.11 X-ray pattern from crystals of a metallic alloy

electrical energy. They provide the current that powers the satellite.

Sapphires (aluminium oxide with impurities) can be grown as whisker-shaped crystals. They have amazing strength. When they are combined with metals, they give materials which are strong even at high temperatures. They are used in the construction of supersonic aircraft. The wings and fuselage reach high temperatures because of the heat generated by friction at such high speeds.

Lasers are intense beams of light. They can drill holes, cut through metals and destroy cancers. Laser beams shoot from ruby crystals (aluminium oxide with impurities). A flash tube coiled around the crystal gives a sudden powerful burst of light. This interacts with the ruby to give rise to a laser beam.

Silicon crystals are the basis of the computer industry. The crystals are sliced into 'chips'. Miniature electronic circuits are built on to the chips to make **integrated circuits** (ICs). These ICs are the brainpower of the microcomputer. (See Section 3.4.)

Why are substances crystalline? The reason for the regular arrangement of faces is that the particles of which the crystal is made are arranged in a regular manner. Figure 1.11 shows an X-ray pattern produced by passing a beam of X-rays through a crystal on to a photographic plate. The dark area in the centre is produced by X-rays which have passed straight through the crystal. The pattern of dots is produced by X-rays which had to change direction because they met particles. Since the pattern of dots is regular, the arrangement of particles in the crystal must be regular. In this way, X-ray photographs give evidence that matter consists of particles.

Elements and compounds. There are two classes of pure substances: **elements** and **compounds**. **Elements** are substances which cannot be split up into simpler substances. Copper is an element; whatever you do with it, you cannot split copper into simpler substances.

Compounds are pure substances which *can* be split into simpler substances. Often, they can be split into elements. Usually, energy must be supplied in the form of heat or light or electricity to split up a compound. A chemical reaction takes place when a compound splits up. A compound contains two or more elements chemically combined. You will learn more about compounds in Chapter 3.

SUMMARY NOTE

Many pure solids are crystalline. Some crystals have important uses. Radio transmitters, light meters, solar cells, construction materials, lasers and microcomputers all depend on crystals.

X-ray photographs of crystals provide evidence for the particle theory of matter.

'Elementary, my dear Watson!'

'By **elementary**, do you mean **simple**, Holmes?'

'It's the same in chemistry, Watson. An **elementary** substance, an **element**, is a **simple** substance: whatever you do, you can't split it up into simpler substances.'

The atom. Elements are made up of minute particles. The smallest particle of an element is called an **atom**. All the atoms in an element behave in the same way. Atoms are so small that it is difficult to imagine just how small they are. It takes 4 million hydrogen atoms to stretch across 1 millimetre.

In some elements, atoms join together by chemical bonds to form larger particles called **molecules** (Fig. 1.12).

SUMMARY NOTE

Pure substances are either elements or compounds. Compounds are pure substances which are composed of two or more elements. Elements are pure substances which cannot be split up into simpler substances.

The smallest particle of an element is an atom. Molecules are groups of atoms joined by chemical bonds.

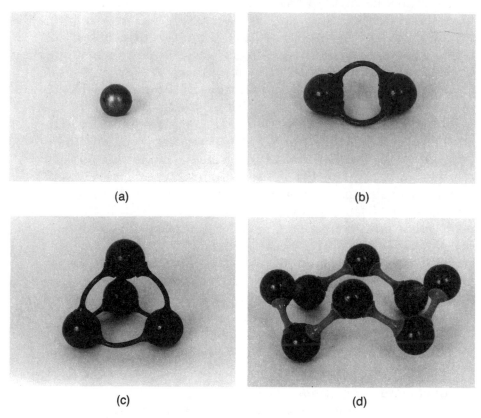

(a)

(b)

(c)

(d)

Fig. 1.12   Molecules of (a) helium, (b) oxygen, (c) phosphorus, (d) sulphur

P 11, 12/50

Mixtures

There are two kinds of mixtures:
- **Solutions**: Every part of a solution has the same composition. A solution is a **homogeneous mixture**; it is the same all through.
- **Heterogeneous mixtures**: When a mixture is not the same all through (that is, when different parts of the mixture have different compositions), the mixture is described as **heterogeneous**.

Solutions. A solution consists of a **solvent** and a **solute**. The solid or liquid or gaseous solute **dissolves** in the solvent, which is usually a liquid. Water is the most common solvent, but there are many others, e.g. alcohols such as ethanol (Chapter 17) and chloro-compounds such as trichloroethane (Chapter 16).

Dissolving is another change that can be explained in terms of particles. Figure 1.13 shows a coloured substance dissolving. Coloured particles split off from the crystal and move through the solution until they are evenly spread out.

A **concentrated** solution is one which contains a high

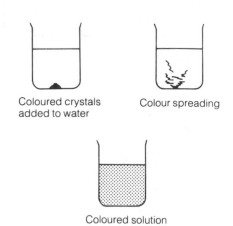

Coloured crystals added to water

Colour spreading

Coloured solution

Fig. 1.13   Crystals dissolving

The solution must be saturated: no more solute will dissolve.

Undissolved crystals

Fig. 1.14 A saturated solution

proportion of solute. A **dilute** solution is one which contains only a small proportion of solute.

A **saturated** solution is a solution which has as much solute dissolved in it as is possible at that temperature. If there is undissolved solute present in the bottom of the container, you know that the solution must be saturated (Fig. 1.14).

The concentration of solute in a saturated solution is the **solubility** of the solute. The solubility of a solute is the mass (in grams) of the solute that will saturate 100 grams of solvent at a certain temperature. You must state the temperature because solubility changes with temperature. A graph of solubility against temperature is called a **solubility curve** (see Fig. 1.15).

For most solutes, the solubility increases with temperature. It follows that when a saturated solution is cooled, the solution can hold less solute at the lower temperature. Some solute comes out of solution: it **crystallises** (see Experiments 1.2, 1.3). In contrast, gases are less soluble at higher temperatures (see Chapter 8).

SUMMARY NOTE

Mixtures can be homogeneous or heterogeneous.

Solutions are homogeneous mixtures. They may be dilute, concentrated or saturated. The concentration of solute in a saturated solution is the **solubility** of the solute. Solubility is the maximum mass of solute that will dissolve in 100 g of solvent at a stated temperature.

Fig. 1.15
Solubility curves for some solutes

Potassium nitrate   Potassium bromide
Potassium chlorate(V)
Potassium chloride
Sodium chloride
Potassium sulphate

Solubility (Mass (in grams) of solute in 100 g solvent)

Temperature in °C

JUST TESTING 3

1 Figure 1.15 shows some solubility curves.
  a 1 kg of a saturated solution of sodium chloride is cooled from 100 °C. What mass of sodium chloride crystallises out?
  b A solution is saturated with both potassium chloride and potassium chlorate(V). If 1 kg of the solution is cooled to 60 °C, what mass of (i) potassium chloride and (ii) potassium chlorate(V) crystallises out?
  c A solution containing enough potassium nitrate and potassium bromide to saturate it at 60 °C is cooled to 20 °C. What masses of the two solutes will separate from 1 kg of the solution?

2 A concentrated solution of copper(II) sulphate is deep blue. When you dilute it with water, it becomes a paler blue. How can you explain this in terms of the particle theory of matter?

Heterogeneous mixtures. In a heterogeneous mixture, particles of one substance are dispersed (spread) through another substance (see Table 1.2).

Table 1.2 Some heterogeneous mixtures

Type	Description	Example
Suspension	Solid particles dispersed in liquid	Clay
Emulsion	Liquid droplets dispersed in liquid	Milk, mayonnaise
Foam	Gas bubbles dispersed in liquid	Soap suds, whipped cream
Mist	Liquid droplets dispersed in gas	Fog, aerosol products
Smoke	Solid particles dispersed in gas	Dust-laden air, smoke

JUST TESTING 4

1 Copy this scheme and fill in the blanks.

Matter: the three chief states are _____, _____ and _____.

```
                    Matter
            /                    \
  Pure substances            Mixtures
  two kinds                  two kinds
    /        \                /        \
_____    _____        _____    _____
```

*1.6 Equilibrium

Vaporisation (Section 1.4) and dissolving (Section 1.5) are physical changes. Let us have a closer look at what happens to the particles during these changes.

The element bromine is a brown liquid which vaporises easily at room temperature. Figure 1.16 shows what happens when a few cm^3 of the brown liquid, bromine, are dropped into a gas jar and the lid is replaced.

Two new terms for you to get to grips with in the following discussion are **property** and **system**. We use the word **property** in chemistry to mean a characteristic. We say that brown colour is a property of bromine. We use the word **system** for any part of the universe which we want to study quite separately from the rest of the universe. The gas jar and its contents can be described as a system. There are two kinds of system:
- **A system in a state of change:** the properties of the system are changing.
- **A system at equilibrium:** its properties are not changing.

Lid

Gas jar

Bromine

Time 1
The mixture of gases inside the gas jar begins to look brown as liquid bromine vaporises.

Time 2
A few minutes later, the gas has become darker brown.

Time 3
After about 15 minutes, the colour of the gas stops darkening. There is no further change.

Fig. 1.16 Vaporisation

In the gas jar shown at time 1 and time 2, you can see that changes are occurring. The gas jar and contents are a system in a state of change. At time 3, however, the amounts of liquid bromine and bromine vapour are no longer changing. The system is at equilibrium: no changes in its properties are occurring. If you could see the bromine molecules, however, you would see plenty of movement. Molecules of bromine are still vaporising – leaving the liquid phase to enter the gas phase. Molecules of bromine are also condensing – leaving the gas phase to enter the liquid phase. The rate of vaporisation is equal to the rate of condensation, so the properties of the system do not change: the system is at equilibrium. Since movement is occurring in the system, the equilibrium is described as a **dynamic equilibrium** (see Fig. 1.17).

There are two kinds of equilibrium:
- **Static equilibrium:** there is no movement.
- **Dynamic equilibrium:** there is movement.

Dissolving is another physical change. Figure 1.18 shows what happens when you stir copper(II) sulphate crystals into a beaker of water.

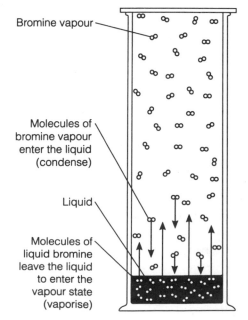

Bromine vapour

Molecules of bromine vapour enter the liquid (condense)

Liquid

Molecules of liquid bromine leave the liquid to enter the vapour state (vaporise)

Fig. 1.17 Dynamic equilibrium – the rate at which molecules condense is equal to the rate at which molecules vaporise.

Time 1
Copper(II) sulphate crystals and water

Time 2
The crystals start to dissolve and the water begins to change into a blue solution.

Time 3
After a while, no more crystals can dissolve. The solution is saturated, and the colour stops changing.

Fig. 1.18 Dissolving

At time 3, the saturated solution and the undissolved crystals are in a state of equilibrium. If you could see the particles of copper(II) sulphate, you would see that the equilibrium is dynamic. You would see that copper(II) sulphate is still dissolving, but, as fast as crystals dissolve, dissolved copper(II) sulphate crystallises from the solution.

We have looked at physical changes here. Later, you will meet chemical changes that come to equilibrium. They are important in the manufacture of cement (Section 13.3), the manufacture of sulphuric acid (Section 14.6) and the manufacture of nitric acid (Section 15.3).

SUMMARY NOTE

The terms **property** and **system** are defined. There are two kinds of system:
- **A system in a state of change:** the properties are changing.
- **A system at equilibrium:** no change in properties is occurring.

There are two kinds of equilibrium:
- **Static equilibrium:** there is no movement.
- **Dynamic equilibrium:** there is movement.

Physical changes and chemical changes can reach a state of equilibrium.

Exercise 1

1 Name some common substances which are **a** solids, **b** liquids and **c** gases.

2 At room temperature, oxygen is a gas, water is a liquid and sugar is a solid. Which of these substances has the strongest forces of attraction between its particles? Which has the weakest?

3 When mothballs are put into a cupboard, they slowly disappear. Do they **a** melt, **b** condense, **c** sublime or **d** distil?

4 If the sun comes out after a rainshower, the puddles dry up faster than if it stays cloudy. Explain why this happens.

5 Of the processes:
Evaporation, Condensation, Distillation, Filtration, Sublimation,
select the process which
  a makes water collect on window panes in cold weather
  b makes water disappear from puddles
  c can be used to separate water from sand
  d includes the changes:
      water → steam → water
  e describes the change:
      ice → water vapour.

6 A weather balloon is being inflated. It will rise 11 km into the atmosphere. It is only partially filled when it is inflated on the ground. Why should it not be filled completely?

7 Copy this passage and fill in the blanks.
Ice is solid _____. Dry ice is solid _____ _____. Ice feels wet because _____. Dry ice feels dry because _____. When ice takes heat from the surroundings, it _____. When dry ice takes heat from the surroundings, it _____. As dry ice cools the surrounding air, water vapour condenses out of the air. This is why when pop groups use dry ice on stage you see _____.

8 The air pressure in the tyres on a car was measured on a cool morning. The car was driven all through the day, which turned out to be sunny and hot. What happened to the pressure in the tyres? Give an explanation according to the kinetic theory of gases.

9 Which goes 'flat' faster, an open bottle of Coke on the kitchen table or an open bottle in the fridge? Explain your answer.

10 One 2 litre balloon is filled with helium. A second 2 litre balloon is filled with air at the same temperature and pressure. It takes 0.32 g of helium to fill the first balloon and 2.4 g of air to fill the second. If the two balloons are punctured (with the same size holes), which balloon will deflate faster? Give a reason for your answer.

11 Name some common substances which are **a** homogeneous solids, **b** heterogeneous solids, **c** homogeneous liquids and **d** heterogeneous liquids.

12 Name some common substances which are **a** solutions, **b** solutes present in solutions, **c** solvents.

Study Fig. 1.19 before answering questions **13–15**.

13 What is the solubility of potassium sulphate at 80 °C?

14 a What mass of copper(II) sulphate-5-water will dissolve in 100 g of water at 100 °C?
   b What happens when the solution is cooled to 50 °C?

15 a What is the solubility at 60 °C of
   (i) potassium nitrate, (ii) sodium chloride?
   b What is the solubility at 20 °C of
   (i) potassium nitrate, (ii) sodium chloride?

Fig. 1.19   Some solubility curves

c A solution is saturated at 60 °C with potassium nitrate and with sodium chloride. A 100 g sample of solution is cooled from 60 °C to 20 °C. What mass of crystals forms?

Career sketch: The vet

Alison is a vet. She had to study very hard at school to obtain three good A-levels including chemistry and biology. Then she spent three years at university before further training. Alison now shares a surgery with her partners, and here she treats small animals. She enjoys the variety her job offers, dealing with children and their pets, farmers and their herds. She has the satisfaction of seeing sick animals transformed into healthy animals.

CHAPTER 2 Pure substances from mixtures

2.1 The gold rush

In the Gold Rush days, some prospectors found nuggets of pure gold. They were the lucky ones. Most gold miners had to separate particles of gold from a large mass of rock or sand. Figure 2.1 shows an old-timer separating gold dust from sand. He is swirling the mixture with water in his miner's pan. Sand is less dense than gold dust. Therefore it swishes out of the pan with the wash water, while gold dust settles in the bottom of the pan. This is not an efficient method, but many people made a living using it.

Very few substances are found pure in nature. It is more usual to find the materials we want to use mixed with other materials. Chemists have to find ways of separating useful substances from the materials with which they are mixed.

SUMMARY NOTE

We need to find ways of separating useful substances from natural sources.

Fig. 2.1 Panning for gold

16

2.2 Separating solids

Dissolving one of the substances

Salt is mined in Cheshire. There are two ways of getting it out of the ground (see Section 16.1). One way is to dissolve it out: salt is soluble, whereas rock is not. A hole is bored into the salt deposit and two pipes are lowered into it. Water is pumped down one pipe and allowed to dissolve the salt. Brine (a solution of salt) is pumped up to the surface through the second pipe (Fig. 2.2). The brine obtained in this way is used by industry in manufacturing processes. In Experiment 2.1, you can find out how to obtain pure salt from rock salt.

Fig. 2.2 Solution mining: dissolving salt in an underground mine

1 A hole is drilled.

2 Two pipes are lowered. Water is sent down one pipe.

3 Brine is pumped up the other pipe.

2.3 Separating a solid from a liquid

From a heterogeneous mixture: by filtration

Filtration separates a solid from a liquid by using a sieve which allows liquid to pass through but does not allow solid particles to pass through. In the laboratory, the sieve used is often **filter paper**. A liquid can pass through pores in the filter paper; a solid cannot. Figure 2.3 shows laboratory apparatus for filtration. Figure 2.4 shows a faster method: filtering under reduced pressure.

◁ Fig. 2.3 Filtration

Filter funnel

Filter paper

Support

The solid remains in the filter as the **residue**.

The liquid which **filters** through is called the **filtrate**.

A Buchner funnel has a perforated plate which is covered by a circle of filter paper.

The side-arm flask is connected to a suction pump. This pulls the liquid through the holes in the funnel, and speeds up filtration.

Fig. 2.4 Filtration under ▷ reduced pressure

17

Fig. 2.5 Salt pans in Australia

From a solution: by crystallisation

In Fig. 2.5, you see how sea water has been allowed to flow into large **salt pans**. They are in Australia where the sun is hot enough to evaporate much of the water. When the brine has become a saturated solution, the solute (salt) begins to crystallise. Scoops are used to remove salt crystals from the sea water.

Experiment 1.2 enables you to grow crystals. A laboratory method of evaporating a solution until it crystallises is shown in Fig. 2.6.

SUMMARY NOTE

A solute separates from a saturated solution by crystallisation. If a solution is unsaturated, some of the solvent has to be removed by evaporation before crystals will form.

From time to time, dip a glass rod into the solution. Do crystals form on the rod? When they do, the solution can be removed from the water bath and left to crystallise.

Solution in evaporating basin

Steam bath (or water bath)

Heating element

Fig. 2.6 Evaporating a solution to obtain crystals of solute

Fig. 2.7 A biochemist at work

From a suspension: by centrifuging

Suppose the biochemist in Fig. 2.7 wants to separate blood **cells** (which are solid) from blood plasma (which is liquid). Blood cells are very small solid particles. Because they are small they **disperse** (spread out) through the plasma and remain **in suspension**. They do not settle to the bottom of a container as heavy particles would. How can small solid particles be separated from the liquid around them? The method of **centrifuging** (or centrifugation) provides the answer. A **suspension** (such as blood) is put into glass tubes inside a centrifuge. This instrument spins round at high speed. The solid particles (in this case, blood cells) are flung to the bottom of the centrifuge tubes. After the machine has been stopped, the liquid (plasma) can be **decanted** (poured off) from the mass of solid at the bottom of the tube. This method is used for many different types of suspension, not just blood.

Fig. 2.8 How a centrifuge works

2.4 *Separating a solute and a solvent from a solution*

In some parts of the world, drinking water is obtained from sea water. The solvent (water) is separated from the solute (salt) by **distillation**. This process uses a great deal of heat. It is only in

Thermometer records the boiling point of the liquid.

Distillation flask

Anti-bumping granules assist smooth boiling.

Heat

Water out

Liebig condenser

Cold water in

Receiver

Distillate

Fig. 2.9 Distillation

the Persian Gulf that the need for water is great enough and the price of oil is low enough to make this method of obtaining drinking water a practical proposition. Figure 2.9 shows a laboratory-scale distillation apparatus. The processes that take place are

- in the distillation flask, **vaporisation** (liquid → vapour)
- in the condenser, **condensation** (vapour → liquid).

Vaporisation followed by condensation is called **distillation**.

SUMMARY NOTE

Distillation is used to separate a solvent from a solution.

2.5 Separating miscible liquids

Distillation

A simple distillation apparatus like that in Fig. 2.9 will separate a liquid solvent from a solid solute. Often, people want to separate **miscible** liquids, that is, liquids that have dissolved in one another to form a solution. For example, whisky manufacturers need to separate alcohol from water in a solution of the two liquids. Alcohol is the substance called **ethanol**, which boils at 78 °C. Water boils at 100 °C. Figure 2.10 shows laboratory apparatus which will separate a mixture of ethanol and water into its parts or **fractions**. The process is called **fractional distillation**.

The **fractionating column** has a large surface area. Three designs of fractionating column are shown in Fig. 2.11a. Vaporisation of the liquid followed by condensation of the vapour takes place many times on the surface of the fractionating

Thermometer. The temperature stays constant at the boiling point of each liquid as it distils separately.

Liebig condenser

The fractionating column is packed with glass rods to give a large surface area. Vaporisation followed by condensation takes place many times. Eventually the liquid with the lower boiling point reaches the top of the column and distils over.

Water out

Cold water in

Distillation flask

Anti-bumping granules

Receiver. The receiver is changed to catch each distillate separately.

Heat

Fig. 2.10 Fractional distillation

Fig. 2.11 (a) Three designs of fractionating column; (b) a distillation column at B.P. Chemicals

column. The liquid with the lower boiling point (ethanol) reaches the top of the column first and distils over. The temperature stays constant at 78 °C while all the ethanol distils into the receiver. Then the temperature starts to rise, and the receiver is changed. At 100 °C, water starts to distil, and a fresh receiver is put into position to collect it.

Fractional distillation

Fractional distillation can be made to run continuously. This is done in the petroleum industry. Crude oil is not very useful in its raw state. By fractional distillation, it can be separated into a number of fractions which are very useful indeed (Fig. 2.12). These fractions are not pure substances. Each is a mixture of substances which boil at similar temperatures. The fractions with low boiling points are collected from the top of the column. Fractions with high boiling points are collected from the bottom of the fractionating column.

Fig. 2.12 Continuous fractional distillation in the oil industry

SUMMARY NOTE

Fractional distillation is used to separate a mixture of miscible liquids. It can be made to run continuously, e.g. in the fractionation of crude petroleum oil.

2.6 Separating immiscible liquids

A cook who wants to separate oil from gravy skims off the oil as it floats on top of the gravy (Fig. 2.13). Chemists have a better way of separating **immiscible** liquids (liquids which do not mix). They use a separating funnel (Fig. 2.14).

◁ Fig. 2.13 A cook separating immiscible liquids

1 Pour in the mixture of liquids. It will settle into two layers.

2 Open the tap. Let the bottom layer run into a receiver.

3 Close the tap. Change the receiver Let the top layer run into a fresh receiver.

Fig. 2.14 A separating funnel ▷

SUMMARY NOTE

Immiscible liquids can be separated by means of a separating funnel.

JUST TESTING 5

1 A crew has to abandon ship. They find themselves in a lifeboat which has tins of food, a tin opener, a packet of plastic straws, a camping stove, matches, but no drinking water. They know that it is fatal to drink sea water. How can they obtain drinking water?

2 Describe how you could separate the oil and the vinegar in a salad dressing.

3 Somehow the car wax in your house has become mixed with sand. Describe how you could remove the sand from it.

2.7 Separating the solutes in a solution: chromatography

You can start this topic by doing Experiments 2.7–2.9. These experiments all separate the solutes present in a solution. They all work with a small volume of solution. They use the method called **chromatography**. When a spot of solution is applied to the chromatography paper, the paper **adsorbs** the solutes, that is, binds them to its surface. As solvent rises through the paper, a competition takes place. The paper can adsorb the solutes; the solvent can dissolve them. Which one wins depends on the individual solute. Some solutes stay put; others dissolve in the solvent and travel in it up the paper. A

2 The chromatography paper must be suspended so that it does not touch the sides of the beaker. The spot must be above the level of solvent in the beaker.

4 The solvent rises up the paper to this level.

5 As the solutes travel at different speeds, they become separated. A **chromatogram** is obtained.

1 A drop of solution is applied to chromatography paper. The solvent evaporates to leave a spot. The solutes have been adsorbed on the paper.

3 Solvent

Fig. 2.15   Chromatography

solute which is very soluble in the solvent travels through the paper faster than a solute which is only slightly soluble. When the solvent reaches the top of the paper, the process is stopped. Different solutes will have travelled different distances. The result is a **chromatogram** (Fig. 2.15).

Water is not the only solvent that can be used (see Experiment 2.9). It is necessary to experiment to find out which solvent gives a good separation of the solutes. When you are using a solvent other than water, you should use a closed container so that the chromatography paper is surrounded by the vapour of the solvent (Fig. 2.16).

Frequently, chemists use chromatography to **analyse** a mixture. **Analysis** of a mixture means finding out which substances are present in it. What they do is to make a chromatogram of the unknown mixture together with known substances which they suspect may be present. For example, a food chemist might use known food additives as well as the unknown mixture. Figure 2.17 shows how results can be obtained by this method.

Bung

Clip to hold chromatography paper.

Boiling tube

Spot

Solvent

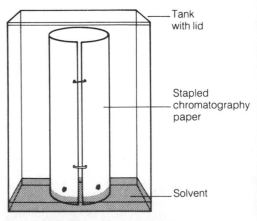

Tank with lid

Stapled chromatography paper

Solvent

Fig. 2.16   Chromatography with a solvent other than water

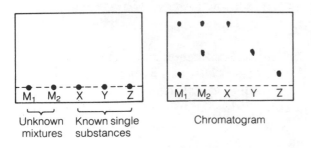

Unknown mixtures   Known single substances

Chromatogram

The results show that M_1 is a mixture of X and Z and M_2 is a mixture of X and Y.

Fig. 2.17   How to obtain results from the chromatograms

JUST TESTING 6

1

Mr Dunn writes a cheque for £7 to Mr Fixit. Mr Fixit alters the amount. Mr Dunn reports the matter to the police. How can the police chemist prove that the 'ty' and the '0' have been added by a different person?

2 A biochemist treats a protein food with an enzyme. She uses chromatography to separate the mixture that she obtains. Her chromatogram is shown in Fig. 2.18a. She knows that the mixture is a mixture of **amino acids**. She suspects that glycine, arginine, aspartic acid, serine, histidine and phenylalanine may be present. When she runs chromatograms on these amino acids one at a time, she obtains the result shown in Fig. 2.18b. What conclusion can you draw from her experimental results?

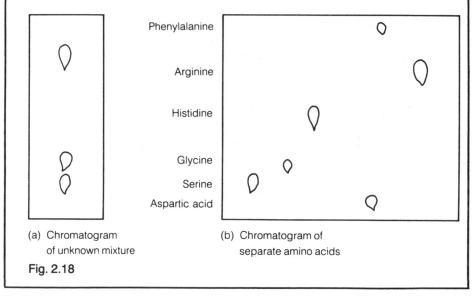

(a) Chromatogram of unknown mixture

(b) Chromatogram of separate amino acids

Fig. 2.18

2.8 Testing for purity

Solids

If a solid consists of a single substance, it is said to be a **pure** substance. If the solid is a mixture of substances, it melts gradually over a range of temperature. If the solid is a pure

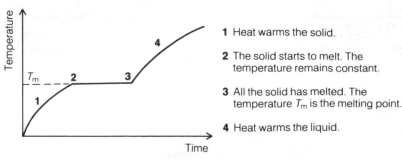

1 Heat warms the solid.

2 The solid starts to melt. The temperature remains constant.

3 All the solid has melted. The temperature T_m is the melting point.

4 Heat warms the liquid.

Fig. 2.19 The temperature changes that occur when a pure solid is heated

substance, it melts suddenly at a definite temperature, the **melting point** of the solid. While a solid is melting, its temperature stays constant as long as there is some solid left. This is because all the heat entering the solid is used to change the solid into a liquid, and not to raise its temperature (see Fig. 2.19).

To find out whether a solid is pure, you need to find its melting point (see Fig. 2.20). If an impurity is present, it lowers the melting point and also makes the impure substance melt over a range of temperatures.

People have listed the melting points of solids at standard pressure, that is, atmospheric pressure at sea level. When you know the melting point of a solid, you can find out what the solid is. Look through the list of melting points until you find the name of a solid with that melting point.

SUMMARY NOTE

The melting point of a solid can be used to test its purity. When a pure solid melts, the temperature stays constant as long as there is some solid left. The solid can be identified from tables of melting points. The presence of an impurity lowers the melting point.

Stirrer

Solid

Water

Heat

1 Heat the water in the beaker until the solid in the tube melts. Switch off the Bunsen.

2 Let the molten solid cool. Stir. Watch the thermometer.

3 While the liquid begins to solidify, the temperature stops falling. It stays constant until no liquid remains. This temperature is the melting point of the solid (and also the freezing point of the liquid).

Fig. 2.20   Finding the melting point of a solid. (When water is used in the beaker, the solid must melt below 100 °C. If the solid has a higher melting point, a different liquid must be used. See Fig. 2.19 for a graph of the way the temperature falls.)

Liquids

A mixture of liquids boils over a range of temperatures. While a pure liquid is boiling, its temperature remains constant at its

1 Heat warms the liquid.

2 It starts to boil. The temperature remains constant at the boiling point as long as there is some liquid left.

Fig. 2.21   The temperature changes that occur when a pure liquid boils

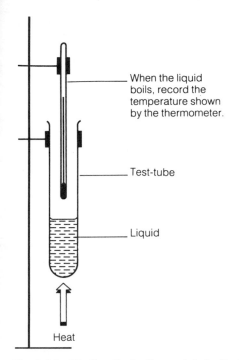

When the liquid boils, record the temperature shown by the thermometer.

Test-tube

Liquid

Heat

Fig. 2.22   Finding the boiling point of a liquid

SUMMARY NOTE

The boiling point of a liquid can be used to test its purity.
A pure liquid boils at a constant temperature.
Impurities raise the boiling point of a liquid.
The boiling point of a liquid depends on the surrounding pressure.

boiling point. If you heat the liquid more strongly, it will boil faster but the temperature will not go up. Heat going into the liquid is used to convert the liquid into vapour and not to raise its temperature (see Fig. 2.21).

To find out whether a liquid is pure, you find its boiling point (Fig. 2.22). A pure liquid boils at a certain temperature. A mixture of liquids boils over a range of temperatures. If a solid is dissolved in the liquid, it raises the boiling point.

The boiling point of a liquid depends on the surrounding pressure. A drop in the surrounding pressure makes the liquid boil at a lower temperature. An increase in the surrounding pressure makes the liquid boil at a higher temperature.

JUST TESTING 7

1 On high mountains, the atmospheric pressure is low.
   Does water boil above or below 100 °C on a high mountain?
   Do mountaineers find it easy or difficult to make a pot of strong tea?
   Explain your answers.

2 In a pressure cooker, food cooks at a pressure greater than atmospheric pressure.
   Is the temperature of water boiling in a pressure cooker above or below 100 °C?
   Does food cook more quickly or more slowly in a pressure cooker than in a saucepan?
   Explain your answers.

Tables of boiling points at standard pressure (that is, atmospheric pressure at sea level) have been drawn up. By checking through these lists, you can find the name of the liquid which has the boiling point you have just measured.

Alternatively, you can find the freezing point of a liquid (Fig. 2.23).

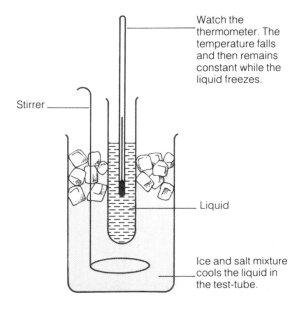

Stirrer

Watch the thermometer. The temperature falls and then remains constant while the liquid freezes.

Liquid

Ice and salt mixture cools the liquid in the test-tube.

Fig. 2.23   Finding the freezing point of a liquid

1 A solid melts at 43 °C. Which of the solids listed below could it be?
   a phenol (m.p., 41 °C), **b** benzoic anhydride (m.p., 42 °C), **c** chlorophenol (m.p., 43 °C), **d** nitrophenol (m.p., 45 °C).

2 An impure sample of a solid X melts at 83 °C. Which of the solids in this list could be X?

Substance	Melting point in °C
Dibromobenzene	87
Naphthalene	80
Di-iodoethane	81
Glycollic acid	79

3 An impure sample of a liquid Y boils at 66 °C. Which of the liquids in this list could be Y?

Liquid	Boiling point in °C
Chloroform	61
Hexene	64
Hexane	69
Benzene	80

Exercise 2

1 Say which of the pure substances listed below are **a** solids, **b** liquids and **c** gases at room temperature and standard pressure. Which substance cannot be a metal? In which substance are the forces of attraction between particles the greatest?

Pure substance	Melting point in °C	Boiling point in °C
A	29	690
B	−101	−35
C	−7	59
D	114	184
E	−39	357
F	820	1100

2 The magnetic separator shown in Fig. 2.24 is in use in a metal recycling plant. It is separating iron and steel (which are magnetic)

1 The mixture of metals is fed in.

2 It passes along a conveyor belt . . .

3 . . . and over a magnetic roller.

Pile A   Pile B

Fig. 2.24 A magnetic separator

from aluminium (which is non-magnetic). Which pile, A or B, is aluminium? Explain how the machine works.

3 Select the correct ending to this sentence: A solid can be purified by crystallisation from water because

A it dissolves in cold water but not in hot water.

B it is insoluble in hot and cold water.

C it is very soluble in hot and cold water.

D it is more soluble in hot water than in cold water.

E it is more soluble in cold water than in hot water.

4 Figure 2.25 shows the changes that occur when a pure liquid is cooled. Explain what changes are occurring **a** in region 1, **b** between point 2 and point 3, **c** in region 4. What do you call the temperature shown as *T*?

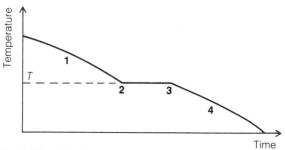

Fig. 2.25   A liquid cools

5 The melting point of a sample of a solid compound A is 133 °C. Which of the solids in this list could be A?

Solid	Melting point in °C
Benzoic acid	122
Maleic acid	130
Urea	136
Oxalic acid	190

6 If you sprinkle salt on to ice, some of the salt will dissolve. Can you explain why this leads to the ice melting?

7 A mixture contains two liquids, A and B. A boils at 70 °C, and B boils at 110 °C. Draw the apparatus you would use to separate A and B. Label the drawing.

8 A chemist extracts an acidic solid from rancid butter. What should he do to find out whether it is a pure substance or not?

9 The police are investigating a case of forged £5 notes. When they search a suspect's premises, they find paper and ink but no counterfeit money. How can they compare the ink they have found with the ink in the forged £5 notes?

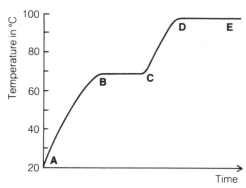

Fig. 2.26   Distillation of a mixture of hexane and heptane

10 Figure 2.26 shows how the temperature changes during the distillation of a mixture of hexane and heptane. The boiling points of the two liquids are: hexane, 69 °C; heptane, 98 °C. Explain what is happening over the regions A–B, B–C, C–D and D–E.

11 In Fig. 2.27, point A shows ice at −25 °C. The graph shows how the temperature changes when ice is heated at a constant rate. What changes take place in regions A–B, B–C, D–E and E–F?

*12 Ethanol (alcohol) melts at −117 °C and boils at 78 °C. Draw a heating curve for ethanol similar to Fig. 2.27, and label

a the melting point

b the boiling point

c the region where ethanol is a gas

d the region where ethanol is a liquid

e the region where ethanol exists as both solid and liquid

f the region where ethanol exists as both liquid and gas.

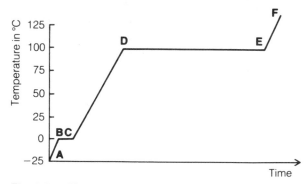

Fig. 2.27   Temperature–time graph

CHAPTER 3 Elements and compounds

3.1 Diamond

Probably the most famous of diamonds is the Hope diamond. This is a huge (20 g) blazing diamond with a bluish tint. It once formed the single eye of a statue of Sita, a Hindu goddess. The diamond was stolen from the statue, and disappeared for many years. It eventually turned up in France in 1668, by which time a legend had grown up around it. The 'French blue', as it was called, was said to carry the curse of the goddess Sita, who resented the theft. Certainly, the diamond brought no luck to one wearer, Marie Antoinette, who was guillotined during the French Revolution in 1792. Part of the French crown jewels, the diamond was stolen again at the time of the Revolution. In 1830, it turned up in London where it was bought by the banker, Henry Hope. The Hope diamond, as it has been called ever since, brought no luck to his family. They lost all their father's wealth and died bankrupt. The diamond passed to an Eastern European prince. He gave it to an actress in the Folies Bergères, but afterwards shot her in a fit of jealous rage. Later, a Greek owner drove over a precipice with his family in a car accident. Sultan Abdul Hamid II of Turkey had owned the diamond for only a few months when he was overthrown by a military revolt in 1909. An American woman, Mrs Evalyn Walsh, then bought the Hope diamond. She did not believe the story of Sita's curse, and wore the diamond as a necklace. Her children died in accidents, and mental illness afflicted her husband. When she died, a dealer bought her jewels, and donated the Hope diamond to the American people. It is now on view at the Smithsonian Institute in Washington, DC.

Why have people always been fascinated by diamonds? The brilliance of diamonds is due to their ability to reflect light. A skilful diamond cutter can increase this brilliance (Fig. 3.1). The 'fire' of a diamond is a result of its ability to split light into flashes of colour. Diamond is the hardest of natural materials. The only thing that can scratch a diamond is another diamond, so 'diamonds are for ever'. This is why diamonds are so often used in engagement rings.

Eye surgeons now use diamond knives to remove cataracts. The edges of these knives are so sharp and so even that a clean cut is made with no tearing.

That space capsule the Americans sent to Venus — it had a window in it! They had to have one to let in infrared radiation for their scientific instruments to record. What could the window have been made of?

Well it's hot on Venus (about 500 °C) and there's about 100 atmospheres pressure. But in space it's cold and there's a vacuum. The only transparent material I can think of which could stand up to all those conditions is diamond.

In a well-cut diamond the rays of light are reflected.

This diamond has been cut too deep and 'leaks' light.

This diamond has been cut too shallow. It also 'leaks' light.

Fig. 3.1 How diamonds are cut

Fig. 3.2   A diamond-edged saw cutting
concrete

Fig. 3.3   Diamond-edged drill bits

Diamond is the hardest naturally occurring substance. In industry there are thousands of applications for diamonds. Diamonds are used for grinding, cutting, grooving, sharpening, etching and polishing. Stone, metals, ceramics, glass and concrete are all cut with diamond-edged tools (Fig. 3.2). The bits of oil-rig drills are studded with small diamonds. Often they have to drill 7000 metres through hard rock. This was almost impossible before the diamond bit (Fig. 3.3).

What is diamond, this beautiful and useful material? What gives it such extraordinary properties? Diamond consists only of carbon atoms. It is a form of the element carbon. **An element is a pure substance which cannot be separated into simpler substances** (see Section 1.5).

Deep down in the Earth the temperature and pressure are both very high. There, millions of years ago, carbon atoms crystallised in a regular solid arrangement. You can see from Fig. 3.4 how

SUMMARY NOTE

Diamonds have always been valued for their sparkle and fire. Diamond is a very hard material. It is used in industry for cutting, grinding and drilling. Diamond is a form of the element carbon. The carbon atoms are joined by chemical bonds to form a giant molecular structure.

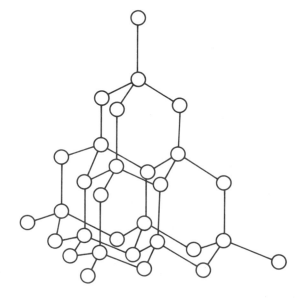

Fig. 3.4   The structure of
diamond

each carbon atom is joined by chemical bonds to four other carbon atoms. A crystal of diamond contains millions of carbon atoms. It is very difficult to break them apart. This is the reason why diamonds are so hard. You will read in Chapter 6 that the structure of diamond is described as a **macromolecule** or **giant molecule**.

3.2 Graphite

Graphite is a shiny dark grey solid. It is soft and, when you rub it, comes off on to your fingers. Mixed with clay, graphite is used to make pencil 'leads'. It is also used as a lubricant, in cars for example. Graphite conducts electricity (as in Experiments 5.1 and 5.2).

Diamond is brilliant. It is one of the hardest substances and is a non-conductor of electricity. Graphite is only slightly shiny. It is so soft that it is used as a lubricant, and it is an electrical conductor. Yet these two substances are both forms of the element carbon. Both diamond and graphite consist of atoms of carbon and nothing else. The reason for the difference in properties lies in the arrangement of atoms in the two solids. They are both crystalline solids: the atoms are arranged in a regular, ordered manner. Graphite has the layer structure shown in Fig. 3.5. The carbon atoms in each layer are joined by chemical bonds. Between the layers, there are only weak forces of attraction. These are weak enough to allow one layer to slide over the next layer.

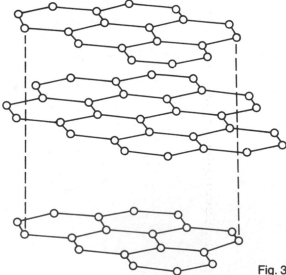

Fig. 3.5   The structure of graphite

Diamond and graphite are **allotropes** of carbon. **Allotropy** is the existence of different crystalline forms of the same element. It is possible to make diamonds from graphite by keeping graphite at a high temperature under high pressure.

Did you know that in 1985 a batch of new carbon allotropes was discovered? The molecules are like a cage of carbon atoms – 50, 60 or 70 carbon atoms. They call the new allotropes **fullerenes** or **bucky balls**.

I bet that's after Buckminster Fuller who designed geodesic domes, those roof structures made of polygons.

The C_{60} molecule is a perfect sphere of carbon atoms. It's called **buckminsterfullerene**. The molecules look like a football, with 20 hexagons and 12 pentagons on the outside.

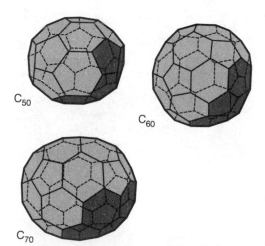

Fig. 3.6   Fullerenes C_{50}, C_{60} and C_{70}

I can see where the nickname 'bucky balls' comes from. Are they any use?

They could be used as semiconductors, superconductors, lubricants, catalysts and in batteries.

3.3 Charcoal

There are also impure forms of the element carbon. Wood charcoal and animal charcoal are made by burning wood or bones in a limited supply of air. Animal charcoal is used as an **adsorbent**. It will adsorb the natural brown colour from sugar during the manufacture of white sugar. It is also used in the gas masks which industrial workers wear when they have to deal with poisonous gases.

JUST TESTING 9

1 What are diamonds made of? What other forms of this element do you know? How does diamond differ from the other forms of the element in **a** behaviour and **b** structure?

2 What is the advantage of using diamond as a surgical knife?
   Why are diamonds often chosen as engagement rings?
   List the characteristics of diamond which make it useful in industry.
   What do the following people have in common: oil prospectors, glass carvers, stone cutters, eye surgeons?

3.4 Silicon

Radios and television sets contain electronic circuits. These circuits used to contain devices called **vacuum tubes**. Their job was to allow current to pass in one direction only. In the 1950s, **transistors** made from silicon replaced vacuum tubes. A

Fig. 3.7   A silicon chip magnified 1000 times

transistor made from a speck of crystal the size of the letter 'o' on this page can do the job of a vacuum tube. Transistors led to the miniaturisation of electronic circuits:

- Transistor radios could be made small enough to be held in the hand.
- Computers the size of a typewriter did the job of the older computers which needed a room full of vacuum tubes.
- Aeroplanes and spacecraft became able to use computers (the size and weight of the valve type of computer had made this impossible).

A second giant step was the packing of an entire electronic circuit (transistors, resistors etc.) on to a single chip of silicon. This saves weight, space and cost. The chip is little affected by moisture, ageing or vibration. This device is called an **integrated circuit** (Fig. 3.7).

Silicon is an element. It is a **semiconductor**: its electrical properties lie between those of an electrical insulator and an electrical conductor. (You can read in Section 13.10 how silicon is obtained.) The first step in making an integrated circuit is to slice large crystals of silicon into wafers. A thousand integrated circuits are then put on to each wafer. This is done by treating tiny areas of the silicon wafer with other elements which make it become a conductor.

The silicon wafer is cut into identical silicon **chips**. Each chip is sealed in plastic or metal. Fine gold wires (finer than human hair) are bonded to the chip to provide connections to an external circuit. This is done by operators looking at the chip through a microscope and using very delicate tools.

The uses of the integrated circuit are many and increase daily. Computers are used in business, commerce, education and medicine.

SUMMARY NOTE

The element silicon is a semiconductor of electricity. This property enables silicon to be used as a **transistor** (which allows current to flow in one direction only). Integrated circuits built on to silicon chips are the basis of the microcomputer industry.

3.5 Gold

People have always treasured gold. It never tarnishes, so the gold ornaments in the tombs of the pyramids are as bright today as when they were put there 3000 years ago.

Gold is a metallic element and like most metals it is shiny. Unlike most metals, however, it does not tarnish. It is not affected by air or water or any other chemicals in the environment. Like most metals, gold can be easily hammered into different shapes and it can be pulled into the form of a wire.

There are scientific uses for gold. Integrated circuits (see Section 3.4) operate at low current and low voltage. Contacts and switches must therefore have low resistance. At these low currents, even small areas of corrosion on the electrical contacts can increase the resistance. Extremely non-corrodable metals must therefore be used, and gold is the best choice. Not only is it an excellent electrical conductor, it is also one of the most unreactive of metals. It is expensive, of course, but it is used in small quantities to plate contacts made of less expensive metals.

SUMMARY NOTE

Gold is a beautiful metal which never tarnishes. It is an element. Its ability to be worked into different shapes is typical of metals.

Gold is used for jewellery and for electrical circuits which demand an electrical conductor which never tarnishes.

Fig. 3.8   (a) Gold jewellery   (b) Gold ingot

Satellites are covered with gold foil protected by glass ceramic. I wonder why.

It's probably to reflect some of the heat from the sun. If a satellite got very hot, the scientific instruments inside it would be damaged.

Fig. 3.9   A satellite

3.6 Iron

Iron is another metal which has been used by the human race for thousands of years. It is an element. Between 2000 and 1000 B.C., people discovered how to obtain iron from iron-bearing rocks. They did not value it for its beauty, like gold, but for the useful tools they could make from it. Iron is hard and strong. It can be hammered into flat blades and then ground with a stone to give it a cutting edge. People were able to make hammers, chisels, axes and knives which were not brittle like their stone tools or easily bent like the bronze tools they were used to. The development of iron tools and weapons made a huge difference to the way people lived. The human race entered a new 'age', called by historians the Iron Age.

You can read about iron and steel, which is an alloy of iron, in Section 11.12.

SUMMARY NOTE

Iron is a metallic element. Being hard and strong, it has been used for thousands of years for making tools.

3.7 Elements

The properties of gold and iron are **typical** of metallic elements. They conduct electricity. Many of the metals we use are not elements. Bronze, brass, solder, steel and many others are **alloys**. They are combinations of two or more metallic elements and sometimes non-metallic elements also. The other elements you have read about in this chapter, carbon and silicon, are non-metallic elements. Some of their properties are typical of non-metallic elements, but some are **atypical** (not typical). The diamond allotrope of carbon is atypical in being shiny; most non-metallic elements are dull. The graphite allotrope of carbon is the only non-metallic element that conducts electricity. Silicon is atypical in being a semiconductor.

Table 3.1 lists some metallic elements and non-metallic elements with their state symbols. In all, there are 92 natural elements found on the Earth. Other elements have been made artificially (see Chapter 4). Table 3.2 summarises the differences in physical properties between metallic elements and non-metallic elements. You will discover the chemical differences later; in particular, their reactions with oxygen (Section 11.4).

Table 3.1 Some elements and their state symbols

Metallic elements	Non-metallic elements
Aluminium (s)	Carbon (s)
Copper (s)	Chlorine (g)
Gold (s)	Iodine (s)
Iron (s)	Hydrogen (g)
Lead (s)	Neon (g)
Mercury (l)	Nitrogen (g)
Silver (s)	Oxygen (g)
Sodium (s)	Silicon (s)
Zinc (s)	Sulphur (s)

SUMMARY NOTE

Gold and iron are metallic elements. Combinations of metallic elements are called **alloys**.

Carbon and silicon are non-metallic elements. Other than graphite and semiconductors like silicon, non-metallic elements do not conduct electricity. This distinguishes them from metals, which are good electrical conductors. The differences between metallic and non-metallic elements are listed in Table 3.2.

Table 3.2 Physical properties of metallic and non-metallic elements

Metallic elements	Non-metallic elements
Solids (except mercury) Dense and hard	Gases, liquids and solids Most of the solid elements are softer than metals; diamond is exceptional.
A fresh surface is shiny; many metals tarnish in air, e.g. iron rusts.	Most are dull; diamond is exceptional.
Can be hammered into shape without breaking: are **malleable**. Can be pulled out into wire form: are **ductile**.	Solid non-metallic elements are easily fractured when attempts are made to change their shape. Diamond is exceptional.
Conduct heat, although highly polished surfaces reflect heat.	All are poor thermal conductors.
Are good electrical conductors.	Most are poor electrical conductors. Graphite is the exception. There are semiconductors, such as silicon.
Make a pleasing sound when struck: are **sonorous.**	Are not **sonorous**.

good test to check if an element is a metal or non-metal, is to check to see if it conducts electricity.

3.8 Compounds

This story from *The Times* shows what can happen when elements **combine**. Mr Martin had been using a mixture which is sold in the USA for unblocking drains. It reacts with water to form hydrogen. He had also been using a bleach which reacts with water to form chlorine. Hydrogen and chlorine are elements. In strong sunlight, an explosive chemical reaction takes place between the two elements. They combine to form the compound hydrogen chloride:

hydrogen + chlorine → hydrogen chloride
element + **element** → **compound**

A compound of chlorine with one other element is called a **chloride**.

What is a compound?

Compounds are pure substances which contain two or more elements chemically combined (see Section 1.5). Water is a compound. You can split it up by passing a direct electric current through acidified water (see Section 5.3). A chemical reaction takes place to give the elements hydrogen and oxygen. Water is a compound of these elements. You could call it hydrogen oxide. A compound of oxygen and one other element is called an **oxide**. Water can be made by a chemical reaction between hydrogen and oxygen (see Section 9.8). Making a compound by combining elements is called **synthesis**.

water ⇌ (A chemical reaction can decompose the compound into elements) *Decomposition* → hydrogen + oxygen

The elements can combine in a chemical reaction to give the compound *Synthesis*

Some compounds can be split up by heat. A chemical reaction of this kind is called **thermal decomposition**. The compound mercury oxide decomposes when it is heated to give the elements mercury and oxygen. This is how oxygen was discovered by the British chemist, Joseph Priestley, in 1774 (see Fig. 3.10). Mercury oxide can be **synthesised** from mercury and oxygen.

To define the term compound:

A compound is a pure substance which consists of two or more elements chemically combined.

You can synthesise some compounds in Experiments 3.1–3.4.

Fig. 3.10   Thermal decomposition of mercury oxide. (Note: This experiment must be done in a fume cupboard because mercury vapour is poisonous)

What is the difference between a compound and a mixture?

There are differences between a compound of elements and a mixture of elements (see Experiments 3.1–3.4). A mixture can contain its components in any proportions. A compound has a **fixed composition**. It always contains the same elements in the same percentages by mass. Calcium carbonate is a compound of calcium, carbon and oxygen. It is quarried as limestone, as chalk and as marble. Wherever it comes from, calcium carbonate always has the composition by mass:

calcium 40%; carbon 12%; oxygen 48%.

Table 3.3 summarises the differences between mixtures and compounds.

Table 3.3 Differences between mixtures and compounds

Mixtures	Compounds
1 A mixture can be separated into its parts by physical methods, such as those used in Chapter 2.	A chemical reaction is needed to split a compound into simpler substances.
2 No chemical change takes place when a mixture is made.	A chemical reaction takes place when a compound is made. Often heat is given out or taken in when a compound is formed.
3 A mixture behaves in the same way as the substances in it.	A compound does not have the properties of its elements. It has a new set of properties.
4 A mixture can be made by mixing elements in any proportions.	A compound always contains its elements in fixed proportions by mass; for example, aluminium iodide always contains 6.6% of aluminium and 93.4% of iodine by mass.

SUMMARY NOTE

A compound is a pure substance which consists of two or more elements chemically combined. The components of a mixture are not chemically combined. The differences between compounds and mixtures are listed in Table 3.3.

JUST TESTING 10

1 How could you tell the difference between **a** a compound of iron and sulphur and **b** a mixture of iron and sulphur?

2 How can a mixture of oxygen and hydrogen be separated? How can the compound water be separated into hydrogen and oxygen?

3 Group the following into **a** mixtures and **b** compounds: sea water, air, common salt, rock salt, gold chloride, aluminium oxide, ink.

4 Name an element which can be used for each of the following uses:
earrings, surgical knife, pencil 'lead', decolourising agent, integrated circuit, chisel, thermometer, plumbing, electrical wiring, coloured lights, saucepans, disinfecting swimming pools.

5 Explain the difference between a compound and a mixture.

3.9 Symbols

Chemists use **symbols** to represent atoms. Every element has a different symbol. For example, the symbol for carbon is C. The letter C stands for one atom of carbon.. Sometimes, two letters are needed. The letters Ca stand for one atom of calcium: the symbol for calcium is Ca. The symbol for chlorine is Cl, and the symbol for chromium is Cr. **The symbol of an element is a letter or two letters which stand for one atom of the element.** Sometimes the letters are taken from the Latin name of the element, e.g. Cu from cuprum (copper) and Fe from ferrum (iron). A short list of symbols is given in Table 3.4. A complete list can be found on p. 410.

Table 3.4 Symbols of some common elements

Element	Symbol	Element	Symbol	Element	Symbol
Aluminium	Al	Gold	Au	Oxygen	O
Barium	Ba	Hydrogen	H	Phosphorus	P
Bromine	Br	Iodine	I	Potassium	K
Calcium	Ca	Iron	Fe	Silver	Ag
Carbon	C	Lead	Pb	Sodium	Na
Chlorine	Cl	Magnesium	Mg	Sulphur	S
Copper	Cu	Mercury	Hg	Tin	Sn
Fluorine	F	Nitrogen	N	Zinc	Zn

JUST TESTING 11

1 A well-educated crook sends this message to his partner in crime. If you have looked at the symbols on p. 410, you should be able to decipher it.

Au	Ba	In	V
Cu	Sn	Ru	Ni
Te	Sr	Kr	Ac

Write down the names of all the elements in the message. Can you see the message? (You have to use some of the letters in the names, and ignore others.)

3.10 Formulas

Formulas are written for compounds. The **formula of a compound** consists of the symbols of the elements present and some numbers. The numbers show the ratio in which the atoms are present. The compound carbon dioxide has the formula CO_2. The formula tells you that carbon dioxide contains two oxygen atoms for every carbon atom. The 2 below the line multiplies the O in front of it. Carbon dioxide consists of particles. Each particle contains one carbon atom joined by chemical bonds to two oxygen atoms (Fig. 3.11). The particle is called a **molecule** of carbon dioxide. To show three molecules, you write $3CO_2$. You cannot assume that every compound consists of molecules (see Section 6.2). The formulas of some of the compounds mentioned in Section 3.8 are given in Table 3.5.

The formula for sulphuric acid is H_2SO_4. This tells you that the compound contains two hydrogen atoms and four oxygen

Fig. 3.11   A molecule of carbon dioxide

Fig. 3.12   A molecule of sulphuric acid

Table 3.5 Some formulas

Compound	Formula
Hydrogen chloride	HCl (one H atom and one Cl atom)
Water	H_2O (two H atoms and one O atom; the 2 multiplies the H in front of it)
Sodium chloride	NaCl (one Na, one Cl)
Mercury oxide	HgO (one Hg, one O)
Mercury iodide	HgI_2 (one Hg, two I)

atoms for every sulphur atom. The numbers below the line multiply the symbols immediately in front of them. Sulphuric acid consists of molecules containing two hydrogen atoms, one sulphur atom and four oxygen atoms (Fig. 3.12). To write three molecules, you write $3H_2SO_4$. The 3 in front of the formula multiplies everything after it. In $3H_2SO_4$, there are 6 H, 3 S and 12 O atoms; a total of 21 atoms.

The formula for calcium hydroxide is $Ca(OH)_2$. The 2 multiplies the symbols in the brackets. There are 2 oxygen atoms, 2 hydrogen atoms and 1 calcium atom. To write $4Ca(OH)_2$ means that the whole of the formula is multiplied by 4. It means 4 Ca, 8 O and 8 H atoms. Section 6.6 deals with how to work out the formula of a compound. Table 3.6 lists the formulas of some common compounds.

SUMMARY NOTE

Compounds have formulas. A formula is a set of symbols and numbers. The symbols tell you what elements are present in the compound. The numbers tell you the ratio in which the atoms of different elements are present.

Table 3.6 The formulas of some compounds

Water	H_2O	Aluminium chloride	$AlCl_3$
Sodium hydroxide	NaOH	Aluminium oxide	Al_2O_3
Sodium chloride	NaCl	Carbon monoxide	CO
Sodium sulphate	Na_2SO_4	Carbon dioxide	CO_2
Sodium nitrate	$NaNO_3$	Sulphur dioxide	SO_2
Sodium carbonate	Na_2CO_3	Ammonia	NH_3
Sodium hydrogencarbonate	$NaHCO_3$	Ammonium chloride	NH_4Cl
		Hydrogen chloride	HCl
Calcium oxide	CaO	Hydrochloric acid	HCl(aq)
Calcium hydroxide	$Ca(OH)_2$	Sulphuric acid	H_2SO_4(aq)
Calcium chloride	$CaCl_2$	Nitric acid	HNO_3(aq)
Calcium sulphate	$CaSO_4$	Copper(II) oxide	CuO
Calcium carbonate	$CaCO_3$	Copper(II) sulphate	$CuSO_4$

aq = aqueous solution

JUST TESTING 12

1 How many atoms are present in the following?
 a CCl_4, b SO_2Cl_2, c $COCl_2$, d $C_2H_3Cl_3$, e $CuSO_4$, f $4CuSO_4$, g $Pb(NO_3)_2$, h $Al_2(SO_4)_3$, i $3Fe(NO_3)_3$, j $2Al(OH)_3$.

2 What are the formulas of
 a water, b hydrochloric acid, c sodium hydroxide, d calcium oxide, e sodium chloride, f carbon dioxide, g calcium carbonate, h sulphuric acid?

3.11 Equations

You have studied symbols for elements and formulas for compounds. These enable you to write **equations** for chemical reactions. Zinc and sulphur combine to form zinc sulphide. You can write this information as a **word equation**:

zinc + sulphur → zinc sulphide

The arrow means 'form'. If you put symbols for the elements and a formula for the compound, you can write:

$Zn + S → ZnS$

This is a **chemical equation**. On the left-hand side, you have one atom of zinc and one atom of sulphur. On the right-hand side, you have one atom of zinc and one atom of sulphur combined as zinc sulphide. The two sides are **equal**, and this is why the expression is called an equation.

It gives more information if you include **state symbols** in the equation. These are (s) for solid, (l) for liquid, (g) for gas and (aq) for aqueous solution (in water).

Zinc carbonate decomposes to give zinc oxide and carbon dioxide. A word equation for this reaction is

zinc carbonate → zinc oxide + carbon dioxide

The chemical equation is

$ZnCO_3 → ZnO + CO_2$

Putting in the state symbols

$ZnCO_3(s) → ZnO(s) + CO_2(g)$

tells you that solid zinc carbonate decomposes to form solid zinc oxide and carbon dioxide gas.

Magnesium reacts with sulphuric acid to give hydrogen gas and a solution of magnesium sulphate. The word equation is

magnesium + sulphuric acid → hydrogen + magnesium sulphate

The chemical equation is

$Mg(s) + H_2SO_4(aq) → H_2(g) + MgSO_4(aq)$

Hydrogen is written as H_2 because hydrogen gas consists of molecules containing two atoms.

There is more about equations in Section 6.8.

JUST TESTING 13

1 Write chemical equations for these reactions:
   a Iron and sulphur combine to form iron sulphide, FeS.
   b Mercury and sulphur combine to form mercury sulphide, HgS.
   c Copper carbonate decomposes to form copper oxide and carbon dioxide.
   d Silicon and oxygen combine to form silicon oxide, SiO_2.
   e Zinc and sulphuric acid react to form hydrogen and zinc sulphate.

Exercise 3

1 Write down from memory the symbols for: sulphur, sodium, potassium, magnesium, lead, copper, iron, zinc, aluminium.

2 In the word square are the names of 20 elements. They may read across, in reverse, upwards, downwards and diagonally. Write down the names of all the elements you can find.

```
T  I  N  E  O  N  C  T  R  Y  M  O
P  R  R  B  U  C  A  L  C  I  U  M
H  O  R  O  T  H  R  U  O  S  I  O
O  N  D  R  N  L  B  I  P  M  N  X
S  G  R  O  P  O  O  E  P  U  I  Y
P  O  A  N  Q  R  N  T  E  I  M  G
H  L  D  O  Z  I  N  C  R  S  U  E
O  D  B  I  R  N  I  C  K  E  L  N
R  E  N  O  U  E  Z  C  L  N  A  D
U  C  U  E  W  M  O  L  E  G  T  A
S  L  T  S  I  L  V  E  R  A  I  E
F  H  Y  D  R  O  G  E  N  M  N  L
```

3 Say whether each of the changes listed is a chemical reaction or a physical change. Give reasons for your answers.
 a Letting off a firework
 b Adding sugar to tea
 c Breaking an egg
 d Frying an egg
 e Baking a cake
 f Making an ice lolly
 g Writing on a piece of glass with a diamond 'pencil'.

4 Can you decipher this message? You will need the symbols on p. 316. Write down the name of each element. Using some of the letters and ignoring others, see if you can spot the message.

```
Ar  Kr  Ru  Ba  At  W
Te  Sb  Kr  Md  Ru  Al
Ru  Ti  V   Bi  Br  Sc
Ru  Ag  K   Bi  Cf  Ru
```

5 How could you prove that the change that takes place when salt is added to water is a physical change?
How could you prove that the change that takes place when iron filings are added to water is a chemical change?

6 How could you find out whether the following substances are mixtures or compounds?
 a salt, b wine, c city air, d honey, e brass.

7 Can you recall the formulas for these important compounds?
sodium chloride, sodium hydroxide, hydrochloric acid, sulphuric acid, calcium oxide, copper(II) sulphate, ammonia, water.

8 Write chemical equations for the following reactions:
 a Copper and sulphur form copper(II) sulphide, CuS.
 b Mercury and iodine combine to form mercury iodide, HgI_2.
 c Carbon burns in oxygen to form carbon dioxide.
 d Zinc carbonate decomposes to form zinc oxide and carbon dioxide.
 e Iron reacts with sulphuric acid to form hydrogen and iron(II) sulphate, $FeSO_4$.

Career sketch: Nursing

Andrew is a charge nurse. He works in the intensive care unit of a hospital. This is the ward into which desperately ill people are rushed after heart attacks and road accidents. The ward is full of instruments which record a patient's pulse, or supply a steady stream of air or drip-feed a patient. Patients in intensive care can do nothing for themselves; the machines are all-important. Andrew has to supervise the instruments. He has A-levels in chemistry and biology and has studied in the nursing school of the hospital to become a State Registered Nurse.

CHAPTER 4 *The atom*

4.1 A momentous discovery

In Paris in 1898 a young physicist called Marie Curie began her research work. She had decided to look for an explanation of a peculiar property of uranium salts. They can 'fog' photographic film, even when the film is some distance away. Could the uranium salts be giving off some kind of rays that travel through air?

Marie Curie soon found that this strange effect happened with all uranium salts. It depended only on the *amount* of uranium present in the salt and *not* on the chemical bonds that were present. She realised that this ability to give off rays must be a property of the *atoms* of uranium. It was a completely new type of property, quite different from the chemical reactions of uranium salts. This was an adventurous new idea. Marie Curie called this property of the uranium atom **radioactivity**.

Marie's husband, Pierre, left his own research work to help her in this exciting new science of radioactivity. In 1898, they discovered two new radioactive elements. They called one polonium, after Madame Curie's native country, Poland. The second element they called radium, meaning 'giver of rays'.

The Curies worked in dismal conditions. A scientist called Wilhelm Ostwald asked to be shown the laboratory in which they had discovered radium. He said it was 'a cross between a horse stable and a potato cellar' and that 'if I had not seen the work table with the chemical apparatus, I would have thought it was a practical joke'.

Marie and Pierre enjoyed their work, despite the miserable shed. While they experimented to obtain a pure specimen of the new element radium they often wondered what it would look like and what colours its salts would be. The radium chloride they obtained surprised them by glowing in the dark. Madame Curie wrote, 'One of our joys was to go into our workroom at night; we then perceived on all sides the feebly luminous silhouettes of the bottles and capsules containing our products. It really was a lovely sight and always new to us. The glowing tubes looked like faint fairy lights.'

Why do the atoms of these elements, uranium, polonium and radium, give off the rays which Marie Curie named radioactivity? The explanation came from the British physicist, Lord Rutherford, in 1902. He suggested that radioactivity is caused by atoms splitting up. This was another revolutionary idea. For many years, scientists had accepted Dalton's view of the atom. The British chemist John Dalton had put forward his Atomic Theory in 1808. He had backed the theory that matter is composed of minute particles called atoms. Atoms, he said, cannot be created or destroyed or split. We know now that a large number of elements have atoms which are unstable and split up to form smaller atoms.

4.2 Protons, neutrons and electrons

Early in the twentieth century, the work of the Curies and of Rutherford and other scientists showed that the atom is made up of smaller particles. These are called **protons**, **neutrons** and **electrons**. These **subatomic particles** differ in mass and in electrical charge (see Table 4.1).

Table 4.1 Subatomic particles

Particle	Mass (in atomic mass units)	Charge (in elementary charge units)
Proton	1	+1
Neutron	1	0
Electron	1/1840	−1

Protons and neutrons both have the same mass as an atom of hydrogen. We call this mass 1 **atomic mass unit** (1 u). (1 $u = 1.67 \times 10^{-27}$ kg.) The mass of an atom depends on the number of protons and neutrons it contains. The number of protons and neutrons together is called the **mass number**. The electrons in an atom contribute very little to its mass.

Electrons carry a negative electric charge of 1 elementary charge unit (−1 e). (1 e $= 1.60 \times 10^{-19}$ coulombs.) Protons carry a positive electric charge of +1 e. Neutrons are uncharged particles. The reason why whole atoms are uncharged is that **the number of electrons in an atom is the same as the number of protons**. The number of protons (which is also the number of electrons) is called either the **atomic number** or the **proton number**. This means that if you know the mass number and the atomic number you can find the number of neutrons:

$$\text{Number of neutrons} = \text{Mass number} - \frac{\text{Atomic (proton)}}{\text{number}}$$

For example, an atom of sodium has a mass of 23 u and an atomic (proton) number of 11. The number of electrons is 11; the same as the number of protons. The number of neutrons in the atom is

$$23 - 11 = 12$$

Relative atomic mass

An atom of hydrogen consists of one proton and one electron. It is the lightest of atoms. Chemists compare the masses of other atoms with that of a hydrogen atom. They use **relative atomic masses**. The relative atomic mass A_r of a uranium atom is 238. This means that one uranium atom is 238 times as heavy as one atom of hydrogen.

$$\frac{\text{Relative atomic mass of}}{\text{an element}} = \frac{\text{Mass of one atom of the element}}{\text{Mass of one atom of hydrogen}}$$

4.3 The arrangement of particles in the atom

How are protons, neutrons and electrons arranged in the atom? One idea was that they are all mixed up together, with the tiny electrons dotted about like currants in a bun, or plums in a plum pudding (see Fig. 4.1). This 'plum pudding' picture of the atom was disproved by the famous physicist, Lord Rutherford, in 1908.

Rutherford showed that most of the volume of an atom is space. The protons and neutrons occupy a tiny volume in the centre of an atom. Rutherford called this the **nucleus** (Fig. 4.2). The nucleus is minute in volume compared with the volume of the atom (see Fig. 4.3).

The electrons are present in the space around the nucleus. They guard the space by repelling the electrons of neighbouring

Fig. 4.1 The plum pudding atom

Fig. 4.2 The Rutherford atom

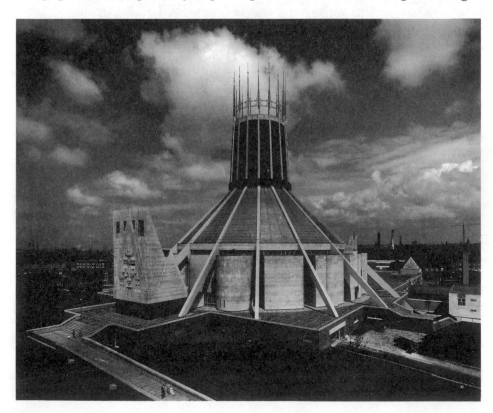

Fig. 4.3 If this building represents the space taken up by an atom, then a pea at the centre of the building represents the size of the nucleus

atoms. Remember that electrons are negatively charged. Repulsion will occur between the like charges on two electrons if they come close enough together. In Fig. 4.3 the electrons furthest away from the nucleus would be at the outside walls of the building.

JUST TESTING 15

1 Element A has atomic number 4 and mass number 9. How many protons, neutrons and electrons are present in one atom of A?

2 Copy this table into your book. Fill in the missing numbers.

Particle	Mass number	Atomic number	Number of protons	Number of neutrons	Number of electrons
Oxygen atom	16	8	—	—	—
Calcium atom	—	20	—	20	—
Bromine atom	80	—	35	—	—
Aluminium atom	27	13	—	—	—

3 State (i) the atomic number and (ii) the mass number of
a an atom with 15 protons and 16 neutrons
b an atom with 80 protons and 120 neutrons
c an atom with 27 protons and 33 neutrons.

4.4 Electrons in orbit

The electrons are in constant motion. They move round and round the nucleus in paths called orbits (see Fig. 4.4).

The scientist Niels Bohr added to our picture of the atom. He had the idea that the electrons in an atom do not all have the same energy. An electron needs more energy to circle the nucleus in an orbit of large radius than in an orbit close to the nucleus. The orbits are grouped together in **shells**. A **shell** is a group of orbits with similar energy. Each shell can hold up to a certain number of electrons (see Fig. 4.5). In any atom, the maximum number of electrons in the outermost group of orbits is 8.

Fig. 4.4   Electrons orbiting the nucleus

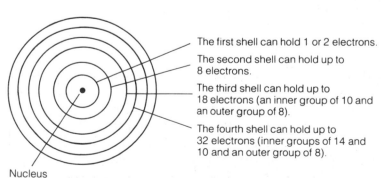

The first shell can hold 1 or 2 electrons.

The second shell can hold up to 8 electrons.

The third shell can hold up to 18 electrons (an inner group of 10 and an outer group of 8).

The fourth shell can hold up to 32 electrons (inner groups of 14 and 10 and an outer group of 8).

Fig. 4.5   Shells of electron orbits in an atom ▷   Nucleus

*4.5 How are the electrons arranged?

If you know the atomic (proton) number of an element, you know the number of electrons in an atom of the element. You can work out how the electrons are arranged by filling the lowest energy shells first. An atom of carbon has 6 electrons. The first shell will be filled by two of the electrons. The other four electrons will go into the second shell (see Fig. 4.6).

An atom of magnesium has atomic number 12. The first shell is filled by 2 electrons, the second shell is filled by 8 electrons, and 2 electrons occupy the third shell (Fig. 4.7). The arrangement of electrons can be written as (2.8.2). It is called the **electron configuration** of the element. Table 4.2 gives the electron configurations of the first 20 elements.

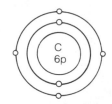

Fig. 4.6   Arrangement of electrons in the carbon atom

Fig. 4.7   The electron configuration of magnesium

Table 4.2 Electron configurations of the first 20 elements

| Element | Symbol | Atomic (proton) number | Number of electrons | | | | Electron config- uration |
			1st shell	2nd shell	3rd shell	4th shell	
Hydrogen	H	1	1				1
Helium	He	2	2				2
Lithium	Li	3	2	1			2.1
Beryllium	Be	4	2	2			2.2
Boron	B	5	2	3			2.3
Carbon	C	6	2	4			2.4
Nitrogen	N	7	2	5			2.5
Oxygen	O	8	2	6			2.6
Fluorine	F	9	2	7			2.7
Neon	Ne	10	2	8			2.8
Sodium	Na	11	2	8	1		2.8.1
Magnesium	Mg	12	2	8	2		2.8.2
Aluminium	Al	13	2	8	3		2.8.3
Silicon	Si	14	2	8	4		2.8.4
Phosphorus	P	15	2	8	5		2.8.5
Sulphur	S	16	2	8	6		2.8.6
Chlorine	Cl	17	2	8	7		2.8.7
Argon	Ar	18	2	8	8		2.8.8
Potassium	K	19	2	8	8	1	2.8.8.1
Calcium	Ca	20	2	8	8	2	2.8.8.2

SUMMARY NOTE

The protons and neutrons make up the nucleus at the centre of the atom. The electrons circle the nucleus in orbits. Groups of orbits with the same energy are called **shells**. The 1st shell can hold 2 electrons; the 2nd shell can hold 8 electrons; the 3rd shell can hold 18 electrons. The arrangement of electrons in an atom is called the **electron configuration**.

JUST TESTING 16

1 The electron configuration of phosphorus is (2.8.5). What does this tell you about the arrangement of electrons in the atom? Sketch the arrangement. (See Figs. 4.6 and 4.7 for help.)
2 Find the names of 4 boys and 2 girls in the names of the elements with the following atomic numbers: **a** 4, **b** 28, **c** 38, **d** 44, **e** 51, **f** 86. (See p. 410 for atomic numbers.)
3 Sketch the arrangement of electrons in the atoms of **a** B, **b** N, **c** F, **d** Al. (See p. 410 for atomic numbers.)

4.6 The repeating pattern of the elements

We have spent time looking at the structure of the atom and the electron configurations of the elements. How does this help with chemistry? If you look at the electron configurations of the atoms, some interesting points may strike you.

First, notice the elements with a full outer shell of electrons. These are helium (2), neon (2.8), argon (2.8.8) and, two elements which are not shown in Table 4.2, krypton and xenon. These elements are **the noble gases,** and are present in air (see Section 8.7). They are the least reactive of the elements. For many years, it seemed as though they took no part in any chemical reactions. Then, in 1960, krypton and xenon were made to combine with the very reactive element fluorine. The noble gases exist as single atoms. Their atoms do not combine in pairs to form molecules as do the atoms of most gaseous elements (e.g. O_2 and H_2). It seems logical to suppose that it is the full outer shell of electrons that makes the noble gases chemically unreactive.

Following each noble gas (that is, with atomic number 1 greater than the noble gas) is a metallic element with one electron in its outer shell. These elements are lithium (2.1), sodium (2.8.1), potassium (2.8.8.1) and (not shown in Table 4.2) rubidium and caesium. They are a set of very similar metallic elements. They all react with cold water to form hydrogen and a solution of the metal hydroxide (see Section 10.3). The strongly alkaline nature of the hydroxides gives these metals the name **the alkali metals**.

Preceding each noble gas (with atomic number 1 less than the noble gas) are the elements fluorine (2.7), chlorine (2.8.7) and (not shown in Table 4.2) bromine and iodine. These elements are a set of very reactive non-metallic elements. They are called **the halogens** because they react with metals to form salts. (Halogen comes from a Greek word and means salt-former.)

Some interesting patterns appear if the elements are first put into the order of their atomic numbers and then arranged in rows. A new row is started every time it is necessary to get a noble gas to fall into place under the preceding noble gas.

Table 4.3 A section of the Periodic Table

	Group 1	Group 2	Group 3	Group 4	Group 5	Group 6	Group 7	Group 0
Period 1	H (1)							He (2)
Period 2	Li (2.1)	Be (2.2)	B (2.3)	C (2.4)	N (2.5)	O (2.6)	F (2.7)	Ne (2.8)
Period 3	Na (2.8.1)	Mg (2.8.2)	Al (2.8.3)	Si (2.8.4)	P (2.8.5)	S (2.8.6)	Cl (2.8.7)	Ar (2.8.8)
Period 4	K (2.8.8.1)	Ca (2.8.8.2)						

(handwritten annotations) Group 1: 1 electron in outer shell · Alkali Metals · Halogens · Noble Gases

49

This arrangement of the elements puts elements which have the same number of electrons in the outermost shell into vertical columns. It is called the **Periodic Table**. It was given this name in 1856 by a Russian chemist called Mendeleev. The Periodic Table simplifies the task of learning about the chemical elements. The eight vertical columns of elements are called groups. The noble gases are in Group 0. For the rest of the elements, the group number is the number of electrons in the outermost shell. The horizontal rows of elements are called periods. The first period contains only hydrogen and helium. The second period contains the elements lithium to argon. The complete Periodic Table is shown on p. 412. You will need to refer to it again in later chapters.

4.7 Isotopes

Sometimes an element has a relative atomic mass which is not a whole number, e.g. chlorine has a relative atomic mass of 35.5. Since

Mass number = Number of protons + Number of neutrons

the mass number *must* be a whole number. The element chlorine consists of two kinds of atoms with different mass numbers. One type has 17 protons and 18 neutrons and mass number 35. The other type of atom has 17 protons and 20 neutrons and mass number 37. All atoms of chlorine have 17 electrons. Since it is the number of electrons which decides the chemical behaviour, all chlorine atoms behave in the same way. The number of neutrons in the nucleus does not affect the chemical behaviour. These different forms of chlorine are called *isotopes*. Isotopes are forms of an element which differ in the number of neutrons in the atom. There are three chlorine atoms with mass 35 *u* for each chlorine atom with mass 37 *u*. The average atomic mass is therefore

$$\frac{(3 \times 35) + 37}{4} = 35.5u$$

This is why the relative atomic mass of chlorine is 35.5.

The isotopes of chlorine are written as $^{35}_{17}Cl$ and $^{37}_{17}Cl$. In general, isotopes are shown as

Mass number
            Symbol
Atomic number

The symbol $^{23}_{11}Na$ tells you that sodium has mass number 23 and atomic number 11. You then know that there are 11 protons, 11 electrons and 12 neutrons in the atom. The isotopes of hydrogen are $^{1}_{1}H$, $^{2}_{1}H$ and $^{3}_{1}H$. They are often referred to as hydrogen-1, hydrogen-2 and hydrogen-3. Hydrogen-2 is also called deuterium, and hydrogen-3 is also called tritium.

Carbon has three isotopes, carbon-12, carbon-13 and carbon-14. The isotope carbon-12 has replaced hydrogen as the reference point for the modern scale of relative atomic masses. Instead of

$A_r(H) = 1.0000$, we use $A_r(C) = 12.0000$. There is very little difference numerically between the two scales. On the carbon-12 scale, $A_r(H) = 1.0080$.

JUST TESTING 17

1 Write the symbol with mass number and atomic number (as above) for each of the following elements:
   a aluminium with 13 protons and 14 neutrons
   b potassium with 19 protons and 20 neutrons
   c iron with 26 protons and 30 neutrons
   d uranium with 92 protons and 146 neutrons.

2 Three atoms are described below. Which two atoms have similar chemical properties?
   Atom A contains 5 protons and 6 neutrons.
   Atom B contains 9 protons and 10 neutrons.
   Atom C contains 13 protons and 14 neutrons.
   Explain your answer.

3 At one time, zinc beryllium silicate was used in the manufacture of fluorescent lights. When workers who came into contact with it developed a disease called 'berylliosis', the substance was banned. The body absorbs zinc beryllium silicate because beryllium follows the same chemical path through the body as a certain harmless element. Which element do you think this might be?

4.8 Radioactivity

Changes of the kind described by Madame Curie as radioactivity are **nuclear reactions**. In a nuclear reaction the atomic nucleus splits, and the protons and neutrons in it form two nuclei. The electrons divide themselves between the two new nuclei. Sometimes protons, neutrons and electrons fly out when the original nucleus divides (Fig. 4.8).

This type of change is quite different from a chemical reaction. In a chemical reaction, old bonds are broken and new bonds are made, but the atoms stay the same. In a radioactive change, new atoms of new elements are formed. Such changes are called **nuclear reactions**. Elements which undergo nuclear reactions are said to be **radioactive**. The breaking-up process is **radioactive decay**. In nuclear reactions, small particles and energy are given out or radiated. These particles and energy are called

Nucleus of unstable radioactive atom

Nucleus starts to divide.

Two new nuclei are formed. Some subatomic particles fly out.

Fig. 4.8   A nuclear reaction ▷

51

radioactivity. Three types of radiation are given off: α-**particles** and β-**particles** and γ-**radiation**. Their characteristics are shown in Fig. 4.9 . α-particles are the nuclei of helium atoms. They consist of 2 protons and 2 neutrons, and carry a positive charge. β-particles are electrons. γ-rays have extremely high penetrating power. They can pass through the skin, penetrate bone, and cause burns and cancers. People who work with sources of γ-rays protect themselves from the radiation by building a wall of lead bricks between themselves and the source (see Fig. 4.15).

Fig. 4.9 The penetrating power of α, β and γ-rays

4.9 The oldest murder in history?

Stonehenge is the most famous ancient monument in the UK. The circle of massive stones has puzzled people for centuries. A ditch which used to surround the monument has become filled in over the years. Recently, an archaeologist, Dr John Evans, was excavating the ditch when, to his surprise, he spotted a skeletal foot sticking out. Carefully, he unearthed the rest of the skeleton. It was the remains of a young man. How long had he lain there? How had he met his end? What Evans saw made him suspect foul play.

The tip of a flint arrowhead was embedded in the breastbone, showing that it had entered the body from behind. Another flint arrowhead was lodged in one of the ribs. A second rib had been chipped by an arrow on its way through the body. Three arrowheads lay nearby. Two had missing tips. The angle of entry showed that the arrows had been fired at close range. It was murder!

Evans used a different kind of detective work to find out the age of the skeleton. He discovered that the skeleton had lain in the ditch since 2200 B.C. This must be the oldest murder ever investigated! How did Evans fix the date?

The scientific method which Evans used is called **radiocarbon dating** or **carbon-14 dating**. This method has shown that parts of Stonehenge go back to 3500 B.C. Other parts are more recent, only 1200 B.C!

Fig. 4.10 Protection from radioactivity

4.10 Making use of radioactivity

Radiocarbon dating

What is radiocarbon dating? Radioactivity is detected by the use of an instrument called a **Geiger–Müller counter** (named after its inventors). Placed near a source of radioactivity, a Geiger–Müller counter (Fig. 4.11) emits a series of clicks. The number of clicks per minute (or counts per minute, c.p.m.) measures the strength of the radioactivity. Alternatively, the radioactivity in c.p.m. can be registered on a digital electronic counter.

If radioactivity is measured at various times and then plotted against the time since measurements were started, the result is a curve like that shown in Fig. 4.12. From this curve you can see that

Fig. 4.11 A Geiger–Müller counter

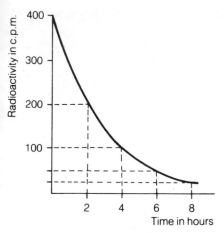

Fig. 4.12 Radioactive decay: a graph of count rate against time

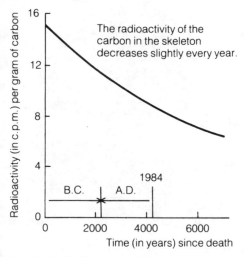

The radioactivity of the carbon in the skeleton decreases slightly every year.

Fig. 4.13 Radiocarbon dating

- the time taken for the count to fall from 400 to 200 c.p.m. is 2 hours
- the time taken for the count to fall from 200 to 100 c.p.m. is 2 hours
- the time taken for the count to fall from 100 to 50 c.p.m. is also 2 hours.

The time for the rate of radioactive decay to fall to half its value is the same, no matter what the original rate of decay is. This time is called the **half-life**. The half-life of the element in Fig. 4.12 is 2 hours.

Carbon is made up of the isotopes carbon-12, carbon-13 and carbon-14. The isotope carbon-14 is radioactive. It has a half-life of 5700 years. A living tree takes in carbon-14 in the carbon dioxide which it uses for photosynthesis. When the tree dies, no more carbon-14 is taken in. The carbon-14 already present decays slowly; carbon-12 does not change. The ratio of the amount of carbon-14 left in the wood to the amount of carbon-12 present can be used to give the age of the wood.

Animals also take in carbon in their food while they are alive. After their death, the proportion of carbon-14 in their bones tells how long it is since they were alive. A carbon-14 decay curve is shown in Fig. 4.13. The radioactivity of the skeleton discovered by John Evans showed that the carbon-14 present had been decaying for 4200 years. This established the time of death as 2200 B.C. By 1984, the trail was too cold for the detective work to result in an arrest!

Other radioisotopes

Radioactive elements differ enormously in their half-lives. Some are listed in Table 4.4.

Table 4.4 Some radioactive isotopes

Isotope	Half-life	Isotope	Half-life
Uranium-238	5000 million years	Gold-198	3 days
Uranium-235	700 million years	Sodium-24	15 hours
Plutonium-239	24 000 years	Uranium-239	24 minutes
Carbon-14	5700 years	Fluorine-17	1 minute
Strontium-90	59 years	Fluorine-22	4 seconds
Cobalt-60	5 years	Polonium-214	1/5000 seconds
Iodine-131	8 days		

Scientists have devised many uses for radioactive isotopes. Some of these are illustrated in Fig. 4.14.

4.11 The dangers of radioactivity

Radioactivity can be of great use to us. If it is mismanaged, however, it can be a serious health hazard. People who work with radioactive sources have to protect themselves from the

(a)

(b)

(c)

Fig. 4.14 Uses of radioactive isotopes: (a) this heart pacemaker contains plutonium-238; (b) measuring the uptake of iodine-131 in kidneys; (c) the technician is wrapping a belt of photographic film round a weld in the pipeline — if the weld is good, no radiation will penetrate it from the radioactive source inside the pipe to affect the film; (d) the diagram shows the production of metal foil (e.g. aluminium baking foil). The detector measures the amount of radiation passing through the foil. If the foil is too thick, the detector reading drops. The detector sends a message to the rollers, which move closer together to make the foil thinner.

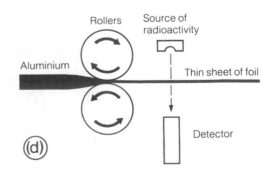

(d)

Rollers

Source of radioactivity

Aluminium

Thin sheet of foil

Detector

Fig. 4.15 Protection from radiation: (a) a long-handled tool is used to deal with a radioactive isotope; (b) a wall of lead bricks shields this scientist from γ-radiation; (c) pressurised suits protect workers from α-radiation

SUMMARY NOTE

The time taken for half the atoms present in a radioactive isotope to decay is called the **half-life** of the isotope. Half-lives vary from a fraction of a second to millions of years. Radioactive isotopes are used in medicine, in research and in industry. Workers handling radioactive materials take precautions to shield themselves from radiation.

radiation they are using. They often use long-handled tools to separate themselves as far as possible from a radioactive source (see Fig. 4.15a). They build walls of lead bricks to protect themselves from γ-emitters (see Fig. 4.15b).

Workers use gloves and protective clothing when working with sources of radioactivity (Fig. 4.15c). This precaution prevents any radioactive material from getting on to their hands or clothes. If radioactive elements get inside the body, they are far more dangerous. They can irradiate the body organs from close quarters, and the risk of cancer is very great. Even α-rays, the rays with least penetrating power, can do damage if they are inside the body.

JUST TESTING 18

1 Refer to the isotopes listed in Table 4.4. If you wanted to detect a leak in an underground water main, which radioisotope would you choose? The radioactivity must last long enough for you to drive along the route taken by the

5 mile long pipe to find out where the leak is. On the other hand, you do not want the radioactivity to contaminate the water for longer than is absolutely necessary.

2 A sample of radioactive isotope was put into a Geiger–Müller counter and the count rate was measured at various intervals.

Time (days)	Count rate (c.p.m.)
0	520
50	410
100	320
200	195
300	115
400	70

Plot a graph of the count rate against the time. Use the horizontal axis for time.
a Use the graph to find the count rate at 150 days and at 250 days.
b After what length of time was the count rate (i) 300 c.p.m., (ii) 150 c.p.m?
c What is the half-life of the radioactive element?

3 Explain the terms 'radioactive decay' and 'half-life'.
A sample of gold-198 has a count rate of 40 000 c.p.m. The half-life of this isotope is 3 days. How long will it take for the count rate to drop to 10 000 c.p.m?

4 Refer to the carbon-14 decay curve in Fig. 4.12.
What was the count rate of the skeleton just after death?
What is the half-life of carbon-14?
What was the count rate which dated the skeleton as 2200 B.C.?

5 Technetium-99 is a radioisotope used for medical diagnosis. It has a half-life of 6 hours. A scientist leaves 1 gram of technetium-99 in the laboratory at 6 p.m. on Friday. How much of the isotope will be left by 6 a.m. on Monday?

6 Strontium-90 is a radioactive isotope formed in nuclear reactors. One of the reasons it is dangerous is that it follows the same chemical pathway through the human body as another element X which is essential for health. By referring to the position of strontium in the Periodic Table, say which element you think is X.

4.12 The missing yellowcake

In November 1968 the cargo vessel Scheersberg sailed out of Antwerp in Belgium. She was loaded with a cargo of metal ore called **yellowcake**. For this voyage, the ship had taken on a new crew. She was bound for Genoa in Italy, but she never arrived. Two weeks later, she arrived at a Turkish port. The £3 million cargo was missing. Government secret agents tried to trace the cargo. The crew could not explain how 200 tonnes of yellowcake could have got lost. With the crew refusing to cooperate, the agents got nowhere. The mystery has never been solved.

Why is yellowcake so important? Why did the disappearance of the cargo cause so much worry? Why did the government take an interest, instead of leaving it to the owners? It was not only the £3 million the government was worried about. The government was afraid that the crew had sold the cargo to another country or to a group of terrorists. **Yellowcake** is an ore containing uranium oxide. There is something very special about uranium: it can be used to make atomic bombs.

4.13 The atomic bomb

In 1939 a German scientist called Otto Hahn did something sensational with uranium atoms. He split them. Hahn had been experimenting on firing neutrons at various elements. When he fired neutrons at uranium, some atoms of uranium-235 split into two new atoms and two neutrons. We call this atom-splitting process **fission** (see Fig. 4.16). When uranium-235 (U-235) atoms are split, an enormous amount of energy is released. Where does the energy come from? The sum of the masses of the atoms and neutrons produced is 0.2 m_u less than the mass of one atom of U-235. The missing mass has been converted into energy, **nuclear energy** (also called **atomic energy**).

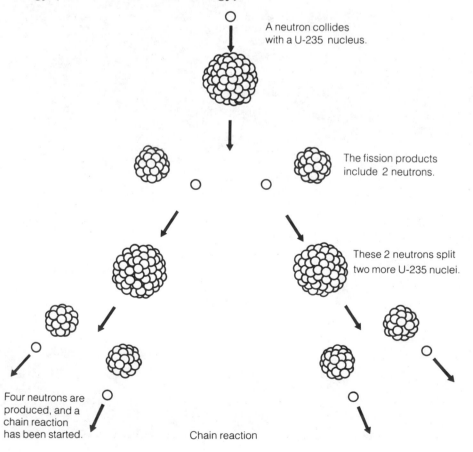

A neutron collides with a U-235 nucleus.

The fission products include 2 neutrons.

These 2 neutrons split two more U-235 nuclei.

Four neutrons are produced, and a chain reaction has been started.

Chain reaction

Fig. 4.16 The chain reaction in uranium fission

Shortly after Hahn's discovery the Second World War broke out. Scientists immediately started work on methods of making bombs which release this new form of energy.

Figure 4.16 shows what happens in a block of uranium-235. The fission of one U-235 atom produces two neutrons. These two neutrons split two more uranium atoms, to give four neutrons. A **chain reaction** is set off. In a large block of uranium-235, this results in an explosion. In a small block of uranium-235, neutrons escape from the surface of the block before producing fission, and an explosion does not occur. There is a **critical mass** below which a block of uranium will not make an atomic bomb. An atomic bomb consists of two blocks of uranium-235, each smaller than the critical mass. The bomb is detonated by firing one block into the other to make a single block which is larger than the critical mass. The detonation is followed by an atomic explosion.

Only two atomic bombs have been used in warfare. The two bombs destroyed two cities in 1945: Hiroshima and Nagasaki in Japan (see Fig. 4.17). The effects were devastating. Thousands of

Fig. 4.17 Devastation

people were killed in the blast. Thousands were burned and many received a large dose of radiation from which they never recovered. There was a great outcry against atomic bombs. The campaign against them continues today. No country has used atomic weapons since 1945, although many nations have huge stockpiles of atomic weapons.

4.14 Nuclear reactors

In nuclear reactors, energy is obtained from the same reaction as in atomic bombs, the fission of uranium-235. This time, the reaction is carried out in a controlled way. The reactors use naturally occurring uranium, which is a mixture of uranium-235 and uranium-238. Only uranium-235 undergoes fission. Figure 4.18 shows a nuclear reactor. Graphite rods are used to slow down the neutrons. Rods of boron control the rate of fission by absorbing some of the neutrons. The nuclear fission generates heat. This heat is used to turn water into steam. The steam drives a turbine, which generates electricity.

Rods of boron absorb some of the neutrons and control the rate of fission.

Tubes loaded with pellets of uranium oxide.

Graphite rods slow down the neutrons.

The heated fluid is used to boil water. The steam produced drives a turbine to generate electricity.

Steam

Water

Pump circulates the coolant.

Concrete shield to absorb radiation.

A coolant fluid circulates through the reactor. It may be water or a gas or liquid sodium.

Fig. 4.18 A nuclear reactor

4.15 Nuclear fusion

When two atoms of hydrogen-2 (deuterium) collide at high speed, the nuclei fuse together:

$$_1^2H + _1^2H \rightarrow _2^3He + _0^1n$$

An isotope of helium and a neutron are produced. The sum of the masses of the helium atom and the neutron is slightly less than the mass of the two hydrogen-2 atoms. The missing mass is converted into energy. The amount of energy released is enormous. This energy gives more hydrogen-2 atoms the energy they need to fuse with other atoms. Thus a chain reaction starts. As hydrogen-2 occurs in water as ^2H_2O, supplies are plentiful.

The fusion process may some day replace the fission of uranium-235 as a source of nuclear energy. It is very difficult, however, to give the hydrogen-2 atoms the energy they need to fuse in the first place. Scientists are still working on the problems of obtaining energy from fusion. The sun obtains its energy from the fusion of hydrogen-2 atoms. In the sun, the temperature is about 10 million °C, and the hydrogen-2 atoms have enough energy to fuse.

*4.16 The hydrogen bomb

The fusion of hydrogen-2 nuclei is the source of energy in the hydrogen bomb. The hydrogen-2 atoms are raised to the temperature at which they will fuse by the explosion of a uranium-235 bomb. The destruction caused by a hydrogen bomb would be so widespread that no nation has dared to use it in warfare.

SUMMARY NOTE

Energy is released in nuclear reactions. This **nuclear energy** can be released in an explosive manner in an **atomic bomb**. The **fission** (splitting) of uranium-235 was used in atomic bombs. The nuclear energy from the fission of uranium-235 is released in a safe, regulated manner in a nuclear power station. The **fusion** (joining together) of small nuclei also releases energy. The fusion of hydrogen-2 nuclei is the source of energy in the hydrogen bomb.

Exercise 4

1 An atom of the element X has atomic number 9 and mass number 19. Sketch the arrangement of electrons in an atom of X. How many protons and neutrons are present in the nucleus?

2 Atom A has atomic number 93 and mass number 239. Atom B has atomic number 94 and mass number 239. How many protons has atom A? How many neutrons has atom B? Are atoms A and B isotopes of the same element? Explain the meaning of the word 'isotope'.

3 Name the elements with the atomic numbers given in this sentence.
She had (29)-coloured hair, a laugh like a (47) bell and a heart of (79), but, as he gazed at her, his heart felt as heavy as (82) because he knew that she had a will of (26) and he would never persuade her to elope with him.

4 Copy and complete this table.

Element	Mass number	Atomic number	Protons	Neutrons	Electrons
X	11	-	-	12	-
Y	-	-	6	6	-
Z	-	8	-	-	16

5 What do a group of elements in the Periodic Table have in common?
What is a *period* of the Periodic Table?

*6 Explain why Mendeleev fitted the elements into vertical groups in his Periodic Table. Why did he fit lithium, sodium, potassium, rubidium and caesium into the same group? Why did he leave some gaps in his table?

7 a Explain the term 'radioactive element'. Give two examples.
  b Name the three types of radiation which are given off by radioactive isotopes. How do they differ in penetrating power? Which type of radiation is the most dangerous?

8 ● Strontium-90 is radioactive and therefore dangerous.
  ● Milk and bones contain more calcium than other tissues of the animal body. Why are babies especially at risk from damage by strontium-90 in the environment? (The clue is in the Periodic Table.)

9 Describe two examples of the way in which radioactive isotopes are used. What advice about safety would you give to someone who was about to use radioactive materials for the first time?

10 Lead-214 is radioactive, with a half-life of 27 minutes. A sample of lead-214 nitrate in a Geiger–Müller counter gives 6000 c.p.m. What will the count rate be after **a** 54 minutes, **b** 1 hour 48 minutes?

11 Complete this chart.

	Atomic number	Mass number	Number of protons	Number of neutrons	Number of electrons
a	3	7	-	-	-
b	32	41	-	-	-
c	20	-	-	16	-
d	-	-	-	45	35
e	-	-	8	8	-

12 A hospital is buying a radioactive source to irradiate cancer patients. Select a suitable isotope from the following list.

Isotope	Radiation	Half-life
Chromium-51	γ	26 days
Nickel-63	β	300 years
Caesium-135	β	2 million years
Caesium-136	β, γ	14 days
Caesium-137	β, γ	37 years
Cobalt-60	β, γ	5.3 years
Zinc-72	β, γ	49 hours
Zirconium-93	β	4 million years

Give reasons for your choice.

13 A doctor needs to put a radioactive isotope into the food of a patient in order to study his digestive system. The isotope chosen must have a suitable half-life. Which of the following list would be suitable?

Isotope	Half-life
Sulphur-35	87 days
Sulphur-37	5 minutes
Calcium-45	152 days
Sodium-24	15 hours
Sodium-25	58 seconds
Nitrogen-13	10 minutes

Give reasons for your choice.

14 Explain the difference between nuclear fusion and nuclear fission.

15 a The fission of uranium-235 is described as a 'chain reaction'. What is meant by a chain reaction?
b Where does the enormous amount of energy liberated in the fission of uranium-235 come from?
c Explain how nuclear energy is used to produce electricity.

16 Is there any real difference between the accident risk which society takes in using cars and the accident risk posed by atomic energy? Is one a worse killer than the other? Explain your answer.

This is a question to which many people do not have an answer. Perhaps you would like to form a group to discuss the issue. The **nuclear debate** comes up again in Chapter 20.

Career sketch: Pharmacologist

Karen is a pharmacologist. She started work as a pharmacist and then returned to university for further study. She now works for a drug company. For every new drug prescribed by doctors, many possible drugs are tested. Karen is a member of a team that does the testing. The organic chemist in the team is expert at making new organic compounds. The laboratory assistants test the new compounds on animals. Karen is an expert on the effects of different drugs on the human body.

CHAPTER 5 *Electrochemical reactions*

5.1 *Electroplating*

The tea service in Fig. 5.1 gleams like silver, but it is made of steel. The reason for the shine is that it has been given a coating of chromium. It will not rust as long as this surface layer is not scratched. Figure 5.2 shows how metal objects are chromium plated. The main reason for this treatment is to make the metal rustproof. Another benefit is that people find a bright shiny finish attractive.

During chromium plating, steel articles are immersed in a solution of a chromium salt. The steel is given a negative electric charge. For some reason, the result of this is that a layer of chromium becomes attached to the surface of the steel. To understand why this happens, you will have to study **electrochemical reactions**. There are two kinds. These are

- chemical reactions which take place when electricity flows through substances
- chemical reactions which produce electricity.

Fig. 5.1   Chromium plating gives this tea service a silvery shine

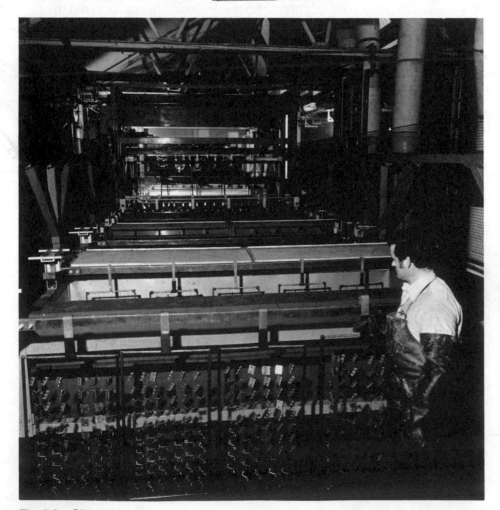

Fig. 5.2   Chromium plating

5.2 Which substances conduct electricity?

You may like to do Experiment 5.1 to find out which substances conduct electricity. Afterwards, you will be able to divide the substances tested into four groups (see Tables 5.1 and 5.2).

Table 5.1 Electrical conductors and non-conductors: solids

Electrical conductors	Non-conductors, i.e. insulators
All metallic elements	Non-metallic elements, e.g. sulphur
All alloys	Many compounds, e.g. polyethene
One non-metallic element, the graphite allotrope of carbon	Crystalline salts, e.g. sodium chloride, copper(II) sulphate

Table 5.2 Electrical conductors and non-conductors: liquids

Electrolytes	Non-electrolytes
Solutions of acids and alkalis and salts. Such liquids are called **electrolytes**. Chemical changes occur at the electrodes. For example, copper(II) chloride solution changes into copper and chlorine and water.	The liquids which do not conduct electricity are organic compounds, such as ethanol, and other liquid compounds, such as water. They are called **non-electrolytes**.

SUMMARY NOTE

Solids: Metals, alloys and graphite conduct electricity.
Liquids: Solutions of acids, alkalis and salts conduct electricity.

5.3 What happens when solutions conduct electricity?

Before you do Experiment 5.2, here are some new words:

A **cell** is a vessel in which either electricity produces a chemical change or a chemical change produces electricity.

The objects which conduct electricity into or out of the cell are called **electrodes**. The electrode connected to the positive terminal of the battery or other source of e.m.f. (electromotive force) is called the **anode.** The electrode connected to the negative terminal is called the **cathode.** The electrodes are usually made of elements such as platinum and graphite which do not react with electrolytes.

The results of Experiment 5.2 may make you wonder. Crystals of copper(II) chloride do not conduct electricity, and distilled water does not conduct electricity. Yet when the two substances are mixed to make a solution, the solution conducts. In the process the solute, copper(II) chloride, is split up. Copper appears as a layer on the negative electrode (the cathode). Chlorine is evolved at the positive electrode (the anode). Copper(II) chloride has been **electrolysed**, that is, split up by an electric current. The process is called **electrolysis**.

The electrodes...which is which?

How to remember:
Ano**D**e
AD → ADD = +
+ is positive
The anode is positive ... and the cathode is negative.

SUMMARY NOTE

Check the meanings of:
● cell
● electrode
● anode
● cathode.

63

How can we explain electrolysis? Copper appears always at the negative electrode, never at the positive electrode. Is there a positive charge associated with copper in copper(II) chloride? We accept that copper, the element, is composed of copper atoms. Does the combined copper in copper(II) chloride consist of atoms with positive charges? Chlorine appears always at the positive electrode, never at the negative electrode. Is there a negative charge associated with the chlorine combined with copper in copper(II) chloride?

The scientist who did the first work on electrolysis was Michael Faraday. In 1834, he suggested a theory to explain his observations. He believed that the evidence of electrolysis pointed to the existence of charged particles of matter. We now call them **ions**.

During electrolysis, positively charged copper ions travel to the negative electrode. When they reach the negative electrode, the ions lose their charge: they are **discharged** to form copper atoms. Negatively charged chloride ions travel to the positive electrode. When they reach the positive electrode, they lose their charge: they are discharged, and molecules of chlorine are formed. According to Faraday's theory, the compound copper(II) chloride consists of positively charged copper ions and negatively charged chloride ions.

Solid copper(II) chloride does not conduct electricity, yet when it is dissolved in water its aqueous solution does conduct. Is it the water in the solution that makes it an electrolyte? No, Experiment 5.1 shows that water is a very poor electrical conductor. To explain this difference, scientists suggested that, in a solid, the ions are fixed in position. They are held together by strong attractive forces between positive and negative ions. In a solution of a salt, the ions are free to move (Fig. 5.3). Another way to free the ions so that they can move to the electrodes might be to melt the solid (see Section 5.4).

Water, a non-conductor, is not ionic.

A crystalline solid is a non-conductor. The ions are fixed in a three-dimensional structure.

The solution is a good conductor. Ions from the crystalline solid are now free to move.

Non-electrolytes

Some of the liquids tested in Experiment 5.1 do not conduct electricity. It follows that these substances do not contain ions (see Section 6.3).

Weak electrolytes

Some substances conduct electricity to a very slight extent. In Experiment 5.1, you saw that ethanoic acid is a poor conductor,

---

The ions .. which is which?

How to remember:
think of the 5 Cs . . .
'Current carries copper cations to the cathode.'
Cations travel to the cathode . . .
Anions travel to the anode.

◁ Fig. 5.3   The ions must be free to move

SUMMARY NOTE

When a direct electric current is passed through solutions of some compounds, they are **electrolysed**, that is, split up by the current. Chemical changes occur in the **electrolyte**, resulting in the formation of new substances. Electrolysis is evidence that compounds which are electrolytes consist of positively and negatively charged particles called **ions**.

a weak electrolyte. A solution of ethanoic acid contains a small concentration of ions, which make it conduct (see Section 7.2).

5.4 Molten salts

The theory put forward to explain electrolysis is that some compounds consist of ions. In a solution of a salt, the ions must be free to move. Another way of enabling the ions to move might be to melt the salt. Figure 5.4 shows an apparatus which can be used to test this idea. Lead(II) bromide is a convenient salt to use because it has a fairly low melting point.

The experiment shows that molten lead(II) bromide is electrolysed. In the molten salt, ions are free to move.

3 Carbon anode. The reddish-brown vapour of bromine appears.

4 Carbon cathode. After cooling, lead can be seen on the cathode.

1 Lead(II) bromide. While the salt is solid, no current flows through the cell.

2 The crucible is heated. When the salt melts, the bulb lights, showing that an electric current is flowing. Molten lead(II) bromide is a conductor.

Pipeclay triangle

Heat

Fig. 5.4 Electrolysis of molten lead(II) bromide

5.5 What is the difference between an ion and an atom?

Atoms are uncharged. The number of protons in an atom is the same as the number of electrons (see Section 4.2). If an atom either gains or loses an electron, it will become electrically charged. Metal atoms and hydrogen atoms form positive ions (cations). For example, a sodium atom loses one electron to form a positively charged sodium ion:

$$\text{sodium atom} \rightarrow \text{electron} + \text{sodium ion}$$
$$\text{Na} \rightarrow \text{e}^- + \text{Na}^+$$

(11 protons, 11 electrons: uncharged)

(11 protons, 10 electrons: charge = +1)

The charge on a cation may be +1, +2 or +3.

- A copper atom loses 2 electrons to become a copper ion, Cu^{2+}.
- An aluminium atom loses 3 electrons to become an aluminium ion, Al^{3+}.

Non-metallic elements form negative ions (anions). They do this by gaining electrons. A chlorine atom gains one electron to become a chloride ion, Cl^-:

chlorine atom + electron → chloride ion
Cl + e^- → Cl^-
(17 protons,   (17 protons,
17 electrons: 18 electrons:
uncharged)   charge = −1)

An oxygen atom gains 2 electrons to become an oxide ion, O^{2-}. Some anions contain oxygen combined with another element. Examples are:

- hydroxide ion, OH^-
- nitrate ion, NO_3^-
- sulphate ion, $SO_4{}^{2-}$.

The ions you meet in this chapter are listed in Table 5.3. You will learn more about ions in Chapter 6.

Table 5.3 Symbols and formulas of some ions

Cations	Anions
Aluminium ion Al^{3+}	Bromide ion Br^-
Copper(II) ion Cu^{2+}	Chloride ion Cl^-
Hydrogen ion H^+	Iodide ion I^-
Lead(II) ion Pb^{2+}	Hydroxide ion OH^-
Sodium ion Na^+	Nitrate ion NO_3^-
Zinc ion Zn^{2+}	Sulphate ion $SO_4{}^{2-}$

(handwritten margin note:) Cations travel to Cathode
Anions travel to Anode.

JUST TESTING 19

1 a Divide the following list into (i) electrical conductors, (ii) non-conductors:
ethanol (alcohol), sodium chloride crystals, limewater, sugar solution, molten magnesium chloride, distilled water, solid sodium hydroxide, molten sodium hydroxide, sodium hydroxide solution.

  b What is the difference between the ways in which a copper wire and molten lead(II) bromide conduct electricity?

  c Some of the conductors in the list are electrolytes. Which are they?

2 Explain the words: cell, anode, cathode, anion, cation, electrolysis.

3 a Why do ions move towards electrodes?

  b Why is solid copper(II) chloride not an electrical conductor?

5.6 What happens at the electrodes?

Copper(II) chloride solution

Copper ions travel to the negative electrode, the cathode, where they form atoms of copper (see Fig. 5.5). When a copper ion reaches the cathode, this electrode, being negatively charged, can supply two electrons to the copper ion turning it into a copper atom. The equation for this electrode process is

$$\text{copper(II) ion} + 2 \text{ electrons} \rightarrow \text{copper atom}$$
$$Cu^{2+}(aq) \qquad + 2e^- \qquad \rightarrow Cu(s)$$

Fig. 5.5 Electrode processes in the electrolysis of copper(II) chloride at carbon electrodes

Chloride ions travel to the positive electrode, the anode, where chlorine gas is evolved. Being positively charged, the anode can take away an electron from a chloride ion. The chloride ion loses its electron — is **discharged** — to form a chlorine atom. Then two chlorine atoms join to form a chlorine molecule. The electrode process is

$$\text{chloride ion} \rightarrow \text{chlorine atom} + \text{electron}$$
$$Cl^-(aq) \qquad \rightarrow Cl(g) \qquad + e^-$$

followed by

$$2Cl(g) \rightarrow Cl_2(g)$$

The electrons given up by the chloride ions at the positive electrode travel round the external circuit (the wires outside the cell) to the negative electrode. There they combine with copper ions to form copper atoms. A constant stream of electrons therefore flows through the external circuit (Fig. 5.5). This stream of electrons is an **electric current**.

SUMMARY NOTE

When electrolysis occurs, ions conduct the electric current through the cell. Positive ions (cations) travel to the negative electrode (the cathode). Negative ions (anions) travel to the positive electrode (the anode).

At the electrodes, ions are **discharged**. Positive ions take electrons from the negative electrode to become atoms. Negative ions give up electrons to the positive electrode to become atoms. Electrons travel from the positive electrode to the negative electrode through the circuit outside the cell.

JUST TESTING 20

1 Refer to Fig. 5.4.
  a Write the symbols for the lead(II) ion and the bromide ion.
  b At which electrode do you see (i) lead, (ii) bromine?
  c Write equations for the processes which occur at the two electrodes.
  d What is happening in the circuit which connects the electrodes outside the crucible?

ay in which a solution of copper(II) chloride
tricity. What type of particle conducts
through the cell and **b** through the circuit
cell?

3 Mo... assium iodide can be electrolysed. Name the
products formed at **a** the positive electrode and **b** the
negative electrode. Write equations for the electrode
processes which result in the formation of these products.

*5.7 More complicated examples of electrolysis

Copper(II) sulphate solution

When copper(II) sulphate is electrolysed, copper is deposited on
the cathode and oxygen is evolved at the anode. To explain how
this happens, we have to think about the water present in the
solution. Water is a covalent liquid, which is ionised to a very
small extent into hydrogen ions and hydroxide ions:

water $\rightleftharpoons$ hydrogen ions + hydroxide ions
$$H_2O(l) \rightleftharpoons H^+(aq) \quad + OH^-(aq)$$

At the positive electrode there are hydroxide ions, OH^-, as well
as sulphate ions, $SO_4{}^{2-}$. Sulphate ions are more stable than
hydroxide ions. It is easier for hydroxide ions to lose their
electrons, and hydroxide ions are discharged. The OH groups
which are formed exist for only a fraction of a second before
rearranging to give oxygen and water:

$$OH^-(aq) \rightarrow OH(aq) + e^-$$
$$4OH(aq) \rightarrow 2H_2O(l) + O_2(g)$$

Although only a tiny fraction of water molecules are ionised,
once hydroxide ions have been discharged, more water molecules
ionise to replace them with fresh hydroxide ions.

Sodium chloride solution

When molten sodium chloride is electrolysed, the products are
sodium and chlorine. When a solution of sodium chloride is
electrolysed, chlorine forms at the positive electrode and
hydrogen forms at the negative electrode. At the negative
electrode, sodium ions and hydrogen ions are present. Sodium
ions are more stable than hydrogen ions. It is easier for an
electron to join a hydrogen ion than it is for it to join a sodium
ion, so the discharge of hydrogen ions takes place. The hydrogen
atoms formed join in pairs to form hydrogen molecules:

$$H^+(aq) + e^- \rightarrow H(g)$$
$$2H(g) \quad \rightarrow H_2(g)$$

At the positive electrode, there is a small concentration of
hydroxide ions from the ionisation of water molecules. Chloride
ions are, however, discharged in preference to hydroxide ions.

Fig. 5.6 The electrolysis of dilute sulphuric acid

Dilute sulphuric acid

The electrolysis of dilute sulphuric acid is shown in Fig. 5.6.

5.8 Which ions are discharged?

You will have realised by now that some ions are easier to discharge at an electrode than others.

Anions. Sulphate ions and nitrate ions are very difficult to discharge. In solutions of these ions, hydroxide ions are discharged instead, and oxygen is evolved.

Cations. The ions of very reactive metals, such as sodium, are difficult to discharge. Sodium atoms are very ready to react to form compounds containing sodium ions. It is difficult to reverse the process and force a sodium ion to accept an electron and become a sodium atom (see Fig. 5.7). The cations of less reactive metals, such as copper and lead, are easy to discharge.

Fig. 5.7 Sodium atoms want to become sodium ions; sodium ions are happy as they are

It is possible to construct a 'league table' of metals, arranging them in order of how easily they are discharged at a negative electrode. The metals with ions that are difficult to discharge are at the top of the table. The order is called the **electrochemical series.** Table 5.4 shows a section of the electrochemical series including hydrogen. It also puts metals in the order of how easily they react, that is, the order in which their atoms give up electrons to become ions (see Section 11.5).

Table 5.4 Part of the electrochemical series

Potassium, K	
Calcium, Ca	
Sodium, Na	Ions discharged
Magnesium, Mg	in electrolysis
Aluminium, Al	less easily
Zinc, Zn	
Iron, Fe	Electrons lost
Hydrogen, H	to form positive
Copper, Cu	ions (cations)
Silver, Ag	more easily
Gold, Au	

(arrow pointing upward beside the list indicating direction)

---

*JUST TESTING 21

1 A solution of potassium bromide is electrolysed. A brown colour appears at one electrode.
   a At which electrode does the brown colour appear?
   b What is produced at the other electrode?
   c Write equations for the two electrode processes.

2 Sodium nitrate solution is electrolysed with carbon electrodes. Name the ions present. Which ions are discharged **a** at the positive electrode and **b** at the negative electrode? Write equations for the electrode processes.

3 An aqueous solution of sodium chloride is electrolysed.
   a What two kinds of ion are present at the positive electrode? Which is discharged? Which kind of ion accumulates?
   b What two kinds of ion are present at the negative electrode? Which is discharged? Which kind of ion accumulates?
   c As these changes take place, the solution of sodium chloride is turning into a solution of something else. What is it becoming?

4 In the electrolysis of acidified water (Fig. 5.6) the gases formed are in the ratio:

   2 volumes of hydrogen : 1 volume of oxygen

   When you have studied Section 12.4, return to this question. Use the information to work out the equation for the reaction:

   water → hydrogen + oxygen.

SUMMARY NOTE

Water is ionised to a very small extent to form $H^+(aq)$ ions and $OH^-(aq)$ ions. These ions are sometimes discharged when aqueous solutions are electrolysed.

The ions of very reactive metals, e.g. Na^+, are difficult to discharge. In aqueous solution, hydrogen ions are discharged and hydrogen is evolved at the negative electrode. The anions SO_4^{2-} and NO_3^- are difficult to discharge. In aqueous solution, OH^- ions are discharged instead, and oxygen is evolved at the positive electrode.

5.9 Electrolysis with reactive electrodes

In all the electrode processes that we have covered so far the electrodes have supplied electrons to the cell or removed electrons from the cell. They have been **inert**: they have not taken part in the chemical reactions. Sometimes, electrodes do take part in the cell reaction.

When copper(II) sulphate is electrolysed with carbon electrodes, as in Experiment 5.5, copper is discharged at the negative electrode and oxygen is evolved at the positive electrode. With copper electrodes, copper is discharged at the negative electrode as before.

Cathode (negative): $Cu^{2+}(aq) + 2e^- \rightarrow Cu(s)$

At the positive electrode, there are three possible processes which would release electrons. These are:

- the discharge of SO_4^{2-} ions
- the discharge of OH^- ions
- the ionisation of Cu atoms from the anode.

In fact, the third of these reactions happens:

Anode (positive): $Cu(s) \rightarrow Cu^{2+}(aq) + 2e^-$

The combined result of the reactions at the two electrodes is a transfer of copper from the positive electrode to the negative electrode.

JUST TESTING 22

1 Different products are obtained in the electrolysis of copper(II) sulphate solution with **a** carbon electrodes and **b** copper electrodes. What products are formed in each case? Write equations for the electrode processes which occur.

5.10 Applications of electrolysis

Electroplating

Often, people want to coat a relatively cheap metal with a more beautiful and more expensive metal. A thin layer of silver or gold can be used to beautify metal objects (Fig. 5.8). To limit the cost, a method of applying a thin layer only is needed. Electrolysis can be used to produce a thin even film of metal which adheres well to the surface being coated. The technique is called **electroplating** (Fig. 5.9).

Electroplating is used for protection as well as for decoration. You will remember from Section 5.1 that steel is chromium plated to prevent it from rusting. Chromium does not stick well

Fig. 5.8 Silverplate

1 The object to be plated is made the negative electrode (the cathode).

2 The electrolyte is a solution of one of the salts of the metal.

3 The positive electrode (the anode) is usually made of the plating metal. Metal atoms dissolve to form metal ions. This keeps the concentration of ions in solution constant.

Fig. 5.9 Electroplating

to steel. Before steel is chromium plated, it is first electroplated with copper, which does adhere well to steel. It is then nickel plated. Nickel is not corroded by air or water. The final step is chromium plating. The result is a bright, non-corrodible surface.

The rusting of iron is a serious and expensive problem (see Section 11.12). In the manufacture of food cans, a layer of tin is electroplated on to iron. Tin is an unreactive metal, and the juices in foods do not react with it. A layer of zinc is applied to iron in the manufacture of **galvanised** iron. Electroplating is often employed. (See Experiments 5.7 and 5.8.)

Extraction of metals from their ores

It is difficult to extract the most reactive metals from their ores. For many of them, e.g. sodium and aluminium, electrolysis is the only method which works (see Section 11.10).

An electrolytic method is also used to obtain pure copper from a slab of impure copper (see Section 11.10).

Manufacture of sodium hydroxide

If brine (sodium chloride solution) is electrolysed, hydrogen ions and chloride ions are discharged at the electrodes. Sodium ions and hydroxide ions accumulate in the solution. Gradually, the sodium chloride solution turns into a solution of sodium hydroxide. Figure 5.10 shows a diaphragm cell, an industrial method of carrying out this electrolysis continuously. The three important chemicals, sodium hydroxide (Section 7.3), chlorine (Section 16.5) and hydrogen (Section 9.17), are all obtained from the plentiful starting material, brine.

1 Purified saturated brine flows in.

Chlorine

Hydrogen

2 Chloride ions are discharged at the anode. Chlorine is evolved.

3 Ions diffuse through the porous asbestos diaphragm.

4 Hydrogen ions are discharged at the cathode. Hydrogen is evolved.

5 The liquid leaving the diaphragm cell contains sodium hydroxide and sodium chloride.

It is evaporated until sodium chloride crystallises out.

Then it is sold as slightly impure sodium hydroxide solution.

Anode

Cathode

Fig. 5.10 The diaphragm cell for the electrolysis of brine (sodium chloride solution)

Fig. 5.11 Diaphragm cells used for the electrolysis of brine

JUST TESTING 23

1 a You need to plate an iron nail with nickel. Draw the apparatus and the circuit you would use. Say what the electrolyte is, what the electrodes are made of and what charge they carry.

 b Explain why it is worth while going to the trouble and expense of electroplating iron nails.

2 Some parts of a car body are protected from rusting by a coat of paint.

   a What advantage does chromium plating have over painting?

   b Why do you think the door handles are chromium plated, not painted?

   c What precautions are taken to ensure that the layer of chromium adheres well to the steel?

3 Why is the manufacture of gold-plated watches and jewellery big business? What two advantages do gold-plated articles have over articles made of cheaper metals? What is the advantage of gold plate over pure gold? Why is pure gold not used?

5.11 *Chemical cells*

There are two kinds of cells:

Electrolytic cells

Electric current flows into the cell. The result is that a chemical reaction takes place.

Chemical cells

A chemical reaction takes place in the cell. The result is that an electric current flows through the external circuit.

In the chemical cell shown in Fig. 5.12, the chemical reaction that takes place is

zinc + copper(II) ions → zinc ions + copper
$$Zn(s) + Cu^{2+}(aq) \rightarrow Zn^{2+}(aq) + Cu(s)$$

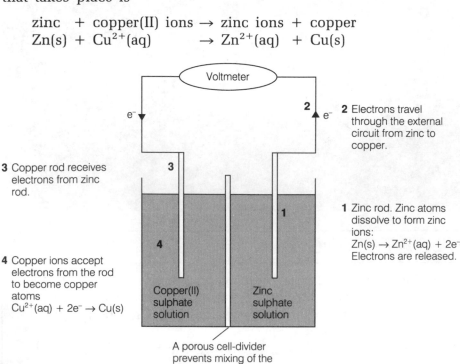

2 Electrons travel through the external circuit from zinc to copper.

3 Copper rod receives electrons from zinc rod.

1 Zinc rod. Zinc atoms dissolve to form zinc ions:
$Zn(s) \rightarrow Zn^{2+}(aq) + 2e^-$
Electrons are released.

4 Copper ions accept electrons from the rod to become copper atoms
$Cu^{2+}(aq) + 2e^- \rightarrow Cu(s)$

A porous cell-divider prevents mixing of the two solutions without breaking the circuit.

Fig. 5.12   The Daniell cell

As a result of this reaction, an electric current flows through the external circuit.

This cell is called the **Daniell cell** after its inventor. Electrons flow from zinc to copper through the external circuit. The difference in electric potential between the two electrodes is called the **electromotive force** (e.m.f.) of the cell. The Daniell cell has an e.m.f. of 1.1 volts (1.1 V).

Many metals can be paired up in chemical cells. The further apart the metals are in reactivity, the greater is the e.m.f. produced by the cell. The direction of flow of electrons is from the more reactive metal to the less reactive metal (that is, from the metal higher in the electrochemical series to a metal lower in the series, see Section 5.8).

*The lead–acid accumulator

Cells can be connected in series to form a **battery**. The type of battery in general use in motor vehicles is the lead–acid accumulator. The battery contains three or six 2 V cells to make a battery that delivers 6 V or 12 V. The word 'battery' is sometimes used incorrectly for a single cell. For example, what we call a torch 'battery' is often a single cell. In the lead–acid accumulator, each cell has one lead electrode, one lead(IV) oxide (PbO_2) electrode and sulphuric acid as the electrolyte. When the battery supplies a current, lead and lead(IV) oxide are both converted into lead(II) ions. When the reactants have been used up, the battery can no longer supply a current; it is 'flat'. It can, however, be recharged. When the vehicle engine is running, it rotates the dynamo (the alternator) which generates electricity and recharges the battery. If the dynamo is faulty, the battery will become flat. It can then be recharged by connecting it to a battery charger, a transformer connected to the mains. This reverses the sign of each electrode and reverses the chemical reactions that have occurred at the electrodes. Lead and lead(IV) oxide are reformed, and the battery is again able to supply an e.m.f.

*Dry cells

Dry cells are chemical cells in which the electrolyte is a damp paste. They can be used in torches, radios, etc., where a Daniell cell is not suitable because the electrolyte might leak out.

The zinc–carbon dry cell. You will have used the zinc–carbon type of dry cell (see Figs. 5.13, 5.14 and 5.15), which has an e.m.f. of 1.5 V. Cells of this type are 1–2 cm in diameter and 3–10 cm in length. They are used in flashlights, portable radios, toys, etc. The chemical reactions that take place oxidise zinc atoms to zinc ions and reduce manganese(IV) oxide to manganese(III) oxide. (For oxidation–reduction, see Section 9.18). When the chemicals have been used up, the cell can no longer operate: it is flat.

The alkaline manganese cell. The alkaline manganese cell uses zinc as the negative electrode and manganese(IV) oxide as the positive electrode. The electrolyte contains potassium hydroxide.

Fig. 5.13 A pocket calculator uses a dry cell.

Fig. 5.14 Zinc–carbon dry cells

1 A layer of cardboard or metal acts as a seal.

2 The zinc case is the negative electrode.

3 A porous bag contains a moist paste of ammonium chloride, manganese(IV) oxide and carbon powder.

4 A graphite rod immersed in the paste is the positive electrode.

5 When a circuit connects the metal cap on the carbon rod with the zinc case, electrons flow from zinc to carbon.

Fig. 5.15   The zinc–carbon dry cell

Fig. 5.16   Alkaline manganese cells

The alkaline manganese cell has the same e.m.f. as the zinc–carbon cell, 1.5 V, but delivers more current than the zinc–carbon cell. Alkaline manganese cells do not become flat as quickly in use and have a longer shelf life than zinc–carbon cells.

The silver oxide cell.   Another type of dry cell is the silver oxide cell (Fig. 5.17). Silver oxide cells are tiny: 0.5–1 cm in diameter and 0.25–0.5 cm in height. They are used in electronic wrist watches, cameras and electronic calculators. Such devices draw little current and silver oxide cells have a long life. They are rather expensive. As the cell operates, zinc is oxidised to zinc ions, and silver ions are reduced to silver (see Fig. 5.17).

Cap over zinc electrode

Zinc electrode (negative)

Metal cup

Separator

Silver oxide electrode (positive)

Fig. 5.17   A silver oxide cell

The nickel–cadmium cell. The nickel–cadmium cell (see Fig. 5.18) has a big advantage over other cells: it is rechargeable. As the cell operates, cadmium is converted into cadmium(II) ions and nickel(IV) oxide into nickel(II) hydroxide. When the cell becomes flat, it can be connected to a source of direct current, which reverses the cell reaction. The cell then has a renewed source of e.m.f.

The nickel–cadmium cell has an e.m.f. of 1.4 V. It is sold as a sealed unit ready for use in calculators, photographic flash units, mobile phones, etc.

Fig. 5.18 Nickel–cadmium rechargeable cells

Table 5.5 Dry cells

Type	Electrodes	Electrolyte	Voltage	Uses	Characteristics
Zinc–carbon	Carbon (+) Zinc (−)	Ammonium chloride	1.5 V	Radios, cassette players, electrical toys, torches	Low cost. Relatively short life. Not rechargeable. Leakage of electrolyte occurs in the unsealed types of cell. Operates at low current; voltage drops gradually during discharge.
Alkaline manganese	Manganese(IV) oxide (+) Zinc (−)	Potassium hydroxide	1.5 V	Cassette players, electrical toys, appliances that are in use for long periods	Costs about twice as much as the zinc–carbon cell and lasts twice as long. Long shelf-life. Not rechargeable. Gives a large current; voltage remains steady during discharge.
Silver oxide	Silver oxide (+) Zinc (−)	Potassium hydroxide	1.5 V	Watches, calculators, hearing aids, cameras	Expensive. Long life. Not rechargeable. Small and lightweight. Voltage remains constant in operation.
Nickel–cadmium	Nickel oxide (+) Cadmium (−)	Potassium hydroxide	1.4 V	Cassette players, electrical toys, radios, mobile phones	Expensive. Gives a large current. Rechargeable. There is a danger of explosion during charging if the current is too high or the rate of charging is too high.

1 Why is the silver oxide 'battery' suitable for use in a camera? Why is it expensive?

2 Both the lead–acid accumulator and the nickel–cadmium cell are rechargeable.
   a What does 'rechargeable' mean?
   b What is the advantage of rechargeable cells over others?
   c For what uses is the nickel–cadmium cell more suited than the lead–acid accumulator?
   d What is the most widespread use of the lead–acid accumulator?

3 a Why do car batteries sometimes become flat?
   b How can they be made to function again?

4 Why is the alkaline manganese cell preferred to the silver oxide cell for use in radios?

5 How did the development of mobile phones depend on the nickel–cadmium battery?

6 The following pairs of metals are joined to form chemical cells. Place the pairs in list **a** and the pairs in list **b** in order of the e.m.f. of the cells. The electrochemical series in Section 5.8 will help you.
   a zinc–copper, magnesium–copper, iron–copper
   b magnesium–zinc, iron–magnesium, magnesium–tin

7 Copper and lead are both low in the electrochemical series (Section 5.8). When they are paired up to form a chemical cell, which of the two metals will become the negative electrode?

SUMMARY NOTE

Chemical cells, e.g. the Daniell cell, transform the energy of chemical reactions into electrical energy. A vehicle lead–acid accumulator consists of a series of chemical cells. Chemical reactions in each cell supply an electric current. These reactions are reversed when the battery is recharged.

Examples of dry cells are: the zinc–carbon dry cell, the alkaline manganese cell, the silver oxide cell and the rechargeable nickel–cadmium cell.

Exercise 5

1 What are the electrical symbols for a bulb, a switch, a cell and a battery of three cells?
Draw a circuit which you could use to test various materials to find out whether they are electrical conductors.
Divide the following list into conductors and non-conductors:
copper, steel, wood, PVC, brass, polythene, silver, candle wax, water, petrol, tetrachloromethane (CCl_4), sodium hydroxide solution, sugar solution.

2 Each of these clues has a one-word answer. (The number of letters in the word is given in brackets after the clue.) Write the answers down one beneath the other. What do the initial letters spell out?

1 There are many of these in an electric current. (9)
2 A metal which is easily discharged in electrolysis. (4)
3 A substance which can be split up by electricity. (11)
4 Every metal is one. (9)
5 The number of charges on a sulphate ion. (3)
6 This sort of metal is not discharged in electrolysis. (8)
7 A gas which is often formed at a positive electrode. (6)
8 The negative electrode. (7)
9 A gas which may be formed at a negative electrode. (8)
10 This may take electricity out of the cell. (9)

11 This kind of salt conducts electricity. (6)
12 This will not allow current to pass. (9)
13 Make this if you want a salt to conduct. (8)
14 Good electroplating needs plenty of this. (4)
15 This tends to stop current flowing. (10)
16 A ---- would be too long, even for clue 14. (4)

3 Name the substances A to H in this table. Write equations for the electrode processes which lead to their formation

Electrolyte	Positive electrode	Negative electrode
Dilute sulphuric acid	A	B
Copper(II) chloride solution	C	D
Sodium chloride solution	E	F
Calcium chloride solution	G	H

*4 In the electrolysis of potassium chloride solution, what element is formed **a** at the positive electrode and **b** at the negative electrode? Why does the solution around the negative electrode become alkaline?

5 Copper(II) sulphate solution can be electrolysed between platinum electrodes.
   a Describe what you see at both electrodes.
   b How could you test the product formed at the positive electrode?
   c Write equations for the electrode processes.

Career sketch: Dietician

Molly is a clinical dietician. She works in a hospital, planning diets and supervising the meals served to patients. Molly has to ensure that food is prepared under safe and hygienic conditions. She also confers with doctors about the patients' nutrition. When patients leave hospital, Molly tells them and their families how to keep to their diets. Molly took A-levels, including chemistry, and studied in a university school of nursing.

CHAPTER 6 *The chemical bond*

metallic bond p193

6.1 Getting in the swim with ions

How can we take the sting out of swimming? Chlorine does a good job of killing bacteria in pool water. Unfortunately, it also makes swimmers' eyes sting. It would be an advantage to replace chlorine with another **bacteriocide** which is also kind to the eyes.

A British firm has found an answer to the problem by inventing a new device. Two electrodes made of a silver–copper alloy dip into the water. A low voltage direct current is fed through the electrodes. The current is made to switch every half minute. The electrodes slowly release copper ions and silver ions into the water. Silver ions kill bacteria, and copper ions kill algae. The dead bacteria and algae are electrostatically charged. The charges make them clump together to form a solid which is easily removed by the pool filter.

The new device is priced at about £500 and costs the same to run as a 40 watt bulb. It can be used to purify water in hospitals. It could be used to provide safe drinking water in countries where sanitation is poor. The device makes use of **ions**. It is time to find out more about them.

6.2 The ionic bond

Sodium chloride

In Chapter 5, you studied electrolysis. You found that some compounds are electrolytes: they conduct electricity. Other compounds are non-electrolytes. To explain the results of electrolysis, we accepted the idea that electrolytes consist of small charged particles called **ions**. When molten sodium chloride is electrolysed, sodium is deposited at the negative electrode, and chlorine is given off at the positive electrode. This fits in with the theory that sodium chloride consists of positively charged sodium ions and negatively charged chloride ions, Na^+Cl^-.

Look at the arrangement of electrons in a sodium atom (Fig. 6.1). There is just one electron more than there is in an atom of the noble gas neon.

You have read in Section 4.6 that the noble gases are helium, neon, argon, krypton and xenon. These gases take part in hardly any chemical reactions. All the noble gases have full outer shells of electrons (Fig. 6.2). It seems logical to suppose that it is this electron arrangement that makes them stable, that is, chemically unreactive (Fig. 6.3).

When a sodium atom loses the lone electron from its outermost shell, the outer shell that remains contains 8 electrons. A sodium atom cannot just shed an electron. The attraction between the nucleus and the electrons prevents this. It can,

Fig. 6.1   Atoms of sodium and neon

Fig. 6.2   The electron arrangements in helium, neon and argon

Fig. 6.3 The noble gases do not care to combine ▷

Fig. 6.4 The arrangement of electrons in chlorine and argon

Na
↓
Na⁺ + e⁻

e⁻ + Cl
↓
Cl⁻

Na⁺

Cl⁻

Fig. 6.5 The formation of sodium chloride

Na atom

Na⁺ ion

Fig. 6.6 The sodium atom and the sodium ion

Cl atom

Cl⁻ ion

Fig. 6.7 A chlorine atom and a chloride ion

however, give an electron to a chlorine atom. In fact, sodium burns vigorously in chlorine to form sodium chloride.

Why should a chlorine atom want an electron? Look at the electron arrangement (Fig. 6.4). With one more electron, chlorine would have the same electron arrangement as argon. A full outer shell brings with it stability.

Figure 6.5 shows what happens when an atom of sodium donates an electron to an atom of chlorine. A full outer shell is left behind in sodium, and a full outer shell is created in chlorine. To make clear what happens, the sodium electrons have been shown as **x** and the chlorine electrons as **o**. This dot-and-cross diagram does not imply that there are two kinds of electrons!

A sodium atom has 11 electrons, 11 protons and 12 neutrons. After it loses one electron, it is left with 11 protons and 10 electrons. The total charge is $+11-10 = +1$ charge unit. It is not a sodium atom, Na, any longer: it is a sodium ion, Na⁺ (see Fig. 6.6).

A chlorine atom has 17 protons and 17 electrons. After it gains an electron, making 17 protons and 18 electrons, the charge is $+17-18 = -1$ charge unit. The chlorine atom, Cl, has become a chloride ion, Cl⁻ (see Fig. 6.7).

Remember this from Chapter 5. An ion is an atom or group of atoms which carries an electric charge. A positively charged ion, e.g. Na⁺, is called a **cation**. A negatively charged ion, e.g. Cl⁻, is called an **anion**.

There is electrostatic attraction between oppositely charged ions (Fig. 6.8). This is what holds the ions, Na⁺ and Cl⁻, together. This electrostatic attraction is the **chemical bond** in the compound, sodium chloride. It is called an **ionic bond** or **electrovalent bond**. Sodium chloride is an ionic or electrovalent compound. The compounds which conduct electricity when they are melted or dissolved (Section 5.3) are electrovalent compounds.

A pair of ions, Na⁺Cl⁻, does not exist in isolation. Other ions are attracted to them. Sodium ions are attracted to chloride ions, and chloride ions are attracted to sodium ions. The result is a three-dimensional structure of alternate Na⁺ and Cl⁻ ions (Fig. 6.9). This is a **crystal** of sodium chloride. The crystal is uncharged because the number of sodium ions is equal to the number of chloride ions. The forces of attraction between positive and negative ions are strong. This is why solid sodium chloride does not conduct electricity and is not electrolysed. Electricity is conducted by the ions of an electrolyte travelling to the electrodes. In solid sodium chloride, the ions cannot move out of their positions in the three-dimensional structure. When the salt is melted or dissolved, the ions are free to move and can travel towards the electrodes.

Fig. 6.8   There is an attraction between oppositely charged ions

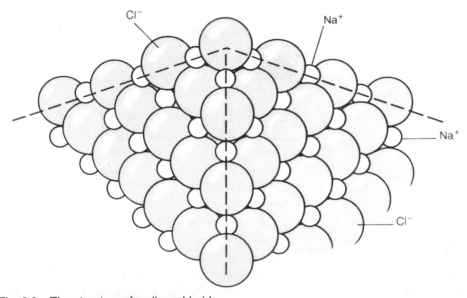

Fig. 6.9   The structure of sodium chloride

Magnesium fluoride

There are thousands of ionic compounds in addition to sodium chloride. Magnesium fluoride is one. Magnesium (2.8.2) has two electrons in the outermost shell. It has to lose these to attain a stable, full outer shell of electrons. Fluorine (2.7) needs to gain an electron. If a magnesium atom wants to lose two electrons and a fluorine atom needs to gain only one electron, a magnesium atom has to combine with two fluorine atoms (Fig. 6.10).

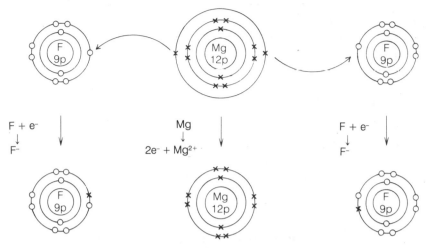

Fig. 6.10   The formation of magnesium fluoride

Magnesium oxide

Magnesium combines with oxygen to form magnesium oxide. One atom of magnesium, Mg (2.8.2), gives two electrons to one atom of oxygen, O (2.6). The ions Mg^{2+} (2.8) and O^{2-} (2.8) are formed. The electrostatic attraction between them is an ionic bond (Fig. 6.11).

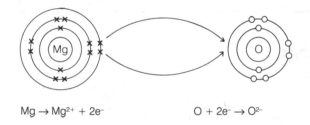

$$Mg \rightarrow Mg^{2+} + 2e^- \qquad\qquad O + 2e^- \rightarrow O^{2-}$$

Fig. 6.11   The formation of an ionic bond between atoms of magnesium and oxygen

SUMMARY NOTE

Metallic atoms can lose 1, 2 or 3 outer electrons, called **valency** electrons. The ions formed have a charge of +1, +2 or +3. Some non-metallic elements can gain 1, 2 or 3 electrons to form ions with charge −1, −2 or −3. The valency of an element is the charge on its ions. Ionic compounds are uncharged because the number of positive charges is equal to the number of negative charges.

Ions and valency

Electrovalent compounds (ionic compounds) are formed when a metallic element combines with a non-metallic element. The charge on the ions formed by an element is the **valency** of that element. Magnesium forms Mg^{2+} ions: magnesium has a valency of 2. Sodium forms Na^+ ions: sodium has a valency of 1. Oxygen forms O^{2-} ions: oxygen has a valency of 2. Iodine forms I^- ions: iodine has a valency of 1. Some elements have a variable valency. Iron forms Fe^{2+} ions and Fe^{3+} ions: iron uses a valency of 2 in some compounds and 3 in others. In general,

$$\text{Maximum valency employed by a metallic element} = \text{Number of electrons in the outermost shell}$$

$$\text{Maximum valency employed by a non-metallic element} = 8 - \text{(Number of electrons in the outermost shell)}$$

Non-metallic elements often form oxo-ions (which contain oxygen), e.g. sulphate, SO_4^{2-}, which has a valency of 2, and nitrate, NO_3^-, which has a valency of 1.

1 Lithium, like sodium, is an alkali metal. It has the electron arrangement Li (2.1). Fluorine has the electron arrangement F (2.7). Draw the arrangement of electrons in the atoms of Li and F. Explain how an ionic bond is formed in lithium fluoride.

2 Sodium is a silvery-grey metal which reacts rapidly with water. Chlorine is a poisonous green gas. Sodium chloride is a white crystalline solid. Explain how the sodium in sodium chloride differs from sodium metal. Explain how the chlorine in sodium chloride differs from chlorine gas.

3 Which of the following elements give **a** positive ions, **b** negative ions: magnesium, potassium, barium, zinc, iron, sulphur, oxygen, iodine, fluorine? (The Periodic Table on p. 318 may help you.)

4 Use dot-and-cross diagrams to show how the following atoms combine:
a Na (2.8.1) and O (2.6); **b** Al (2.8.3) and F (2.7); **c** Be (2.2) and F (2.7); **d** Ca (2.8.8.2) and O (2.6).

5 Name two differences between
a a sodium ion, Na$^+$ (2.8), and a neon atom, Ne (2.8)
b a chloride ion, Cl$^-$ (2.8.8), and an argon atom, Ar (2.8.8).

6.3 The covalent bond

There are compounds which are not electrolytes. Since they do not conduct electricity, they cannot consist of ions. Non-electrolytes contain a type of chemical bond different from the ionic bond.

Two atoms of chlorine combine to form a molecule, Cl_2. Both chlorine atoms have the electron arrangement Cl (2.8.7). Neither chlorine atom wants to give an electron: both want to gain an electron. They achieve a full outer shell of electrons by sharing electrons. The pair of chlorine atoms shown in Fig. 6.12 is sharing the pair of electrons **ox**. One electron comes from each of the chlorine atoms. The atoms have come close enough together for their outer shells to overlap. Then the shared pair of electrons can orbit round both the chlorine atoms. Each chlorine atom therefore has eight electrons in the outermost orbit. **When two atoms share a pair of electrons, this is called a covalent bond**.

In hydrogen chloride, two electrons are shared between the hydrogen and chlorine atoms to form a covalent bond. The arrangement gives the hydrogen atom a full shell of 2 electrons, like the noble gas helium. The chlorine atom then has a full outer shell of 8 electrons, like the noble gas neon (Fig. 6.13).

The arrangement of electrons in water, H_2O, and in ammonia, NH_3, is shown in Fig. 6.14.

A molecule of water, H_2O, contains covalent bonds between one O atom and two H atoms. Each O atom has 8 electrons in

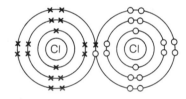

The pair of electrons **ox** is shared between the 2Cl atoms One electron comes from each Cl.

Fig. 6.12   The chlorine molecule

With 2 electrons, the outer shell of the H atom is full.

With 8 electrons, the outer shell of the Cl atom is full.

Fig. 6.13   A molecule of hydrogen chloride

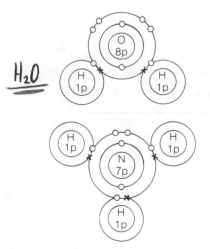

Fig. 6.14 H_2O and NH_3

its outer shell, and each H atom has two. Since the O atom shares two pairs of electrons, oxygen has a valency of 2. Since each H atom shares one pair of electrons, hydrogen has a valency of 1.

In ammonia, NH_3, each nitrogen atom shares three of its electrons, one with each of three hydrogen atoms. In this way, nitrogen obtains a full outer shell of 8 electrons, and hydrogen obtains a full shell of two. Nitrogen has a valency of 3, and hydrogen has a valency of 1.

*Double covalent bonds

In carbon dioxide, CO_2, the carbon atom shares 2 electrons with each of the 2 oxygen atoms. Each oxygen atom shares two of its electrons with the carbon atom (see Fig. 6.15). The two pairs of shared electrons are a **double bond**.

Fig. 6.15 CO_2

SUMMARY NOTE

Another type of chemical bond is the covalent bond. Atoms share electrons. By sharing, the bonded atoms both gain a full outer shell of electrons. The valency of the element equals the number of pairs of electrons which an atom of the element shares with other atoms in a covalent compound.

JUST TESTING 26

1 Sketch the arrangement of electrons in F (2.7) and H (1). Show by means of a sketch like those in the figures what happens when a covalent bond forms in HF.

2 Sketch the arrangement of electrons in the covalent compound CH_4 (C (2.4), H (1)).

*3 By means of a dot-and-cross diagram like those in the figures, sketch the arrangement of electrons in the outer shells of C and Cl in the molecule CCl_4 (C (2.4), Cl (2.8.7)).

6.4 Shapes of covalent molecules

The shapes of some covalent molecules are shown in Fig. 6.16. Covalent substances can be solids, liquids or gases. Gases consist of individual molecules.

In liquids, there are forces of attraction between the molecules. In some covalent substances, the attractive forces between molecules are strong enough to make the substances solids. Iodine is a shiny black crystalline solid. Forces of attraction hold molecules of iodine in a three-dimensional structure (Fig. 6.17). It is described as a **molecular structure**. There are two kinds of chemical bonds in it:

- the strong covalent I–I bonds
- the weak forces of attraction between I_2 molecules.

Diamond is an **allotrope** of carbon. Diamond has a structure (Fig. 3.4) in which every carbon atom is joined by covalent bonds to four other carbon atoms. Millions of carbon atoms form a giant molecule. The structure is **giant molecular** or **macromolecular**.

Graphite, the other allotrope of carbon, has a **layer structure** (Fig. 3.5). Strong covalent bonds join the carbon atoms within each layer. The layers are held together by weak forces of attraction.

SUMMARY NOTE

Some covalent substances are composed of individual molecules. Others are composed of larger units. These may be chains or layers or macromolecular structures.

Fig. 6.16 The shapes of some covalent ◁ molecules

Name	Formula	Structure	Molecular model
Chlorine	Cl_2	Cl – Cl	
Hydrogen chloride	HCl	H – Cl	
Oxygen	O_2	O = O	
Water	H_2O	H–O–H	
Ammonia	NH_3	N with H H H	
Methane	CH_4	H–C with H H H	
Ethene	$H_2C = CH_2$	H H C = C H H	
Carbon dioxide	CO_2	O = C = O	

Fig. 6.17 The structure of an iodine crystal

JUST TESTING 27

1 Why is it difficult to rub away any carbon atoms from a diamond?

2 Why is graphite used as a lubricant?

3 Why does diamond have a high boiling point?

4 Solid iodine consists of shiny black crystals. Iodine vapour is purple. What is the difference in chemical bonding between solid and gaseous iodine?

6.5 Ionic and covalent substances

The physical characteristics of substances, for example, whether they are solids, liquids or gases, depend on the type of chemical bonds in the substances. Chemical behaviour also depends on the types of bonds present.

Table 6.1 Differences between ionic and covalent substances

Ionic bonding	Covalent bonding
1 Ionic compounds are formed when a metallic element (on the left-hand side of the Periodic Table) combines with a non-metallic element (on the right-hand side of the Periodic Table).	1 Atoms of non-metallic elements combine with each other by sharing pairs of electrons in their outer shells. A shared pair of electrons is called a covalent bond.
2 **a** Atoms of metallic elements form positive ions. Elements in Groups 1, 2 and 3 of the Periodic Table form ions with charges +1, +2 and +3, e.g. Na^+, Ca^{2+}, Al^{3+}.	2 The maximum number of covalent bonds that an atom can form is equal to the number of electrons in the outer shell. Often, an atom does not use all its electrons in covalent bond formation.
b Elements in Group 7 of the Periodic Table (non-metals) form anions, X^-, as each atom gains one electron from a metallic element.	
c Elements in Group 6 of the Periodic Table (non-metals) can form Y^{2-} ions as each atom gains 2 electrons from a metal atom.	
3 There is a strong electrostatic attraction between ions of opposite charge. This is what gives ionic solids a close, regular structure. Ionic compounds are crystalline because of this regular structure. The strong force of attraction between ions of opposite charge makes it difficult to separate the ions. This is why ionic compounds have high melting points and high boiling points.	3 There are three types of covalent substances.
	a Many covalent substances are composed of small individual molecules. The bonds holding the atoms together are strong, but there are negligible forces of attraction between molecules. Such covalent substances are gases, e.g. HCl, SO_2, CO_2, CH_4.
	b Other covalent substances consist of small molecules with weak forces of attraction between the molecules. Such covalent substances are low-boiling point liquids, e.g. ethanol, C_2H_5OH, or low-melting point solids. The low-melting point solids are molecular crystals, e.g. iodine (Fig. 6.17).
	c Some covalent substances consist of giant molecules. Atoms may link in chains or sheets, e.g. graphite (Fig. 3.5) or in three-dimensional networks e.g. diamond (Fig. 3.4) and quartz (Fig. 1.9). Substances with giant molecular structures have high melting and boiling points.
4 Ionic compounds are electrolytes. They conduct electricity when molten or in solution and are split up in the process (see Section 5.3).	4 Covalent compounds are non-electrolytes.
5 Ionic compounds are insoluble in organic solvents, that is, solvents which have covalent bonds.	5 Covalent compounds are soluble in organic solvents, e.g. ethanol, tetrachloromethane.

1 What kind of bonding would you expect between the following pairs of elements?
   a K and Cl; **b** Ca and Br; **c** Mg and S; **d** Cu and O; **e** S and O; **f** Na and H.
   (The Periodic Table on p. 412 may help you.)

2 From the information in the table, say what you can about the chemical bonds in A, B, C and D.

Solid	State	Melting point in °C	Does it conduct electricity when molten?
A	Solid	660	Conducts electricity when molten
B	Solid	720	Does not conduct electricity when molten
C	Solid	85	Does not conduct electricity when molten
D	Gas	−100	Does not conduct electricity

SUMMARY NOTE

The type of chemical bonds present, ionic or covalent, decides the properties of a compound, e.g. its physical state (solid, liquid or gas), boiling and melting points, solubility and electrolytic conductivity.

*6.6 Formulas of ionic compounds

You have seen how electrovalent compounds consist of oppositely charged ions. The compound is neutral because the charge on the positive ion (or ions) is equal to the charge on the negative ion (or ions). In calcium chloride, $CaCl_2$, one calcium ion, Ca^{2+}, is balanced in charge by two chloride ions, $2Cl^-$.

Fig. 6.18 The charges must balance

This is how you can work out the formulas of electrovalent compounds.

Compound:	Calcium chloride
Say which ions are present:	Ca^{2+}, Cl^-
Now balance the charges:	One Ca^{2+} ion needs two Cl^- ions
Ions needed are:	Ca^{2+} and $2Cl^-$
The formula is:	$CaCl_2$

Table 6.2 The symbols of some common ions

Cation	Symbol
Aluminium	Al^{3+}
Ammonium	NH_4^+
Barium	Ba^{2+}
Calcium	Ca^{2+}
Copper(II)	Cu^{2+}
Hydrogen	H^+
Iron(II)	Fe^{2+}
Iron(III)	Fe^{3+}
Lead(II)	Pb^{2+}
Magnesium	Mg^{2+}
Mercury(II)	Hg^{2+}
Potassium	K^+
Silver	Ag^+
Sodium	Na^+
Zinc	Zn^{2+}

Anion	Symbol
Bromide	Br^-
Carbonate	CO_3^{2-}
Chloride	Cl^-
Hydrogencarbonate	HCO_3^-
Hydroxide	OH^-
Iodide	I^-
Nitrate	NO_3^-
Oxide	O^{2-}
Phosphate	PO_4^{3-}
Sulphate	SO_4^{2-}
Sulphide	S^{2-}
Sulphite	SO_3^{2-}

SUMMARY NOTE

The formula of an ionic compound is worked out by balancing the charges on the ions.

Compound: *Sodium carbonate*
Say which ions are present: Na^+, CO_3^{2-}
Now balance the charges: Two Na^+ are needed to balance one CO_3^{2-}
Ions needed are: $2Na^+$ and CO_3^{2-}
The formula is: Na_2CO_3

Compound: *Copper(II) hydroxide*
Ions present are: Cu^{2+}, OH^-
Now balance the charges: Two OH^- ions balance one Cu^{2+} ion
Ions needed are: Cu^{2+} and $2OH^-$
The formula is: $Cu(OH)_2$
(The brackets tell you that the 2 multiplies everything inside them. There are 2O atoms and 2H atoms, in addition to the 1Cu ion.)

Compound: *Iron(II) sulphate*
Ions present are: Fe^{2+}, SO_4^{2-}
Now balance the charges: One Fe^{2+} ion balances one SO_4^{2-} ion
Ions needed are: Fe^{2+} and SO_4^{2-}
The formula is: $FeSO_4$

Compound: *Iron(III) sulphate*
Ions present are: Fe^{3+}, SO_4^{2-}
Now balance the charges: Two Fe^{3+} would balance three SO_4^{2-} ions
Ions needed are: $2Fe^{3+}$ and $3SO_4^{2-}$
The formula is: $Fe_2(SO_4)_3$
(The brackets tell you that all the atoms inside them must be multiplied by the 3 that follows them. The formula contains 2Fe, 3S and 12O.)

You need to learn the symbols and charges of the ions in Table 6.2. Then you can work out the formula of any electrovalent compound containing these ions.

You will notice that the sulphates of iron are named iron(II) sulphate and iron(III) sulphate. The roman numerals II and III show which of its valencies iron is using. They are always used with the compounds of elements of variable valency.

Career sketch: Science librarian

Pat works in the library of a research centre. Scientists on the site ask him for books. If the centre does not stock a certain book, Pat asks the British Library to lend a copy. They send it to him, and he passes it on to the scientist who needs it. Pat records the loan on the computer. He left school after GCSE.

*6.7 Formulas of covalent compounds

In a covalent compound, pairs of electrons are shared between
atoms. The number of electrons which an atom of an element
shares in bond formation is the valency of the element. The
formulas of covalent compounds are decided by the sort of dot-
and-cross diagrams shown in Figs. 6.12 to 6.15.

*6.8 Equations: the balancing act

You began your work on equations in Section 3.11. Now you can
tackle 'balancing' equations.

Example 1 Hydrogen and oxygen combine to form water. The
word equation is

hydrogen + oxygen → water

The chemical equation could be

$$H_2(g) + O_2(g) \rightarrow H_2O(l)$$

This equation is not **balanced**. There are 2 oxygen atoms on the
left-hand side (LHS) and only 1 oxygen atom on the right-hand
side (RHS). To balance the O atoms, multiply H_2O on the RHS
by 2:

$$H_2(g) + O_2(g) \rightarrow 2H_2O(l)$$

The O atoms are now balanced, but there are 4H atoms on the
RHS and only 2H on the LHS. Multiplying H_2 on the LHS by 2,

$$2H_2(g) + O_2(g) \rightarrow 2H_2O(l)$$

The equation is now balanced (Fig. 6.19).

Number of atoms on LHS = 4H + 2O
Number of atoms on RHS = 4H + 2O

$$\frac{\text{Number of atoms of}}{\text{each element on LHS}} = \frac{\text{Number of atoms of}}{\text{each element on RHS}}$$

$$\frac{\text{The total mass}}{\text{of the reactants}} = \frac{\text{The total mass}}{\text{of the products}}$$

$$2H_2(g) + O_2(g) \longrightarrow 2H_2O(l)$$

Fig. 6.19   A balanced equation; example 1

Example 2   Sulphur dioxide is oxidised by oxygen to sulphur trioxide:

sulphur dioxide + oxygen → sulphur trioxide
$SO_2(g)$ $+ O_2(g)$ $\rightarrow SO_3(g)$

You can see that the equation is not balanced. There are 4O on the LHS and 3O on the RHS. It is tempting to write O for oxygen on the LHS. You must not do this. Never change a formula. All you can do to balance an equation is to multiply formulas. Instead of changing O_2 to O, multiply SO_2 and SO_3 by 2:

$$2SO_2(g) + O_2(g) \rightarrow 2SO_3(g)$$

The equation is now balanced: 2S + 6O on the LHS; 2S + 6O on the RHS; see Fig. 6.20.

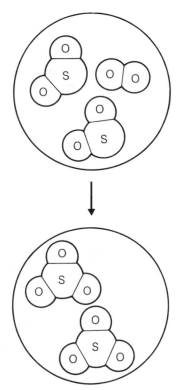

Fig. 6.20   A balanced equation; example 2

The steps in writing a chemical equation are
1 Write a word equation for the reaction.
2 Write the symbols and formulas for the reactants and products.
3 Add the state symbols.
4 Balance the equation. Multiply the formulas if necessary. Never change a formula.
5 Check again:
Number of atoms of each element on LHS   =   Number of atoms of each element on RHS

Take the reaction between sodium and water to form hydrogen and sodium hydroxide solution. Work through the five steps:

1 Sodium + water → hydrogen + sodium hydroxide solution

2 $Na + H_2O \rightarrow H_2 + NaOH$

3 $Na(s) + H_2O(l) \rightarrow H_2(g) + NaOH(aq)$

4 $2Na(s) + 2H_2O(l) \rightarrow H_2(g) + 2NaOH(aq)$

5 Number of atoms on LHS = 2Na + 4H + 2O
  Number of atoms on RHS = 2Na + 4H + 2O

*1 Copy these equations, and balance them.
  a $Fe_2O_3(s) + C(s) \rightarrow Fe(s) + CO(g)$
  b $Fe_2O_3(s) + CO(g) \rightarrow Fe(s) + CO_2(g)$
  c $NH_3(g) + O_2(g) \rightarrow NO(g) + H_2O(l)$
  d $Cr(s) + HCl(aq) \rightarrow CrCl_3(aq) + H_2(g)$
  e $Fe_3O_4(s) + H_2(g) \rightarrow Fe(s) + H_2O(l)$
  f $C_3H_8(g) + O_2(g) \rightarrow CO_2(g) + H_2O(l)$.
*2 Try writing equations for these reactions:
  a hydrogen + copper(II) oxide → copper + water
  b carbon + carbon dioxide → carbon monoxide
  c magnesium + sulphuric acid → hydrogen + magnesium sulphate
  d copper + chloride → copper(II) chloride
  e mercury + oxygen → mercury(II) oxide
  f sodium + oxygen → sodium oxide
  g iron + sulphur → iron(II) sulphide.
*3 Write balanced chemical equations for these reactions:
  a calcium + water → hydrogen + calcium hydroxide solution
  b iron + hydrochloric acid → iron(II) chloride solution + hydrogen
  c iron + chlorine → iron(III) chloride
  d aluminium + chlorine → aluminium chloride
  e zinc + steam → zinc oxide + hydrogen.

*6.9 The shapes of covalent molecules – an explanation

Is there an explanation for the different shapes of the molecules in Fig. 6.16? Why are the four bonds in methane, CH_4, arranged in space as you see them?

Since the bonds are shared pairs of electrons, they are negatively charged. As a result, the bonds repel one another and take up positions in space which place them as far apart as possible. Fig. 6.21 shows how the bonds in CH_4 manage this. The bonds are directed towards the corners of a regular tetrahedron, with the carbon atom at the centre. (A tetrahedron has four faces. In a regular tetrahedron, all the sides and angles are equal.) The angle between each pair of bonds is 109.5°. If you make a model of the CH_4 molecule, you can try making the angle between one pair of bonds greater than this. You will find that you have decreased the angle between another pair of bonds. An angle of 109.5° between each pair of bonds maximises the bond angle and so minimises the repulsion between the electrons.

In a molecule of ammonia, NH_3, there are three covalent bonds. An atom of nitrogen shares an electron with each of three hydrogen atoms. However, the nitrogen atom has five electrons in its outer shell. (The electron arrangement is 2.5.) In total,

Fig. 6.21 (a) The arrangement of bonds in space in CH₄ (b) A model

therefore, there are three shared pairs of electrons and one unshared pair of electrons. The four electron pairs are directed towards the corners of a regular tetrahedron. The three bonds are as shown in Fig. 6.22.

Fig. 6.22 (a) The arrangement of bonds in space in NH₃ (b) A model

In a molecule of water, H₂O, there are two covalent (electron pair) bonds. The oxygen atom, however, has six electrons in its outer shell. (The electron arrangement is 2.6.) Two electrons are shared in bonds, leaving four electrons (two pairs) unshared. The two bonds and the two unshared pairs of electrons are directed towards the corners of a regular tetrahedron (see Fig. 6.23).

Fig. 6.23 (a) The arrangement of bonds in space in H₂O (b) A model

In ethene, $CH_2{=}CH_2$, there is a double bond between the carbon atoms. You can use a model set with flexible bonds to assemble two $H_2C{=}$ groups with a tetrahedral arrangement of bonds (as in Fig. 6.21). If you join two pairs of bonds between two carbon atoms, you will find that the four hydrogen atoms all lie in the same plane (see Fig. 6.24a).

To make a model of a molecule of carbon dioxide, you need to fit four flexible bonds into a model carbon atom (with a tetrahedral arrangement of bonds). Then bend the bonds so that you can fit two of the bonds into each of two oxygen atoms. You will find that the molecule of CO_2 is linear (see Fig. 6.24b).

Fig. 6.24 (a) A model of $CH_2{=}CH_2$
(b) A model of CO_2

Exercise 6

Note You will need the electron arrangements shown on p. 48.

1 What happens to their electrons when atoms combine by means of an ionic bond? Illustrate your answer with a diagram showing the valency electrons (the outermost electrons) in **a** sodium fluoride, **b** magnesium chloride, **c** lithium oxide.

2 What happens to their electrons when atoms combine by means of a covalent bond? Illustrate your answer with a dot-and-cross diagram of the valency electrons in **a** HF; **b** CH_4; **c** PH_3; **d** CH_2Cl_2; **e** H_2S.

3 **a** Explain why the ionic compound $PbBr_2$ melts at a higher temperature than the covalent compound CH_2Br_2.
  b You can smell the compound $CHCl_3$, chloroform. You cannot smell the compound KCl. Explain the difference in terms of the chemical bonds in the two compounds.

4 Write the formulas of **a** mercury(II) oxide, **b** copper(II) nitrate, **c** aluminium nitrate, **d** aluminium sulphate, **e** barium nitrate, **f** calcium carbonate, **g** calcium hydrogencarbonate.

Note Question 5 is a revision question. You should tackle it *after* you have met the reactions.

*5 Copy out these equations into your book, and then balance them.

  a $H_2O_2(aq) \rightarrow H_2O(l) + O_2(g)$
  b $Fe(s) + O_2(g) \rightarrow Fe_3O_4(s)$
  c $Mg(s) + N_2(g) \rightarrow Mg_3N_2(s)$
  d $P(s) + Cl_2(g) \rightarrow PCl_3(s)$
  e $P(s) + Cl_2(g) \rightarrow PCl_5(s)$
  f $SO_2(g) + O_2(g) \rightarrow SO_3(g)$
  g $Na_2O(s) + H_2O(l) \rightarrow NaOH(aq)$
  h $KClO_3(s) \rightarrow KCl(s) + O_2(g)$
  i $NH_3(g) + O_2(g) \rightarrow N_2(g) + H_2O(g)$
  j $Fe(s) + H_2O(g) \rightarrow Fe_3O_4(s) + H_2(g)$
  k $H_2S(g) + O_2(g) \rightarrow H_2O(l) + SO_2(g)$
  l $H_2S(g) + SO_2(g) \rightarrow H_2O(l) + S(s)$.

CHAPTER 7

Acids, bases and salts

7.1 The acid taste

The Californian wine industry owes much of its success to a device called a pH meter. 'pH' is a term chemists use to describe how acidic or alkaline a solution is, and a pH meter measures acidity. In California, pH meters are used to measure how acidic the grape juice is. Picking the grapes at the right pH is one of the most important factors in producing a good wine. The right degree of acidity gives wine a fresh tart taste. Too much acidity results in an undrinkable sour wine, tasting like vinegar. Too little acidity gives wine a flat uninteresting taste.

As grapes ripen, their sugar content increases, and their acidity decreases. In the hot sun of California, grapes ripen early in the year, and their sugar content is high. Sometimes the pH meter tells growers that their grapes lack acidity. The acids in grapes include tartaric acid and citric acid. Producers use the reading on the pH meter to tell them how much tartaric acid they should add to bring the natural concentration of tartaric acid in grape juice up to the level that produces a good wine.

Fig. 7.1 A pH meter

SUMMARY NOTE

The names and formulas of some acids are
- hydrochloric acid, HCl(aq), a strong acid
- sulphuric acid, H_2SO_4(aq), a strong acid
- nitric acid, HNO_3(aq), a strong acid
- ethanoic acid, CH_3CO_2H(aq), a weak acid.

7.2 Acids

Thousands of years ago, people found out how to ferment grapes to make wine. They also found out that if the fermentation process went on for too long they got vinegar (sour wine). Centuries ago, chemists distilled vinegar and obtained a sour-tasting substance which we now call ethanoic acid. They obtained other acids also from plant and animal sources: methanoic acid from ants, citric acid from fruits and lactic acid from sour milk. Acids such as these, which were obtained from plant and animal sources, were named **organic acids**.

Later, chemists found ways of making sulphuric acid, hydrochloric acid and nitric acid from minerals. They called these acids **mineral acids**. They are much more reactive than organic acids. We describe mineral acids as **strong** acids and organic acids as **weak** acids. Mineral acids played a big part in the advance of chemistry. They made it possible for chemists to carry out new reactions and make new compounds.

What chemical reactions are typical of acids? Experiment 7.1 will enable you to answer this question.

1 Acids have a sour taste. You can test the truth of this statement with lemon juice (which contains citric acid) or vinegar (which contains ethanoic acid). **Do not try any of the strong acids**.

2 Acids can change the colour of certain substances, called **indicators**. For example, acids turn blue litmus red.

3 Acids react with many metals to produce the gas hydrogen.

Some metals, e.g. copper, are slow to react with acids. Some other metals, e.g. sodium, react dangerously fast. Metals which react at a safe speed are magnesium, aluminium, zinc, iron and others. Chapter 11 will tell you more about metals.

4 When aqueous solutions of acids are electrolysed, hydrogen is evolved at the negative electrode (see Section 5.9).

5 Acids neutralise **bases** (see Section 7.3).

6 Acids react with carbonates and hydrogencarbonates to give the gas carbon dioxide. Carbonates are compounds which contain carbonate ions, CO_3^{2-}, e.g. calcium carbonate, $CaCO_3$, and sodium carbonate, Na_2CO_3. Hydrogencarbonates contain the ion HCO_3^-, e.g. sodium hydrogencarbonate, $NaHCO_3$.

What is an acid?

A Swedish chemist called Svante Arrhenius made a deduction from these observations. He theorised that aqueous solutions of acids contain hydrogen ions, $H^+(aq)$. This theory explains many reactions of acids, including the two listed below.

1 On electrolysis, hydrogen gas is evolved at the negative electrode. This can be explained by the discharge of hydrogen ions:

hydrogen ions + electrons → hydrogen molecules
$$2H^+(aq) \quad + \quad 2e^- \quad \rightarrow \quad H_2(g)$$

2 In a reaction with a reactive metal M, hydrogen gas is given off and a salt of the metal is formed:

metal atoms + hydrogen ions → metal ions + hydrogen molecules
$$M(s) \quad + \quad 2H^+(aq) \quad \rightarrow \quad M^{2+}(aq) + H_2(g)$$

Arrhenius gave this definition of an acid:
An acid is a substance that releases hydrogen ions when dissolved in water.

7.3 Bases

Another class of substances has been known for centuries, the substances we call **bases**. Sodium hydroxide, NaOH, is an example. Bases have a number of properties in common (see Experiment 7.2).

1 Soluble bases can change the colour of indicators; for example, soluble bases turn red litmus blue.

2 Soluble bases have a soapy feel to the skin. This is because bases actually convert some of the oil in your skin into soap (see Experiment 7.2). Soluble bases, e.g. ammonia, are used in the home as degreasing agents because they have this ability to react with oil and grease to form a soluble soap.

3 Bases react with acids. They counteract the acid — **neutralise** the acid. The product of the reaction is neither an acid nor a base; it is a neutral substance called a **salt**. The reaction is called **neutralisation**. It is the basis of the definition of a base. **A base**

SUMMARY NOTE

Examples of bases are:
- **metal oxides**, including
  copper(II) oxide, CuO
  zinc oxide, ZnO
  aluminium oxide, Al_2O_3;
- **metal hydroxides**, including
  sodium hydroxide, NaOH
  and magnesium hydroxide,
  $Mg(OH)_2$.
  Most metal oxides and
  hydroxides are insoluble.
  The soluble ones are called
- **alkalis**. They are:
  sodium hydroxide, NaOH
  potassium hydroxide, KOH
  and calcium hydroxide,
  $Ca(OH)_2$.
  Ammonia solution, NH_3(aq),
  is an alkali.

Table 7.1 Coloured insoluble metal hydroxides

copper(II) hydroxide, $Cu(OH)_2$(s)	blue
iron(II) hydroxide, $Fe(OH)_2$(s)	green
iron(III) hydroxide, $Fe(OH)_3$(s)	rust
magnesium hydroxide, $Mg(OH)_2$(s)	white

SUMMARY NOTE

Bases neutralise acids to form salts. Soluble bases change the colours of indicators.

Metal oxides and hydroxides are bases. Soluble bases are called alkalis. Solutions of alkalis contain high concentrations of hydroxide ions, OH^-(aq). They are degreasing agents, and have a soapy 'feel'.

is a substance that reacts with an acid to form a salt and water only.

4 When an alkali dissolves in water, it produces hydroxide ions, OH^-(aq). This is why an alkali will react with metal salts. Most metal hydroxides are insoluble. When hydroxide ions from a solution of an alkali meet metal ions from a solution of a metal salt, an insoluble metal hydroxide is **precipitated** from solution. A solid which forms when two liquids are mixed is called a **precipitate**.

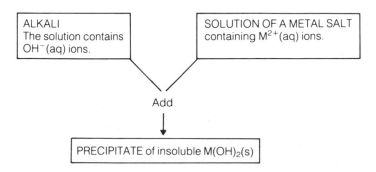

For example, in solution

$$\text{copper(II) sulphate} + \text{sodium hydroxide} \rightarrow \text{copper(II) hydroxide} + \text{sodium sulphate}$$

$$CuSO_4(aq) + 2NaOH(aq) \rightarrow Cu(OH)_2(s) + Na_2SO_4(aq)$$

*Ionic equations

There is another way of writing this equation. The reaction is the combination of copper ions and hydroxide ions. The sodium ions and sulphate ions take no part in the reaction. They are called **spectator ions**. The equation can be written without the spectator ions:

$$Cu^{2+}(aq) + 2OH^-(aq) \rightarrow Cu(OH)_2(s)$$

This is called an **ionic equation**.

The colours of insoluble metal hydroxides can be of help in finding out what metal cations are present in a solution.

JUST TESTING 31

1 Alkalis are a subset of bases. Copy the Venn diagram (Fig. 7.2). Fill in the names of the four common alkalis. Write the names of four insoluble bases.

*2 Write formulas for these bases:
iron(II) hydroxide,
iron(III) hydroxide,
barium oxide, magnesium hydroxide.

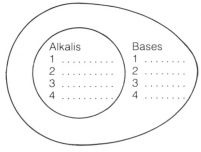

Fig. 7.2

7.4 Neutralisation

What takes place in neutralisation, the reaction between an acid and a base? Consider the reaction between hydrochloric acid and the alkali (soluble base), sodium hydroxide solution:

hydrochloric acid	+	sodium hydroxide	→	sodium chloride	+ water
HCl(aq)	+	NaOH(aq)	→	NaCl(aq)	+ H_2O(l)
acid	+	**alkali**	→	**salt**	+ **water**

When the solutions of acid and alkali are mixed, hydrogen ions, H^+(aq), and hydroxide ions, OH^-(aq), combine to form water molecules:

$$H^+(aq) + OH^-(aq) → H_2O(l)$$

Sodium ions, Na^+(aq), and chloride ions, Cl^-(aq), remain in the solution, which becomes a solution of sodium chloride. If you evaporate the solution, you obtain solid sodium chloride.
Neutralisation is the combination of hydrogen ions from an acid and hydroxide ions from a base to form water. In the process, a salt is formed.

What happens when an acid neutralises an insoluble base (Experiment 7.3)? Consider sulphuric acid and magnesium oxide:

sulphuric acid	+	magnesium oxide	→	magnesium sulphate	+ water
H_2SO_4(aq)	+	MgO(s)	→	$MgSO_4$(aq)	+ H_2O(l)
acid	+	**base**	→	**salt**	+ **water**

Hydrogen ions and oxide ions, O^{2-}, combine to form water:

$$2H^+(aq) + O^{2-}(s) → H_2O(l)$$

The resulting solution contains magnesium ions and sulphate ions: it is a solution of magnesium sulphate. If you evaporate it, you will obtain magnesium sulphate crystals.

7.5 Strengths of acids and bases

Some acids are stronger than others. A strong acid reacts faster than a weak acid with metals, bases and carbonates (see Experiment 7.1). Some bases are stronger than others. Ammonia is a weak base. A strong base will drive ammonia out of an ammonium salt:

$$\text{ammonium salt} + \text{strong base} \rightarrow \text{ammonia} + \text{salt of strong base}$$

For example,

$$\text{ammonium chloride} + \text{calcium oxide} \rightarrow \text{ammonia} + \text{calcium chloride}$$

This reaction is used as a laboratory preparation of ammonia and as a test for ammonium salts (see Section 15.4).

Universal Indicator can distinguish between strong and weak acids. It turns different colours in strongly acidic and weakly acidic solutions. It can also distinguish between strongly basic and weakly basic solutions (see Table 7.2). Each shade of Universal Indicator colour corresponds to a **pH number**. The pH number is a measure of the acidity or alkalinity of the solution. For a neutral solution, pH = 7; for an acidic solution, pH < 7; for an alkaline solution, pH > 7 (see Experiment 7.4). Table 7.3 lists the colours of some other indicators.

SUMMARY NOTE

Some acids are stronger than others. The mineral acids are stronger than organic acids, e.g. ethanoic acid. Some bases are stronger than others. Ammonia is a weak base. Universal Indicator turns different colours in strongly acidic, weakly acidic, neutral, weakly alkaline and strongly alkaline solutions. For each shade of colour, there is a pH number. The pH of a solution is a measure of its acidity or alkalinity.

Table 7.2 The colour of Universal Indicator in different solutions

	Strongly acidic			Weakly acidic		Neutral		Weakly alkaline			Strongly alkaline		
pH	0	1	2	3	4	5	6	7	8	9	10	11	12	13	14
Colour	←—— Red ——→			Orange	Yellow		Green	Blue	←——		Violet		——→	

Table 7.3 The colours of some common indicators

Indicator	Acidic colour	Neutral colour	Alkaline colour
Litmus	Red	Purple	Blue
Phenolphthalein	Colourless	Colourless	Pink
Methyl orange	Red	Orange	Yellow

Career sketch: Laboratory assistant 2

Paul is a laboratory assistant. He works for a manufacturer of agricultural chemicals. Chemists in the company's laboratory are constantly making new compounds. It is Paul's job to try them out to see whether they will do what the chemists hope they will do. He may spray a selection of plants in the laboratory with a new compound which the chemists hope will make plants grow faster or more slowly. He measures the plants' growth and keeps a careful record. If the new chemical does what the chemists hope, then Paul sends it on for large-scale trials. Paul left school after GCSE.

Table 7.4 Some common acids and bases

	Where you find it and why you use it
Acid	
Carbonic acid	In fizzy drinks
Citric acid	In fruit juices
Ethanoic acid	In vinegar
Hydrochloric acid	Used for 'pickling' metals before they are coated
Nitric acid	Used for making fertilisers and explosives
Phosphoric acid	In rust inhibitor; used for making fertilisers
Sulphuric acid	In car batteries; used for making fertilisers (Chapter 14)
Base	
Ammonia	In cleaning fluids as a degreasing agent; used in the manufacture of fertilisers
Calcium hydroxide	Spread on soil which is too acidic
Calcium oxide	Used in the manufacture of cement, mortar and concrete
Magnesium hydroxide	In 'antacid' indigestion tablets and 'milk of magnesia'
Sodium hydroxide	In powerful oven cleaners as a degreasing agent; used in the manufacture of soap

Fig. 7.3   Some common acids

Table 7.5 shows the pH values of solutions of some common acids and alkalis. Some salts do not have a pH value of 7. Carbonates and hydrogencarbonates are alkaline in solution.

Table 7.5 pH values of some solutions

pH	Solution
0	Bench hydrochloric acid
1	Digestive fluids in the stomach
2	
	Lemon juice
3	Vinegar
	Orange juice
4	
	Soda water
5	
6	Rain water
	Cows' milk
7	Pure water
	Blood
8	
	Sodium hydrogencarbonate solution and sea water
9	
10	
11	Bench ammonia solution
	Sodium carbonate (washing soda) solution
12	
	Calcium hydroxide solution (limewater)
13	
14	Bench sodium hydroxide solution

Fig. 7.4   Some common alkalis

JUST TESTING 32

1 Give an example of **a** a weak acid, **b** a strong acid, **c** a weak base, **d** a strong base. Where might you find each of these substances outside the laboratory?

2 Say whether these substances are strongly acidic, weakly acidic, neutral, weakly basic or strongly basic:
a grapefruit juice, pH = 3.0; **b** blood, pH = 7.4; **c** beer, pH = 5.0; **d** rain, pH = 6.2; **e** sea water, pH = 8.5; **f** saliva, pH = 7.0.

3 Why is sodium hydrogencarbonate used to treat indigestion while sodium carbonate is not?

4 Why does stewing apples in an aluminium saucepan leave it clean?

5 Sherbet contains sodium hydrogencarbonate and citric acid (a solid). When you put it in your mouth, it generates carbon dioxide and fizzes. Why does it do this only when wet?

6 Indigestion tablets are of many kinds. They may contain one of the following compounds:

$NaHCO_3$, $Al(OH)_3$, Al_2O_3, $MgCO_3$, $Mg(OH)_2$, MgO, $CaCO_3$.

Which would react fastest with the excess of acid in the stomach?

7 A greasy oven can be cleaned by spraying the inside with a concentrated solution of sodium hydroxide. How does it work?

*7.6 Weak acids and bases

Why are some acids stronger than others? Why are some bases stronger than others? A strong acid is completely ionised in solution. A solution of hydrochloric acid contains oxonium ions (hydrogen ions) and chloride ions. There are no hydrogen chloride molecules present. A weak acid is only partially ionised in solution. A solution of ethanoic acid contains chiefly molecules of ethanoic acid. Very few of the molecules (only 1 per cent) ionise:

ethanoic acid $\rightleftharpoons$ hydrogen ions + ethanoate ions
$$CH_3CO_2H(aq) \rightleftharpoons H^+(aq) + CH_3CO_2^-(aq)$$

The reverse arrows, $\rightleftharpoons$, mean that the ionisation is incomplete. The solution contains hydrogen ions, ethanoate ions and ethanoic acid molecules.

Ammonia is a weak base. In water, it ionises to a small extent:

ammonia + water $\rightleftharpoons$ ammonium ions + hydroxide ions
$$NH_3(aq) + H_2O(l) \rightleftharpoons NH_4^+(aq) + OH^-(aq)$$

The concentration of ammonium ions and hydroxide ions is small, but it is sufficient to account for many of the reactions of

* SUMMARY NOTE

Strong acids are completely ionised; weak acids are partially ionised.
Strong bases are completely ionised; weak bases are partially ionised.

101

ammonia solution. The hydroxide ions present will precipitate insoluble metal hydroxides from solution, as other alkalis do (see Section 7.3).

---

*JUST TESTING 33

1 Hydrogen cyanide, HCN, is a poisonous gas which dissolves in water to form a solution of the weak acid HCN(aq), hydrocyanic acid. Write an equation to show the dissociation of hydrocyanic acid into hydrogen ions and cyanide ions.

---

*7.7 Amphoteric oxides and hydroxides

All metal oxides and hydroxides are basic. They all react with acids to form salts. The oxides and hydroxides of some metals are also acidic: they react with bases to form salts. For example:

Zinc oxide
Zinc hydroxide
— React with hydrochloric acid to form zinc chloride
— React with sodium hydroxide to form sodium zincate

Oxides and hydroxides of this kind are **amphoteric**, that is, both basic and acidic. In sodium zincate, Na_2ZnO_2, the metal zinc is part of the anion, ZnO_2^{2-}. The formation of the zincate salt is

zinc hydroxide + sodium hydroxide → sodium zincate + water
$$Zn(OH)_2(s) + 2NaOH(aq) \rightarrow Na_2ZnO_2(aq) + 2H_2O(l)$$

Other amphoteric oxides and hydroxides are aluminium oxide and hydroxide, Al_2O_3 and $Al(OH)_3$, and lead(II) oxide and hydroxide, PbO and $Pb(OH)_2$.

Al_2O_3 and $Al(OH)_3$
— with acid → Al^{3+} salts
— with base → AlO_2^- salts (aluminates)

PbO and $Pb(OH)_2$
— with acid → Pb^{2+} salts
— with base → PbO_2^{2-} salts (plumbates)

JUST TESTING 34

1 Describe what you see when sodium hydroxide solution is added gradually to a solution of aluminium sulphate.

2 A solution of sodium hydroxide is added to a solution of a metal salt. A white precipitate is formed. The white precipitate dissolves when an excess of sodium hydroxide is added. Could the metal salt be **a** magnesium hydroxide or **b** zinc hydroxide? Explain your answer.

7.8 Salts

Silver bromide, AgBr, is a salt which can give you a lot of fun. The reason why you can take photographs is that light affects silver bromide. Photographic film consists of a paper and cellulose base covered with a film of emulsion. In black and white film, the emulsion consists of grains of silver bromide suspended in gelatin. When the film is exposed, light falls on to some areas of the emulsion. It changes the grains of silver bromide which it meets. In each exposed grain, some silver ions, Ag^+, are converted into silver atoms, which are black. These black atoms form a picture of the object called a **latent image** (Fig. 7.5). When the film is **developed**, the process started by light continues. More silver ions in the areas affected by light are converted into silver atoms. The result is a **negative**. A **fixer** is used to remove unchanged silver bromide. The negative has to be placed on a piece of photographic paper and exposed to light to give a **print** (see Fig. 7.5).

Light from object

Exposing

1 The film is exposed. A **latent image** forms.

Developing
Emulsion of silver bromide in gelatin

Cellulose base

2 **Developer** turns the latent image into the negative. Then **fixer** dissolves unchanged silver bromide.

Light from enlarger

Printing

3 Light from the enlarger can pass through some areas of the negative.

The photograph

4 It falls on to photographic paper. By reducing silver bromide, it makes a **print**.

Fig. 7.5 Photography

Occurrence of salts

This useful salt, silver bromide, does not occur naturally. Many other salts do occur naturally in the Earth's crust. One of the most widespread and useful is sodium chloride, NaCl, which is known as **common salt** (see Chapter 16). Other examples are calcium fluoride, CaF_2 (called **fluorite** or **Blue John**), magnesium sulphate, $MgSO_4$ (called **Epsom salts**), lead(II) sulphide, PbS (called **galena**).

Other salts, including silver bromide, must be made in the laboratory. Many can be made by neutralising acids. In a salt, the hydrogen ions in the acid have been replaced by metal ions or by the ammonium ion. Salts of hydrochloric acid are called **chlorides**. Salts of sulphuric acid are called **sulphates**. Salts of nitric acid are called **nitrates**. (See Table 7.6.)

Table 7.6 Salts of some common acids

Acids	Salts
Hydrochloric acid, HCl(aq)	Sodium chloride, NaCl
	Zinc chloride, $ZnCl_2$
	Iron(II) chloride, $FeCl_2$
	Ammonium chloride, NH_4Cl
Sulphuric acid, H_2SO_4(aq)	Sodium sulphate, Na_2SO_4
	Magnesium sulphate, $MgSO_4$
	Iron(III) sulphate, $Fe_2(SO_4)_3$
Nitric acid, HNO_3	Sodium nitrate, $NaNO_3$
	Zinc nitrate, $Zn(NO_3)_2$

Salts may be soluble or insoluble. When soluble salts are made, the final step is often to allow them to crystallise from solution. The crystals of some salts contain water. Examples are

- copper(II) sulphate-5-water, $CuSO_4 \cdot 5H_2O$
- cobalt(II) chloride-6-water, $CoCl_2 \cdot 6H_2O$
- iron(II) sulphate-7-water, $FeSO_4 \cdot 7H_2O$

In Experiment 7.7 you can see how the water content of crystals gives crystals their shape and their colour. It is called **water of crystallisation**. When blue crystals of copper(II) sulphate-5-water are heated at 100 °C, the water of crystallisation is driven off. The white powdery solid that remains is **anhydrous** (without water) copper(II) sulphate:

copper(II) sulphate-5-water → water + copper(II) sulphate
blue crystals   as steam   white powder, **anyhdrous**

$$CuSO_4 \cdot 5H_2O(s) \rightarrow 5H_2O(g) + CuSO_4(s)$$

SUMMARY NOTE

There are thousands of salts. Many of them are extremely useful to us. Some of them occur naturally, but most of them must be made by the chemical industry.

Some soluble salts crystallise with water of crystallisation. This gives the crystals their shape and, in some cases, their colour.

JUST TESTING 35

1 Name the salts with the following formulas: KI, KNO_3, NaBr, $BaCO_3$, Na_2SO_4, $NiCl_2$, $CrCl_3$, $BaSO_4$, MgI_2, $ZnCl_2$.
*2 Write formulas for these salts: potassium sulphate, potassium chloride, copper(II) chloride, lead(II) sulphate, sodium bromide, ammonium sulphate.

7.9 Uses of salts

We use many different salts for a multitude of different purposes. Photography is one activity which depends on a salt, the salt silver bromide. There are many other applications for salts. A few examples will be given.

Fig. 7.6 Plaster of Paris

SUMMARY NOTE

Salts are used in agriculture, in the home, in medicine and in industry. Methods of making salts are therefore important.

Agricultural uses. Ammonium nitrate and ammonium sulphate are used as fertilisers (Section 15.3). Copper(II) sulphate solution is used on vines and potatoes to kill pests (see Sections 14.8 and 15.7).

Domestic uses. Sodium carbonate-10-water is 'washing soda', used as a water softener (Section 9.13).

Medical uses. Calcium sulphate is mined as calcium sulphate-2-water. When heated it forms calcium sulphate-$\frac{1}{2}$-water. This is plaster of Paris. It combines with water to form a strong material which is used to support broken bones (Fig. 7.6). It is also used for plastering walls.

Iron(II) sulphate-7-water is given in the form of 'iron tablets' to people who suffer from anaemia.

Barium sulphate is given to patients who are suspected of having a stomach ulcer. After a 'barium meal', an X-ray shows the path taken by the salt. Being large, barium ions give good X-ray photographs.

Industrial uses. Anhydrous calcium chloride is used as a drying agent. Sodium chloride has many uses (see Section 16.1).

Some of these salts are mined, e.g. sodium chloride and calcium sulphate. Others must be made by the chemical industry, e.g. silver bromide and copper(II) sulphate.

7.10 Methods of making salts

The methods of making salts fall into three classes:
- Direct combination of the elements, called **synthesis**
- Methods for soluble salts
- Methods for insoluble salts.

Table 7.7 summarises the facts about the solubility of salts.

Table 7.7 Soluble and insoluble salts

Salts	Soluble	Insoluble
Chlorides	Most are soluble	Silver chloride, AgCl Lead(II) chloride, $PbCl_2$
Sulphates	Most are soluble	Barium, calcium and lead(II) sulphates, $BaSO_4$, $CaSO_4$ and $PbSO_4$
Nitrates	All are soluble	None
Carbonates	Sodium and potassium carbonates, Na_2CO_3 and K_2CO_3	Most are insoluble
Ethanoates	All are soluble	None
Sodium, potassium and ammonium salts	All are soluble	None

SUMMARY NOTE

You will need to refer to this information about soluble and insoluble salts.

Direct combination of elements

A reactive metal and a reactive non-metallic element may combine directly (Experiments 3.1–3.4). For example,

aluminium + iodine → aluminium iodide

iron + sulphur → iron(II) sulphide

These are examples of **synthesis**. This method can be used for soluble and insoluble salts. You will meet the synthesis of oxides in Chapter 10 and the synthesis of chlorides in Chapter 15.

Methods for soluble salts

1 ***Reaction between a metal and a dilute acid.*** A reactive metal will displace hydrogen from a dilute acid to give a salt (see Experiment 7.5):

Metal + Acid → Salt + Hydrogen

For example,

zinc + sulphuric acid → zinc sulphate + hydrogen

Figure 7.7a shows how the reaction can be used to prepare a salt.

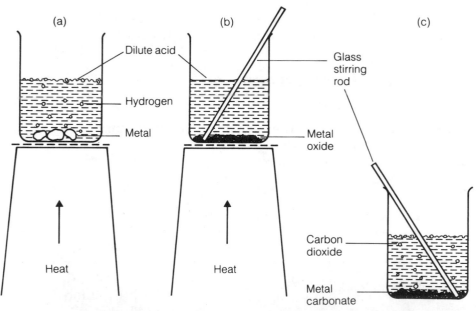

(a)
Dilute acid
Hydrogen
Metal
Heat

(b)
Glass stirring rod
Metal oxide
Heat

(c)
Carbon dioxide
Metal carbonate

1 Use an excess of metal. When no more hydrogen gas is evolved, the reaction is over: all the acid has reacted.

Use an excess of metal oxide. When the solution no longer turns blue litmus red, the reaction is over.

Use an excess of metal carbonate. When the evolution of carbon dioxide stops, the reaction is over.

2 Remove the excess of metal in (a) or metal oxide in (b) or metal carbonate in (c) by filtration.

3 Evaporate the filtrate until crystallisation begins. Crystals of the metal salt form.

Fig. 7.7   Preparation of soluble salts

2 ***Reaction between an insoluble base and a dilute acid.***
A base reacts with an acid to give a salt and water (see Experiment 7.6):

Acid + Base → Salt + Water

Soluble salts are made by the reactions:

Acid + Reactive metal →
   Salt + Hydrogen

Acid + Insoluble base →
   Salt + Water

Acid + Metal carbonate →
   Salt + Water + Carbon dioxide

In these three methods, an excess of the solid reactant is used, and unreacted solid is removed by filtration.
The Acid + Alkali method follows later.

For example,

copper(II) oxide + sulphuric acid → copper(II) sulphate + water

Figure 7.7b shows how the reaction can be used for the preparation of a salt.

3 Reaction between a metal carbonate and a dilute acid.
A metal carbonate reacts with a dilute acid to give a salt and carbon dioxide and water:

Acid + Carbonate → Salt + Carbon dioxide + Water

For example,

barium carbonate + hydrochloric acid → barium chloride + carbon dioxide + water

Figure 7.7c shows how the reaction can be used for the preparation of a salt.

JUST TESTING 36

Refer to Fig. 7.7.

1 How do you know that all the acid has been used up?

2 Why is it necessary to ensure that all the acid is used up?

3 If some acid were left unneutralised in step **1**, what would happen to it in step **3**? How would it affect the result?

4 Why is it easier to remove an excess of base than an excess of acid?

4 Reaction between an acid and an alkali. When an alkali reacts with an acid

Acid + Alkali → Salt + Water

For example,

potassium hydroxide + hydrochloric acid → potassium chloride + water

An alkali is a soluble base. You cannot remove an excess by filtration, as in methods **1**, **2** and **3**. You must add exactly the right amount of alkali to neutralise the acid. **Titration** can be used. You can use this method of adding one reactant to another in a measured way in Experiment 7.8. Figure 7.8 summarises the method.

Soluble salts can be made by the reaction:

Acid + Alkali → Salt + Water

The method of titration is used to add exactly the right amounts of acid and alkali.

Career sketch: Analytical chemist

Gwynneth is an analytical chemist who works for an agricultural advisory service. One of her jobs is to measure the protein content of different foods. She works in a laboratory which is equipped with many kinds of apparatus. She has an automatic instrument to do titrations for her. She must understand how her instruments work and be able to interpret the results they give. Gwynneth has A-level chemistry.

2 *Read* the burette.

3 *Titrate.* Add acid slowly from the burette. Swirl the conical flask. Stop when the indicator changes to its neutral colour.

1 The conical flask holds a measured volume of alkali and some indicator. It sits on a white tile.

4 Read the burette again. What volume of acid has been used?

5 Now take the same volume of alkali *without indicator*. Add the *same volume* of acid as you used in the titration.

6 Evaporate the salt solution until it begins to crystallise.

Fig. 7.8   Titration

JUST TESTING 37

1 Copy and complete the following word equations:

a potassium hydroxide + sulphuric acid → potassium .... + ...

b nickel oxide + hydrochloric acid → .... chloride + ...

c calcium hydroxide + hydrochloric acid → .... + ...

d chromium oxide + hydrochloric acid → .... + ...

e aluminium oxide + sulphuric acid → .... + ...

f magnesium oxide + nitric acid → .... nitrate + ...

g sodium hydroxide + nitric acid → .... + ...

*2 Write chemical equations for the reactions listed in **1a**, **1b** and **1c**.

Method for insoluble salts: precipitation

An insoluble salt can be made by **precipitation** (see Experiment 7.9). When two chosen solutions are added, the insoluble salt **precipitates**. For example, to make the insoluble salt lead(II) sulphate you add two solutions. The reaction that has occurred is

lead(II) nitrate + sodium sulphate → lead(II) sulphate + sodium nitrate

$$Pb(NO_3)_2(aq) + Na_2SO_4(aq) \rightarrow PbSO_4(s) + 2NaNO_3(aq)$$

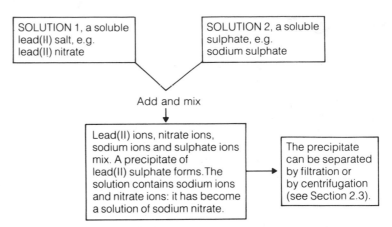

SOLUTION 1, a soluble lead(II) salt, e.g. lead(II) nitrate

SOLUTION 2, a soluble sulphate, e.g. sodium sulphate

Add and mix

Lead(II) ions, nitrate ions, sodium ions and sulphate ions mix. A precipitate of lead(II) sulphate forms. The solution contains sodium ions and nitrate ions: it has become a solution of sodium nitrate.

The precipitate can be separated by filtration or by centrifugation (see Section 2.3).

*When lead(II) ions and sulphate ions meet, they cannot remain in solution because lead(II) sulphate is insoluble. The sodium ions and nitrate ions play no part in the reaction: they remain in solution. They are called **spectator ions**. The equation for the reaction can be written without the spectator ions:

$$\text{lead(II) ions} + \text{sulphate ions} \rightarrow \text{lead(II) sulphate}$$
$$Pb^{2+}(aq) + SO_4^{2-}(aq) \rightarrow PbSO_4(s)$$

This is called an **ionic equation**.

In general, to make an insoluble salt MA you have to choose a soluble salt of M and a soluble salt of A. Table 7.7 will help you. Remember that dilute sulphuric acid can be used to provide sulphate ions, $SO_4^{2-}(aq)$, and dilute hydrochloric acid can be used to provide chloride ions, $Cl^-(aq)$.

JUST TESTING 38

(See Table 7.7 for solubility.)

1 To make lead(II) sulphate, which lead(II) salt other than lead(II) nitrate could you use? Which sulphate other than sodium sulphate could you use?

2 Silver chloride is insoluble. You can make it by adding solutions of a soluble choride and a soluble silver salt.
   a Name a soluble chloride.
   b Name a soluble silver salt.
   c Write a word equation for the reaction that happens when you add the two solutions.
   d Describe how you would obtain a dry specimen of silver chloride.
   e Write an ionic equation for the reaction.

3 Barium sulphate is insoluble.
   a Name two solutions which you could mix to give a precipitate of barium sulphate.
   b Describe what you would do to obtain barium sulphate from the mixture.
   c Write a word equation for the reaction.
   d Write a chemical equation.

4 Nickel carbonate is insoluble.
   a What two solutions would you use to prepare it?
   b Write a word equation for the reaction.

Exercise 7

1 What type of container is used for strong acids?

2 List three salts and their uses.

3 You are given five solutions in bottles labelled A, B, C, D and E. One bottle contains water and the others contain solutions of citric acid (from lemons), sulphuric acid, sodium hydroxide and sodium hydrogencarbonate (which is used as a remedy for indigestion). Given a bottle of Universal Indicator, how could you find out which solution is which?

4 • Teeth become coated with a layer of food and bacteria called **plaque**.

 • Toothpaste contains solid aluminium hydroxide.
 How does solid aluminium hydroxide work to remove plaque from teeth?
 How does it remove the acids which form in plaque?
 Why do we need to remove mouth acids?
 Why is a detergent added to toothpaste to make it foam?
 Why is flavouring, such as mint, added to toothpaste?

5 Scouring powders are strong cleaners for jobs like oven cleaning. They contain an alkali, often sodium hydroxide, and powdered stone.
 How does the powder help in cleaning?
 How does the alkali help in cleaning?

6 a Name the acid used in car batteries.
 b If you spilt some of this acid, what household substance could you use to neutralise it?
 c Name the acid present in vinegar.
 d Name the compound present in bath salts.
 e What gas is formed when vinegar reacts with bath salts?

7 Magnesium sulphate crystals, $MgSO_4 \cdot 7H_2O$, can be made from magnesium oxide and dilute sulphuric acid by the following method.

 Step 1 Add an excess of magnesium oxide to dilute sulphuric acid. Warm.
 Step 2 Filter.
 Step 3 Partly evaporate the solution from Step 2. Leave it to stand.
 Step 4 Filter the solution from Step 3.

 a Explain why an excess of magnesium oxide is used in Step 1.
 b Name (i) the residue and (ii) the filtrate in Step 2.
 c Explain why the solution is partly evaporated in Step 3.
 d What is removed by filtering in Step 4?
 e Would you dry the product by strong heating or by gentle heating? Explain your answer.
 f Write a word equation for the reaction. Write a symbol equation.

8 How would you make potassium nitrate? What starting materials would you use, and what steps would you take to obtain crystals of the product?
 Explain why you have chosen this method. (For solubility information, see Table 7.7.)

9 What method would you use to make copper(II) chloride? Explain why you have chosen this method. Say what starting materials you would need, and what you would do to obtain solid copper(II) chloride. (For solubility information, see Table 7.7.)

10 How would you make barium carbonate? Say what starting materials you would need, and describe what you would do with them. Explain why you chose this method. (For solubility information, see Table 7.7.)

11 When you add lemon juice to tea, the tea changes colour. Suggest a reason for the change.

12 Arrange the following pH values in order of increasing acid strength. Which values show basic, neutral and acidic solutions?
 a 5.0; b 1.5; c 9.5; d 7.0; e 12.0; f 6.5; g 7.4.

13 Silver bromide, the light-sensitive salt in photographic film, is made by mixing solutions of silver nitrate and potassium bromide. Write a word equation and a chemical equation for the reaction. What precaution would you have to take to obtain a useful product?

14 • Sauerkraut is made by allowing cabbage to ferment.
 • Cabbage juice has a pH of 5. Sauerkraut has a pH of 3.
 What kind of substance must be produced when cabbage is fermented?

15 Barium ions are highly poisonous. A person who swallows barium chloride solution should be given sodium sulphate solution to drink. Explain why this is an antidote. Write a word equation and a chemical equation for the reaction that occurs.

16 The label on a bottle of baking soda says that one of its uses is to relieve acid indigestion. The acid in the stomach is hydrochloric acid. Explain how baking soda, sodium hydrogencarbonate, acts as an antacid. Give a word equation for its reaction with stomach acid.

Career sketch: Laboratory technician 1

Jane works for a chemical manufacturer. Her job is to check and test the dyes which her company manufactures. She works in a well equipped laboratory, where she is able to do a number of different tests. The firm's customers want very accurate colour matches. They send Jane small samples of material which she can analyse. Then she can suggest a dye which will give exactly the right shade of colour. Her work takes Jane out of the laboratory. She visits customers to try out her dyes in their colour-printing machinery.

Chemistry was one of Jane's A-level subjects. She is now improving her qualifications by part-time study at a College of Higher Education.

Career sketch: Laboratory technician 2

Ahmed works for an industrial company which manufactures latex paints. He is one of a small team that makes up experimental batches of latex and tests them. If a batch is satisfactory, they add pigment and other substances to make them into paints. Then they test the paints. Ahmed hopes that he will move into the sales area of the firm, dealing with customers' technical problems.

Ahmed started work after A-levels. He attends a day-release course at a College of Further Education.

CHAPTER 8 *Air*

8.1 Saving lives with heroism and oxygen

The clock on the wall of the Credito Mexicano bank in the centre of Mexico City stopped at 7.20 a.m. on Thursday, 19th September, 1985. The windows broke, the floors heaved, the walls swayed, but the bank stood. Next door, the Hotel Regis collapsed into a mountain of rubble, crushing or trapping 500 tourists. Schools, houses and apartment blocks collapsed. By 8 a.m., everyone who was left in Mexico City knew that they were lucky to be alive. They had survived the worst earthquake in their city's history. In the centre of the city, 250 buildings had collapsed and 10 000 people had died.

People who had escaped injury started to search for survivors. Thousands of people lay trapped under masses of twisted steel and fallen concrete. There was a second danger for those who had survived the earthquake: lack of air. The air was heavy with dust and smoke. Broken gas mains caught fire. If there were any survivors in the ruins of the Hotel Regis, the fire smouldering through the ruins took away their oxygen and their chance of being rescued. When survivors were found under the rubble, rescuers fed air to them through plastic pipes, to prevent them suffocating in the dust and smoke-filled ruins.

There were some near-miraculous rescues. When the Juarez Hospital collapsed, its 12 stories folded in, trapping a thousand patients and staff between the floors. Rescuers tunnelled between the collapsed floors finding survivors and removing bodies. After 7 days, rescuers brought out alive some tiny newborn babies who had survived for a week without food. They were rushed to a hospital. Many of the babies survived. In incubators, they were warmed slowly back to a normal temperature, and given food and oxygen (see Fig. 8.1). Pure oxygen from a cylinder can save the life of someone who has been deprived of air.

Fig. 8.1 One of Mexico City's infant miracles

8.2 Air

For people in normal health, there is enough oxygen in the air they breathe. The percentage by volume of oxygen in clean, dry air is 21%. Figure 8.2 shows the percentages of nitrogen and other gases in pure, dry air. Water vapour and pollutants may be present also.

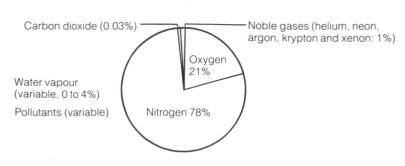

Carbon dioxide (0.03%)

Noble gases (helium, neon, argon, krypton and xenon: 1%)

Oxygen 21%

Water vapour (variable, 0 to 4%)

Pollutants (variable)

Nitrogen 78%

Fig. 8.2 Composition of clean, dry air in percentage by volume

8.3 How to obtain oxygen and nitrogen from air

The method used to separate oxygen and nitrogen from air is fractional distillation (see Section 2.5) of liquid air (Fig. 8.3). Drastic cooling is needed to liquefy air at −200 °C. Two physicists called Joule and Thompson noticed that when a compressed gas is allowed to expand suddenly its temperature drops. This cooling effect is used to liquefy air (Fig. 8.3). Liquid air is distilled in an insulated fractionating column. The temperature is −190 °C at the top of the column and −200 °C at the bottom. Nitrogen, with the lower boiling temperature of −196 °C, can exist as a gas at the top of the column. Oxygen, with the higher boiling temperature of −183 °C, remains as a liquid and is run off from the bottom of the column. Argon is drawn off from the middle of the column. The fractions, oxygen, nitrogen and argon, can be redistilled if very pure gases are required. They are stored under pressure in strong steel cylinders. Many important uses are found for them.

SUMMARY NOTE

Air is a mixture of oxygen, nitrogen, noble gases, carbon dioxide, water vapour and pollutants. Oxygen and nitrogen are obtained by the fractional distillation of liquid air.

Fig. 8.3   Fractional distillation of liquid air

8.4 Uses of oxygen

Hospitals need oxygen for patients who have difficulty in breathing. Tiny premature babies often need oxygen, and people with lung diseases are kept alive by daily sessions with their

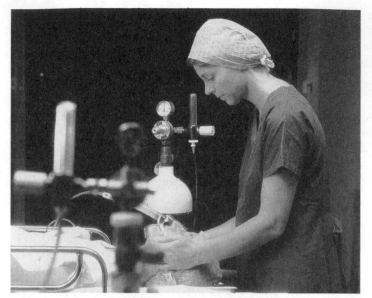

Fig. 8.4   Oxygen in hospitals

Fig. 8.5   Oxygen in industry

breathing machines. Patients who are having operations are given an anaesthetic mixed with oxygen (Fig. 8.4).

Industry has many uses for oxygen. The 'oxy-acetylene' torch burns the gas ethyne (formerly called acetylene) in oxygen to produce a temperature of about 4000 °C. This torch is used for cutting and welding metal plates (Fig. 8.5).

The steel industry uses oxygen to burn off impurities, such as carbon, sulphur and phosphorus. The removal of these impurities turns brittle cast iron into strong steel (see Section 11.11). The consumption of oxygen is high: one tonne of oxygen for every tonne of cast iron turned into steel. Many steel plants make their own oxygen on site.

Aeroplanes which fly at high altitude must carry oxygen. At a height of 5 km, the air pressure is only half that at sea level. Climbers who are tackling high mountains take oxygen with them.

Divers carry oxygen cylinders when they are working under water (Fig. 8.6). They breathe a mixture of oxygen and helium (see Section 8.7). At one time, divers used to carry cylinders of air. Under water, at high pressure, nitrogen dissolves in the blood. When a diver surfaced, nitrogen came out of solution, and if the diver surfaced quickly the bubbles collected in the bloodstream, causing a painful condition called the **bends**. The use of helium instead of nitrogen to dilute oxygen avoids the bends because very little helium dissolves in the blood, even under pressure.

Astronauts must carry oxygen, and even unmanned space flights need oxygen. To lift spacecraft into orbit, rockets burn kerosene in oxygen. After lift-off, the spacecraft burns hydrogen in oxygen (Fig. 8.7).

Oxygen is used to combat pollution. Air or oxygen is used in the treatment of sewage (see Chapter 9). If it were not for this treatment, many rivers and lakes would be spoiled by sewage (Fig. 8.8). Oxygen is used to restore life to polluted lakes and rivers (see Chapter 9).

SUMMARY NOTE

There are many uses for pure oxygen. Hospitals use it to treat patients who have breathing difficulties. Industries, especially the steel industry, use oxygen. Mountaineers, deep-sea divers, high altitude pilots and astronauts all carry oxygen. Oxygen is used to combat pollution.

Fig. 8.6   A diver needs oxygen

Fig. 8.7   Space rockets carry oxygen

Fig. 8.8   Oxygen fights pollution

8.5 Nitrogen

Nitrogen is used by the food industry. When foods such as nuts and bacon are processed, they need to be protected from oxygen. Otherwise, oxygen in the air will oxidise oils in the foods to rancid products. To exclude oxygen, a stream of nitrogen is passed over the processed foods while they are being packed.

Many uses of nitrogen depend on its unreactive nature. Liquid nitrogen is used when an unreactive refrigerant is needed. The food industry uses it for the fast freezing of foods. Hospitals use it to preserve kidneys from a donor until they are transplanted into a patient. Vets use liquid nitrogen to preserve semen, ready for use in artificial insemination. They can transport the semen of a prize bull or a famous racehorse around the country and use it to improve a dairy herd or racing stable. Preserved human semen is used in some infertility clinics. If a husband does not produce normal sperm, the semen from a donor may enable him and his wife to have the baby they want.

Fig. 8.9 These foods are packaged under nitrogen

SUMMARY NOTE

Nitrogen is used when an inert atmosphere is needed.

8.6 Carbon dioxide and water vapour

Although carbon dioxide is only 0.03% by volume of air, we could not do without it. It is essential for photosynthesis in plants (see Section 13.6). Figure 8.10 shows how you can test for the presence of carbon dioxide in air. The test depends on the white precipitate formed when carbon dioxide reacts with a solution of calcium hydroxide, **limewater** (see Section 13.3).

The content of water vapour in the air varies from 0% in a desert to 4% in a rain forest. Figure 8.10 shows how to test air for water vapour. Any substance which contains water turns anhydrous copper(II) sulphate from white to blue (see Section 7.8).

Air is drawn through the apparatus by the suction pump.

To suction pump

Ice-water

Anhydrous copper(II) sulphate turns from white to blue.

Limewater (calcium hydroxide solution): a white precipitate forms.

Fig. 8.10 Testing for carbon dioxide and water vapour in air

SUMMARY NOTE

Air contains
- carbon dioxide
- water vapour.

This is why air
- turns limewater cloudy
- turns anhydrous copper(II) sulphate from white to blue.

8.7 The noble gases

In the 1930s, airships were a popular means of transport. These 'lighter than air' ships contained big gas bags filled with hydrogen. Air is 14 times denser than hydrogen, and the gas bags were able to lift into the air a 200 tonne airship with 50 passengers. Diesel engines attached to the outside of the airships could propel them at up to 140 kilometres per hour (90 m.p.h). Passengers enjoyed the spacious shipboard-type accommodation, together with the comfort of the smooth ride and the excitement of fine views. Transatlantic crossings were particularly popular until disaster struck in 1937. The pride of Germany's fleet of airships, the Hindenburg, caught fire when landing in the USA. Of the 50 passengers, only a few were able to leap to safety. Investigation showed that the fire had been started by an act of sabotage, not by any design fault. Nevertheless, Germany decided to stop using airships, and other nations followed suit.

Nearly 50 years later, the UK-based firm, Airships Industries, pioneered the return of the airship. In June 1985, an airship flew over Lords during the Test Match, over Wimbledon during the tournament and over Henley Regatta. It carried an advertisement (see Fig. 8.11). The manufacturers, besides selling airships for advertising, also make airships which carry passengers. Both civil and military uses have been found for the new airships.

Fig. 8.11 Skyship 500 carries 2 tonnes at 90 km per hour. It is only 1/100 of the size of a 1930s airship

The reason why the new airships are safe is that they use the gas helium. Although helium is denser than hydrogen, it is still much less dense than air. Helium does not burn; in fact, helium takes part in no chemical reactions whatsoever. It is one of the **noble gases**.

The noble gases are a set of elements which make up 1% by

117

Fig. 8.12   Neon lights

volume of air (Fig. 8.2). They are helium, neon, argon, krypton and xenon. So unreactive are these elements that for a long time people believed that they formed no compounds, and called them the **inert gases**. Argon is the most abundant of the noble gases (0.09% of air). It can be obtained by the fractional distillation of liquid air (Fig. 8.3). You met the noble gases in Chapter 4.

Neon lights are well known for their brightness and long life (Fig. 8.12). When an electric discharge is passed through neon at low pressure, it glows brightly. Argon, krypton and xenon are also used in artificial lights. The tungsten filament in an electric light bulb reaches 2500 °C in operation. If oxygen were present, it would oxidise the filament. During manufacture, air is flushed out and the bulb is filled with argon. So many uses have been found for helium (e.g. for divers as well as for airships and balloons) that the supply from air is insufficient. It is obtained from natural gas (Chapter 18).

SUMMARY NOTE

The noble gases take part in few chemical reactions. Helium is used to fill airships. Neon and other noble gases are used in illuminated signs.

JUST TESTING 39

1 Why does an Olympic cyclist fill his tyres with helium instead of air?

2 The Coastguard Service has bought one of the new airships. What advantages does an airship have over a boat for coastal patrol?

3 What would form if a light bulb containing a tungsten filament were filled with air?

8.8 How can oxygen be prepared in the laboratory?

Hydrogen peroxide is often used as a source of oxygen. It decomposes to give oxygen and water:

hydrogen peroxide → oxygen + water
$$2H_2O_2(aq) \rightarrow O_2(g) + 2H_2O(l)$$

Solutions of hydrogen peroxide are kept in stoppered brown bottles to slow down the rate of decomposition. To speed up the

Tap funnel contains a solution of hydrogen peroxide '20 volume'.

Oxygen is collected over water.

Gas jar

Beehive shelf

Trough

Manganese(IV) oxide

Fig. 8.13   A laboratory preparation of oxygen

reaction, you can either warm the solution or add a catalyst (see Chapter 21). The catalyst manganese(IV) oxide, MnO_2, is often used (see Experiments 8.1 and 8.5).

Test for oxygen

Oxygen is a colourless, odourless gas which is only slightly soluble in water. It is neutral. Since only one-fifth of air is oxygen, substances burn much faster in pure oxygen than in air. One test for oxygen is to lower a glowing wooden splint into the gas. If the splint starts to burn brightly, the gas is oxygen. **Oxygen relights a glowing splint** (see Experiment 8.1).

8.9 The reactions of oxygen with some elements

Nearly all elements combine with oxygen. Many elements burn in oxygen. The products of the reactions are **oxides**. An oxide is a compound of oxygen with one other element. Table 8.1 shows the results of the study you made in Experiment 8.1.

Table 8.1 The reactions of some elements with oxygen

Element	Observation	Product	Action of product on water
Copper (metal)	Does not burn; turns black	Copper(II) oxide, CuO (black solid)	Insoluble
Magnesium (metal)	Burns with a bright white flame	Magnesium oxide, MgO (white solid)	Dissolves slightly to give an alkaline solution, pH = 9
Iron (metal)	Burns with yellow sparks	Iron oxide, Fe_3O_4 (blue–black solid)	Insoluble
Sodium (metal)	Burns with a yellow flame	Sodium oxide, Na_2O (yellow–white solid)	Dissolves readily to form a strongly alkaline solution, pH = 10
Sulphur (non-metal)	Burns with a blue flame	Sulphur dioxide, SO_2, a fuming gas with a choking smell	Dissolves readily to form a strongly acidic solution, pH = 2
Carbon (non-metal)	Glows red	Carbon dioxide, CO_2, an invisible gas	Dissolves slightly to give a weakly acidic solution, pH = 4
Phosphorus (non-metal)	Burns with a yellow flame	Phosphorus(V) oxide, P_2O_5, a white solid	Dissolves to give a strongly acidic solution, pH = 2

Fig. 8.14   Oxides

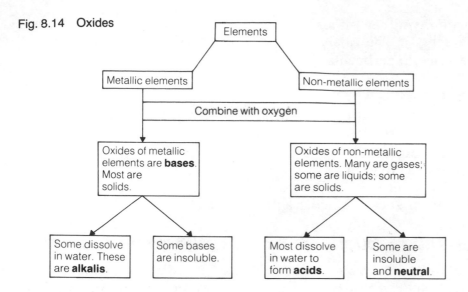

A pattern can be seen in the nature of oxides (see Fig. 8.14). The oxides of metallic elements are **bases**. If the bases dissolve in water, they are called **alkalis**. The oxides of non-metallic elements are mostly **acids**, but some are **neutral**. Acids react with bases to form **salts**. (See Chapter 7.)

When an element or compound combines with oxygen, we say it has been **oxidised**. Oxygen **oxidises** carbon to carbon dioxide. This reaction is an **oxidation**

```
       ┌─── Carbon is oxidised ───────┐
       │                              ▼
carbon + oxygen  →  carbon dioxide
C(s)   + O₂(g)   →  CO₂(g)
       └─── This reaction is oxidation ───→
```

The opposite of oxidation is **reduction**. When a substance loses oxygen, it is **reduced**. See Chapter 9 for more about reduction.

SUMMARY NOTE

Oxygen can be made by the catalytic decomposition of hydrogen peroxide. A test for oxygen is to see whether it relights a glowing splint. Many elements burn in oxygen. Most elements react with oxygen to form oxides. The oxides of metals are bases. The oxides of non-metallic elements are acidic or neutral.

JUST TESTING 40

1 Describe two differences in physical properties between metallic and non-metallic elements. (See Chapter 3 if you need to revise.)
State two ways in which metallic and non-metallic elements differ in their chemical reactions. (See Chapter 6 as well as this chapter.)

2 **a** Why is magnesium used in distress flares?
   b The fireworks called 'sparklers' are coated with iron filings. Write a word equation for the reaction that takes place when you light one.

*3 Write word equations and balanced chemical equations to show what products are formed when the following elements are burned in oxygen:
   a sodium,
   b barium,
   c silicon,
   d aluminium.

8.10 Combustion

Compounds, as well as elements, can be oxidised. An oxidation reaction in which energy is given out is called a **combustion** reaction. If there is a flame, the combustion is described as **burning**. Substances which undergo combustion are called **fuels**.

The combustion of fuels is one of the most important reactions. We need fuels to heat our homes, to cook our food, to run our cars and to generate electricity. Many of our most important fuels, e.g. petrol, kerosene (paraffin), diesel fuel and natural gas, are petroleum oil derivatives (Chapter 18). These fuels are mixtures of **hydrocarbons**. Hydrocarbons are compounds of carbon and hydrogen only. It is important to know what products are formed when these fuels burn. Figure 8.15 shows how you can test the products of combustion of kerosene (paraffin), which is sold for use in domestic heaters. **Do not use petrol in this apparatus**. You can burn a candle instead of kerosene. Candle wax is another hydrocarbon fuel obtained from crude oil.

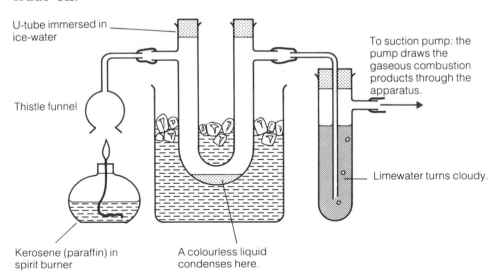

U-tube immersed in ice-water

Thistle funnel

To suction pump: the pump draws the gaseous combustion products through the apparatus.

Limewater turns cloudy.

Kerosene (paraffin) in spirit burner

A colourless liquid condenses here.

Fig. 8.15 Testing the combustion products of a hydrocarbon fuel, e.g. kerosene or candle wax (NOT petrol)

As you see from Figure 8.15, the combustion products are carbon dioxide and water. The same products are obtained with other hydrocarbon fuels:

hydrocarbon + oxygen → carbon dioxide + water vapour

Some fuels, e.g. candle wax, also leave a deposit of carbon (soot) on the inside of the thistle funnel. This proves that the air supply was insufficient to oxidise all the carbon in the hydrocarbon fuel to carbon dioxide, CO_2. There is another product of incomplete combustion which you cannot see or smell. This is the poisonous gas carbon monoxide, CO. When petrol is burned in the cylinders of a vehicle engine, the exhaust gases contain some carbon monoxide, some unburnt hydrocarbons and some soot in addition to the harmless products, carbon dioxide and water. There have been many instances of people being poisoned by carbon monoxide while running a car engine in a closed garage.

For the fire triangle and fire extinguishers, see Chapter 13.

JUST TESTING 41

1 Kerosene (called paraffin by retailers) makes a convenient fuel for use in room heaters. Why is it important that a room should be well ventilated if you are using a kerosene (paraffin) heater in it?

2 People complain of headaches when they are forced to spend time in slow-moving traffic jams. Which of the exhaust gases do you think is responsible?

8.11 Breathing and respiration

Another process which involves air is **breathing**. We **inhale** (breathe in) and **exhale** (breathe out) air to keep alive. We inhale between 15 000 and 20 000 litres of air each day. The differences between inhaled air and exhaled air are shown in Table 8.2.

Table 8.2 The composition of air in percentage by volume

Air	Oxygen	Carbon dioxide	Water vapour	Nitrogen	Noble gases
Inhaled	21%	0.03%	0%	78%	1%
Exhaled	16%	4%	1%	78%	1%

The reason for the differences is that inhaled air takes part in the biochemical reactions called **respiration**. Inhaled air dissolves in the blood supplied to the lungs. In the bloodstream, some of the oxygen in the dissolved air oxidises food materials. The oxidation products are carbon dioxide and water. They are carried by the bloodstream to the lungs. During the oxidation of foods, energy is released. Carbohydrates (sugars and starches) and fats are the main energy-providing foods. The combustion of foods in living tissues is **respiration**.

carbohydrate + oxygen → carbon dioxide + water + energy
(e.g. glucose, a sugar, $C_6H_{12}O_6$)

$$C_6H_{12}O_6(aq) + 6O_2(g) \rightarrow 6CO_2(g) + 6H_2O(l) + energy$$

The energy released is used as heat energy, to keep us warm, and as kinetic energy (energy of motion) to allow us to be active.

JUST TESTING 42

1 What happens when you blow on to a cold window? Explain.

2 What do you see when you breathe out on a very cold, frosty day? Explain.

3 Describe an experiment you could do to show that the air you breathe out contains more carbon dioxide than the air you breathe in.

8.12 Rusting

Another process which involves air is **rusting** (see Experiments 8.3 and 8.4). Rust is the reddish brown solid which appears on the surface of iron and steel. Other metals also can be corroded (Section 11.4), but only iron and steel rust. Rusting is a nuisance. Millions of pounds a year are spent on replacing rusty iron and steel structures. Methods of preventing rust save money. To find methods of preventing rust, you must first find out what causes it.

Your experiments showed that air and water are needed for iron to rust. There must also be a trace of acid present; the carbon dioxide content of the air is sufficient. Of the air, 21% is used up. The remaining gas will not allow a splint to burn in it, so the part of the air that reacts with iron must be oxygen. Like other reactions studied in this chapter, rusting is an oxidation reaction:

iron + oxygen → iron(III) oxide (rust)

Methods of preventing iron from rusting are covered in Section 11.12.

JUST TESTING 43

1 a Describe experiments which you could do to find what percentage by volume of the air is used in (i) the rusting of iron, (ii) the oxidation of magnesium and (iii) respiration.

b What results would you expect to find in each of the three experiments?

8.13 Pollution

The problem

We are constantly exposed to air. Each day we breathe in 15 000 to 20 000 litres of air, to pass over the sensitive tissues of our lungs. The lung diseases of cancer, bronchitis and emphysema

are common illnesses in regions where air is highly polluted.
Through the lungs, pollutants can reach every part of our bodies.
The main air pollutants are shown in Table 8.3.

Table 8.3 The main pollutants in air

Pollutant	Emission*	Source
Carbon monoxide, CO	100	Vehicle engines and industrial processes
Sulphur dioxide, SO_2	33	Combustion of fuels in power stations and factories
Hydrocarbons	32	Combustion of fuels in factories and vehicles
Dust	28	Combustion of fuels; mining; factories
Oxides of nitrogen, NO and NO_2	21	Vehicle engines and fuel combustion

*Emissions are given in millions of tonnes per year in the UK.

This is an alarming list of pollutants. We are now going to
look into the following questions:

- Where do the pollutants come from?
- What harm do they do?
- What can be done to reduce them?

First, we shall look at how we manage to survive at all with all
these pollutants being released into the air.

Air currents and temperature inversions

The sun beating down on the Earth keeps the surface of the
Earth warm, and the Earth warms the lower atmosphere. The air
in the upper atmosphere is cooler. Since warm air is less dense
than cold air, warm air has a tendency to rise and cold air to
sink (Fig. 8.16a). These currents of air mix the lower atmosphere.
The dirty air we produce is carried upwards and dispersed
quickly into the vast upper atmosphere.

Sometimes these air currents disappear for a time. Then the air

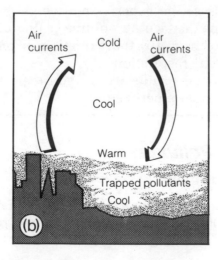

Fig. 8.16   (a) Air currents; (b) a temperature inversion

124

in the higher regions of the atmosphere, warmed by the sun, becomes warmer than air near the ground. There is a **temperature inversion** (Fig. 8.16b). The cooler air near the ground is the denser, and stays put. Pollutants poured into a stagnant layer do not become dispersed. They accumulate near ground level, mainly over cities. Temperature inversions force us to breathe our own pollutants, and sometimes these make us ill. Temperature inversions are most likely to occur in places which have a hot climate and still air.

Carbon monoxide

Worldwide, the emission of carbon monoxide is 350 million tonnes a year. The chief source is the internal combustion engine. As you read in Section 8.10, if the combustion of petrol is incomplete, the exhaust gases contain carbon monoxide and carbon as well as the harmless combustion products, carbon dioxide and water. Incomplete combustion occurs when there is insufficient oxygen for full oxidation of the hydrocarbons in petrol. Car designers find that maximum performance is obtained when fuel-rich mixtures are burned in the cylinders. This design leads to the discharge of carbon monoxide, carbon and unburnt hydrocarbons.

What harm does carbon monoxide do? Carbon monoxide combines with haemoglobin. Haemoglobin is the red susbtance in blood which transports oxygen round the body. It combines with oxygen in the lungs, carries oxygen as oxyhaemoglobin round the body and releases oxygen to the tissues.

In the lungs:

haemoglobin + oxygen → oxyhaemoglobin
$Hb(aq)$ + $O_2(g)$ → $O_2Hb(aq)$

In the tissues:

oxyhaemoglobin → oxygen + haemoglobin
$O_2Hb(aq)$ → $O_2(aq)$ + $Hb(aq)$

The freed haemoglobin then circulates back to the lungs to pick up more oxygen. If carbon monoxide is present in the lungs, it combines with haemoglobin:

carbon monoxide + haemoglobin → carboxyhaemoglobin
$CO(g)$ + $Hb(aq)$ → $COHb(aq)$

Carbon monoxide is 200 times better at combining with haemoglobin than oxygen is. It therefore ties up haemoglobin so that haemoglobin can no longer combine with oxygen. At a level of 0.1%, carbon monoxide will kill quickly; at lower levels, it causes headaches and dizziness and affects reaction times.

Being colourless and odourless, carbon monoxide gives no warning of its presence. Measurements have shown fairly high levels of carbon monoxide in crowded streets during rush hours. Since carbon monoxide is concentrated at street level, it is most likely to affect people when they are driving and need sound judgment and quick reflexes.

What can be done? Nature can deal with carbon monoxide. Soil organisms can convert it into carbon dioxide or methane. In city streets, where the concentration of carbon monoxide is high, there is little soil to remove it.

People are working on a number of solutions to the problem.

- The tuning of vehicle engines can be altered to provide more air and produce only carbon dioxide and water. A snag is that this increases the formation of oxides of nitrogen (see Section 13.6).
- Many cars are now fitted with **catalytic converters**. The hot exhaust gases pass over a catalyst, which helps to oxidise carbon monoxide to carbon dioxide (see Acid Rain). Catalytic converters only work when the petrol contains no lead compounds.
- In the future, vehicles may be powered by fuels which burn more cleanly than hydrocarbons (see Section 18.1).

SUMMARY NOTE

Carbon monoxide is produced when hydrocarbon fuels burn incompletely in an inadequate supply of air. It is a poison which combines with haemoglobin in the blood, thus starving the body of oxygen. Catalytic converters can be fitted in the exhaust pipes of cars to bring about the oxidation of carbon monoxide to the harmless product, carbon dioxide.

Sulphur dioxide

Where does sulphur dioxide come from? Almost all the sulphur dioxide in the air comes from industrial sources. Industrial smelters, which obtain metals from sulphide ores, produce tonnes of sulphur dioxide daily. Half of the output of sulphur dioxide comes from the burning of coal. All coal contains between 0.5 and 5 per cent sulphur.

$$\text{sulphur in coal} + \text{oxygen in air} \rightarrow \text{sulphur dioxide}$$
$$S(s) \qquad\qquad + O_2(g) \qquad\quad \rightarrow SO_2(g)$$

The sulphur dioxide escapes up chimneys into the atmosphere. Worldwide, 150 million tonnes a year are emitted. The emission is growing as countries become more industrialised. Most of the coal is burned in power stations. These are always situated in densely populated regions where the demand for electricity is high and where there are plenty of people to breathe in the sulphur dioxide (see Fig. 8.17).

Fig. 8.17   Sulphur dioxide emission

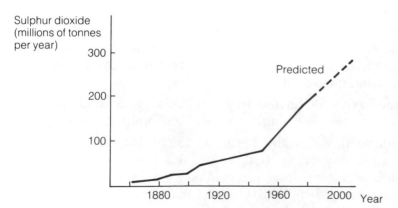

What harm does sulphur dioxide do? Sulphur dioxide is a colourless gas with a very penetrating and irritating smell. It is poisonous; at a level of 0.5%, it will kill. The immediate effects of inhaling sulphur dioxide are coughing, chest pains and shortness of breath. Sulphur dioxide is thought to contribute to bronchitis and lung diseases.

Factories and power stations burn coal, which contains sulphur. They send sulphur dioxide into the air. Metal smelters oxidise sulphides to sulphur dioxide. Sulphur dioxide causes bronchitis and lung diseases. In the upper atmosphere, it reacts with water to form **acid rain**.

Fig. 8.18 The chimneys of a power station

What can be done about it?

- Tall chimneys carry sulphur dioxide away from factories (Fig. 8.18). Unfortunately it comes down to earth again as **acid rain**.
- A number of processes for removing sulphur dioxide from the emission of power plants are being tried (see below).

Acid rain

Tall chimneys carry away the sulphur dioxide and other pollutant gases. They are not allowed to pollute the air breathed by the factory workforce or the local residents.

Unfortunately, the acid gases do not disappear. In the air, sulphur dioxide meets water vapour, and reacts to form sulphurous acid, H_2SO_3. This is slowly oxidised by oxygen in the air to sulphuric acid, H_2SO_4. When it rains or snows, down comes the sulphuric acid as acid rain or acid snow. Oxides of nitrogen are converted into nitric acid, HNO_3 (see Fig. 8.19).

SUMMARY NOTE

Sulphur dioxide and oxides of nitrogen are present in the exhaust gases of coal- and oil-fired power stations. In the atmosphere, these gases react with water vapour to form acid rain.

Fig. 8.19 Sources of acid rain

127

Rain is naturally weakly acidic. Carbon dioxide from the air dissolves in it to form the weak acid, carbonic acid, H_2CO_3. Sulphuric acid is a thousand times stronger than carbonic acid (see Fig. 8.20).

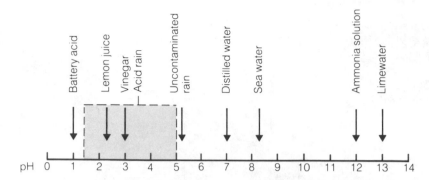

◁ Fig. 8.20 The pH values of rain, acid rain and other solutions (for pH, see Chapter 7)

What harm does acid rain do? The main damage so far has been to lakes and fish, to trees and to building materials such as stone, concrete, metal and cement.

Fish cannot survive in acidic lake water. Thousands of lakes in Canada, Norway and Sweden are now empty of fish. These countries produce very little of the acid rain and snow that falls on them. The pollution is carried to Scandinavia by the prevailing winds from the UK and from Germany, France and other highly industrialised European countries. Canada receives much of its pollution from the USA.

Some countries suffer more than others from attack by acid rain. If the soil contains basic substances, these will partially neutralise the rain as it trickles through the soil. Cold countries like Sweden receive acid snow for many months. During the spring thaw, a huge volume of acidic water is released into the lakes. The soil has no chance to neutralise it. The acidic lake water destroys water plants. As a result, light can penetrate further through the water. Acid lakes look beautifully clear and blue.

The effect of acid rain on trees is shown in Fig. 8.21. It dissolves minerals from the soil, removing the ions Ca^{2+}, K^+, Al^{3+} and Pb^{2+}. Some of these ions are nutrients, which should be absorbed by the roots of the trees. Acid rain deprives the trees of these nutrients.

Building materials suffer from attack by acid rain. Concrete and stone react with acids. Many stone buildings are made of limestone, calcium carbonate. You saw how this reacts with acids in Section 7.2. Cement and concrete contain calcium hydroxide, which reacts with carbon dioxide in the air to form calcium carbonate. So when cement and concrete 'weather', calcium carbonate is formed (see Experiment 12.2). Acid rain attacks all these substances.

Metals are attacked by acids. Iron railings, steel window-frames, motor vehicles and bridges are all corroded faster when rain water is acidic.

What can be done about it? All this damage costs money. Replacing rusty motor vehicles costs money. Restoring stonework

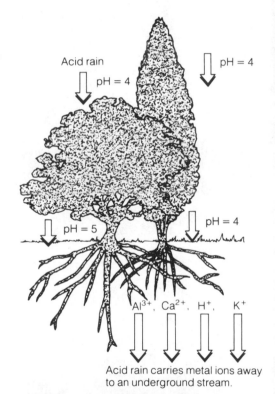

Acid rain carries metal ions away to an underground stream.

Fig. 8.21 Acid rain falls on trees

SUMMARY NOTE

Acid rain makes lakes too acidic for fish to live in. It removes minerals from the soil. Trees are deprived of essential minerals and die. Acid rain attacks construction materials such as limestone, cement, concrete and metals.

Fig. 8.22 Stonework attacked by acid rain

ACID RAIN
S VE YOUR CAR

WASH-IT-HERE

Fig. 8.23 Cashing in on the acid rain scare

SUMMARY NOTE

The damage caused by acid rain is costly. European countries have agreed to stop exporting their pollutants. Industries and power stations are trying methods of reducing their emission of acidic gases.

costs money. The Canadian timber industry is suffering as the growth of trees is affected. Tourism is suffering in Canada and Sweden: tourists do not want to fish in 'dead' lakes. Sweden has adopted the practice of spraying calcium oxide (quicklime) into acid lakes. Being a base, calcium oxide neutralises acids:

calcium oxide + sulphuric acid → calcium sulphate + water
$CaO(s)$ + $H_2SO_4(aq)$ → $CaSO_4(aq)$ + $H_2O(l)$

American companies have started neutralising sulphur dioxide at its source. They use jets of wet lime (calcium oxide) to bombard the combustion gases before they leave the chimney. This process removes sulphur dioxide, nitrogen dioxide and other acid gases from the exhaust gases. Cleaning the exhaust gases in this way costs money. The product is calcium sulphate. Some of this by-product can be used as hardcore in road-making. The rest must be removed and dumped. Another method of removing sulphur dioxide is to 'scrub' the exhaust gases with ammonia. The end product of this process is ammonium sulphate. It can be sold in large quantities as a fertiliser.

In 1979, 31 European countries signed the Convention on Long Range Transboundary Air Pollution. In this agreement, each nation agreed to reduce the amount of pollution that it allows to sweep across its frontiers. When the nations put this agreement into practice, Norway and Sweden will no longer be damaged by pollutants from central European countries and the UK. Canada and the USA have signed a similar agreement.

JUST TESTING 44

1 Why do lakes in a limestone region become less acidic as a result of acid rain than lakes in a granite region?

2 Tall chimneys carry sulphur dioxide away from factories. Explain why this is not a final solution to the problem of pollution.

3 What is formed when marble statues are attacked by air containing sulphur dioxide as well as the gases normally present in air?

4 A thousand Swedish schoolchildren wrote to the Government of West Germany to complain about the pollution of lakes in Sweden. Why did the children think West Germany could help?

5 • A smelter emits 500 tonnes of sulphur dioxide daily. This can produce 800 tonnes of sulphuric acid a day.
  • To make rain acidic (pH = 4) needs 0.01 g of sulphuric acid per kg of water.
  a How many tonnes of rain can be made acidic by this plant in a year? (Round off your answer to give an approximate figure. 1 tonne = 1000 kg.)
  b A yearly rainfall brings 2 million tonnes of rain water to each square mile of the Earth's surface. How many square miles of the Earth's surface would the acid rain in **a** cover?

Note See Exercise 12 for calculations on pollution.

Particles: smoke, dust and grit

The atmosphere contains millions of tonnes of tiny solid and liquid particles. **Particles** are droplets of liquid and small bits of solids. Dust storms, forest fires and volcanic eruptions send particles into the air. Man-made sources of dust and smoke are mining, land-clearing, coal-burning power stations, industries and vehicles. These sources are increasing.

What harm do particles do? Particles make our environment dirty. They scatter light and give air a 'smoggy' appearance. Grime falls on to clothing, buildings and plants.

Particles make our air unhealthy. They increase the danger of **smog**. Smoke consists of particles. Fog consists of water droplets. When smoke and fog mix, the fog prevents the smoke from blowing away. **Smog** is formed (Fig. 8.24). The sulphur dioxide in the smoke reacts with water droplets in the fog to form sulphurous acid and sulphuric acid. When we breathe smog, the acid irritates our lungs and makes them produce mucus. This makes it more difficult to breathe, and can cause the death of people who already suffer from a respiratory disease. In the smog which hit London in 1952 and lasted for 5 days, 5000 people died. In 1956, there was another fatal smog, and in that year Parliament passed the **Clean Air Act**. This created **smokeless zones** in which only low-smoke and low-sulphur fuels can be burned.

There is another effect of dust in the atmosphere: it can affect the climate (see Chapter 13).

How can particles be removed? Some industries use sprays of water to wash out particles from their waste gases. Others circulate air through filters. Electrostatic precipitators are used to remove small particles. They depend on the fact that most particles carry a small amount of electrostatic charge (Fig. 8.25).

The exhaust gases of vehicles are not treated by any of these methods.

Fig. 8.24 Smog

A high voltage between the metal plates will draw the particles to the plates by electrostatic attraction.

Dirty gas in

Clean gas out

Once deposited on the plates, the particles are shaken off. The dust is removed.

Fig. 8.25 An electrostatic precipitator

SUMMARY NOTE

Factories and power stations send smoke, dust and grit into the air. This dirt damages buildings and plants. It pollutes the air we breathe. When it mixes with fog, **smog** is formed.

Oxides of nitrogen

When fuels are burned in the oxygen of the air, nitrogen is also present. At the high temperatures that result, some nitrogen combines with oxygen:

nitrogen + oxygen → nitrogen monoxide
$$N_2(g) + O_2(g) \rightarrow 2NO(g)$$

nitrogen monoxide + oxygen → nitrogen dioxide
$$2NO(g) + O_2(g) \rightarrow 2NO_2(g)$$

In consequence, the gases nitrogen monoxide, NO, and nitrogen dioxide, NO_2, are released from the chimneys of power stations and factories and in the exhaust gases from motor vehicles. This mixture of gases is sometimes shown as NO_x.

What harm do they do? Nitrogen monoxide, NO, is only moderately toxic. It is soon converted into nitrogen dioxide in air. Nitrogen dioxide, NO_2, is highly corrosive and toxic. It irritates the breathing passages. It reacts with oxygen and water to form nitric acid, an ingredient of **acid rain**.

What can be done? One hope of reducing the quantity of nitrogen monoxide in exhaust gases is to bring about the reaction

nitrogen monoxide + carbon monoxide → nitrogen + carbon dioxide
$$2NO(g) + 2CO(g) \rightarrow N_2(g) + 2CO_2(g)$$

The reaction takes place in the presence of a catalyst. **Catalytic converters** are now being fitted in the exhausts of some American cars to reduce the emission of oxides of nitrogen. If lead compounds are present in the exhaust gases, they stop the catalyst working.

SUMMARY NOTE

Oxides of nitrogen, NO and NO_2 (NO_x), are formed in the engines of motor vehicles. They react with air and water to form the strong acid, nitric acid. This strongly irritates the respiratory passages. Catalytic converters can be fitted in the exhaust pipes of cars to convert nitrogen oxides into nitrogen.

JUST TESTING 45

1 In petrol engines, hydrocarbons are burned to form a number of products. What are these products? How does the ratio of carbon dioxide to carbon monoxide in the exhaust gases change as the engine temperature increases?

Nitrogen combines with oxygen in the combustion chamber. What is formed? How does the proportion of these gases in the exhaust gas alter as the engine temperature increases?

Hydrocarbons

Where do they come from? There are natural sources of hydrocarbons. Methane, CH_4, is produced when dead plant material decays in the absence of air. Although only 15 per cent of the hydrocarbons in the air come from our activities, they affect human health because they are concentrated in city air.

What harm do they do? Hydrocarbons by themselves cause little damage. In sunlight, they react with the oxygen and oxides of nitrogen in the air. As a result of these **photochemical** reactions

(reactions which are brought about by light), irritating and toxic compounds are formed. The irritating smog of Los Angeles in the USA is mostly of photochemical origin. It is known as **photochemical smog**.

What can be done? The hydrocarbons emitted by petrol engines can be reduced by increasing the oxygen supply so as to burn the petrol completely. There is a snag. The problem is this:

Chemists are doing research on the problem. The solution may be to run engines at a lower temperature (in order to reduce the combination of oxygen and nitrogen) and employ a catalyst (to ensure the complete combustion of hydrocarbons at the lower temperature).

Other pollutants

Heavy metals and their compounds are serious air pollutants. **Heavy** metals are metals with a density greater than 5 g/cm³. We need small quantities of some heavy metals, e.g. copper and zinc, in our food. Others, e.g. lead and mercury, are toxic.

Mercury. Air contains a small concentration of mercury vapour from natural sources. We add greatly to this by earth-moving activities, such as mining and road-making. By disturbing soil and rock, we allow the mercury which they contain to escape into the air. Many metal ores contain mercury compounds, which are released during the winning of the metals from their ores. The combustion of coal and oil also sends mercury vapour into the air. Both mercury and its compounds cause kidney damage, nerve damage and death.

Lead. Lead is not naturally present in air. Lead and its compounds are discharged by the combustion of coal, by the roasting of metal ores and by vehicle engines (Fig. 8.26). Unlike the other pollutants in exhaust gases, lead compounds have been purposely added to the fuel. Tetraethyl lead, TEL, is added to improve the performance of the engine. City dwellers take in lead from many sources. Many people have blood levels of lead which are nearly high enough to produce the symptoms of lead poisoning. Mild lead poisoning symptoms are depression, tiredness, irritability and headache. Higher levels of lead cause damage to the brain, liver and kidneys.

There is a cure for this type of pollution: the elimination of lead additives to petrol. In the UK, cars manufactured after 1990 run on unleaded petrol. Catalytic converters are 'poisoned' by lead compounds.

Fig. 8.26 Children in pushchairs are particularly at risk from exhaust fumes

The price of clean air

Of the pollutants mentioned in this chapter, carbon monoxide, oxides of nitrogen, hydrocarbons and lead compounds all come from motor vehicles. The UK, like many other countries, has decided to stop adding TEL (tetraethyl lead) to petrol. The addition of TEL turns a low octane fuel into a high octane (four-star) fuel on which engines run smoothly. Without TEL, vehicles need to use the more expensive high octane fuels. This increases the cost of motoring. Research chemists in the petrochemical industry are trying to find other ways of managing without TEL. They are working on methods of turning low octane fuels into high octane fuels.

Now that British cars run on unleaded petrol, they are able to use catalytic converters. These turn oxides of nitrogen, carbon monoxide and hydrocarbons in the exhaust gas into non-toxic products. The cost of fitting converters increases the price of cars. The use of catalytic converters increases the petrol consumption of cars. Pollution control therefore increases both the purchase price and the running cost of a car. Most people believe that the extra cost is worthwhile since it improves the quality of the air we breathe.

Sulphur dioxide and oxides of nitrogen are sent into the air by power stations, metal smelters and factories. Chemists have the means to remove them from the mixtures of exhaust gases produced, but this costs money. Building cleaning systems into the chimneys costs money. The chemicals consumed every day in running a cleaning system cost money. The result is an increase in the price of the electricity or metal or article which is produced. British manufacturers do not want to put up their prices. They are afraid that their competitors in other countries will have an advantage over them.

JUST TESTING 46

1 Why is carbon monoxide such a dangerous pollutant? How does nature remove it from the air?

2 Why are the oxides of sulphur so obnoxious as air pollutants? How does nature remove them?

3 Why are particulate pollutants dangerous, even though they may be chemically unreactive solids?

4 How do lead and its compounds get into the air? What damage do they cause? What is the solution to this problem?

5 Imagine you are a British manufacturer. You run a factory which sends tonnes of sulphur dioxide into the air every day. After reading some books on pollution, you decide to do your bit towards clean air. You look into the cost of installing and running a clean-up system. You calculate how much you will have to raise the price of your products to cover the cost.

Then the factory foreman points out that your chief competitor is doing nothing about pollution control. The foreman is afraid that you will price your product out of the market. You could go bankrupt. Then the workforce will be out of their jobs.

a Write a letter to your competitor, explaining to him why sulphur dioxide is a pollutant. Try to persuade him to cut down the release of sulphur dioxide from his factory if you do the same.

b Write a letter to your Member of Parliament. Tell him or her that you think Parliament should pass a law to make all manufacturers cut pollution by the same percentage. Explain why you think this would be a good idea.

c It is possible that you do not agree with **a** and **b**. In this case, explain what your views are.

6 A question for discussion:

As pollution control devices are added to cars, the number of miles we can get from a litre of petrol decreases. This means that we have to burn more petrol to travel the same number of miles. In this way, we produce more pollutants which have to be removed. Does this make pollution control self-defeating?

8.14 Winds and weather patterns

Land and sea breezes

You will probably have felt the refreshing effect of a **sea breeze**. On a sunny day, the land heats up and a cooling breeze from the sea blows towards the land. After the Sun sets, a **land breeze** flows from the land towards the sea. The Sun's energy falls equally on land and sea. How can we explain land and sea breezes?

Land heats up more easily than sea, and therefore on a sunny day the air in contact with the land becomes warmer and less dense than the air over the sea. As the warm air over the land rises, cooler air from over the sea moves in to take its place. This is a sea breeze.

2 Air warmed by the land rises.

Daytime

3 The air over the sea is cooler and denser. It flows in from the sea to take the place of the warm air. This is a sea breeze.

1 The land warms up more quickly than the sea.

Land

Sea

Fig. 8.27 A sea breeze – daytime

Fig. 8.28 A land breeze – night-time

At night, the land cools more quickly than the sea. As the air over the land cools and becomes denser than the air over the sea, a breeze blows from land to sea (see Figs. 8.27 and 8.28).

Isobars

The atmosphere exerts a pressure on everything within it. At sea level, the atmosphere exerts an average pressure of 101 000 pascals (1.01×10^5 Pa). This is called **standard atmospheric pressure**.

one pascal = one newton per square metre (1 Pa = 1 N/m²)

People who study the weather are called **meteorologists**. They use a unit of pressure called the millibar (mb).

1000 mb = 101 000 Pa = standard atmospheric pressure

On a weather map (see Fig. 8.29), lines join places which have the same atmospheric pressure. The lines are called **isobars**. Air moves, that is, the wind blows, from places with higher atmospheric pressure to places with lower atmospheric pressure.

Isobars join places which have the same atmospheric pressure.

Isobars enclose a region of high pressure. This is an **anticyclone**.

Isobars enclose a region of low pressure. This is a **depression**.

Fig. 8.29 Isobars

A study of isobars therefore tells you in which direction the wind is blowing. If isobars are close together, you know that atmospheric pressure changes rapidly over a short distance and there are strong winds. In regions where the isobars are widely spaced, winds are light and variable.

High pressure and low pressure

A region of high pressure (see Fig. 8.29) is called an **anticyclone** or, sometimes, simply a 'high'. An anticyclone may be warm or cold. Figure 8.30 shows how air flows into an anticyclone from above. As the air descends and becomes warmer, it can hold more water vapour. Clouds therefore disperse.

A region of low pressure enclosed by isobars is called a **depression**, or simply a 'low'. Air flows in from below and rises to flow out at a higher level, that is, in the opposite direction to an anticyclone (see Fig. 8.31). In the UK, depressions occur more frequently than anticyclones.

Figure 8.32 shows what is meant by a **ridge** of high pressure and a **trough** of low pressure.

Clouds

Atmospheric pressure decreases with height above the Earth. When air rises, it moves to regions of lower pressure and it therefore expands. The energy needed for expansion comes from the air and it therefore cools. When air cools, it can hold less water vapour, and water vapour condenses in tiny droplets of water as clouds. The factors that cause air to rise are:

- Air may be forced upwards if it meets hills.
- Convection currents carry air upwards.
- When warm and cold fronts meet, air is forced upwards (see later in this section).

Clouds are divided into three main groups: **cirrus clouds**, **stratus clouds** and **cumulus clouds**.

Cirrus clouds are delicate, white, wispy clouds which form at high levels (above 6000 m). They are called 'mares' tails' and can extend to form a thin veil of white cloud. They do not produce rain.

Stratus clouds are uniform layers of cloud, like fog, formed at 2500–6000 m. They can develop into **nimbostratus clouds**, large flat-topped clouds shaped like a blacksmith's anvil. These produce rain.

Cumulus clouds are 'piles' of thick, lumpy, dome-shaped or cauliflower-shaped clouds with flat bases, which form at low levels (below 2500 m). Light cumulus clouds may give a little rain or none at all. Large cumulus clouds produce light showers. They can grow to become anvil-shaped **cumulonimbus clouds** which give heavy showers and thunderstorms.

Air flows in from above. As it sinks, the air is compressed and warmed so it can hold more moisture.

No clouds.
Sunny days and cold nights.
Fog may form near the ground.

Fig. 8.30 Anticyclone weather

As the air moves upward, it cools and can therefore hold less water vapour. Water vapour condenses.

Clouds form.
There may be rain or snow. Most depressions give rise to strong winds.

Fig. 8.31 Depression weather

Sometimes the isobars round a 'high' bulge out in one direction. This is called a **ridge**.

Sometimes the isobars round a depression bulge out in one direction. This is called a **trough**.

Fig. 8.32 A ridge of high pressure and a trough of low pressure

SUMMARY NOTE

Isobars are lines on maps which join points of equal atmospheric pressure. A region of high pressure enclosed by isobars is called an anticyclone or a 'high'. A region of low pressure enclosed by isobars is called a depression or a 'low'.

Fig. 8.33   How clouds form

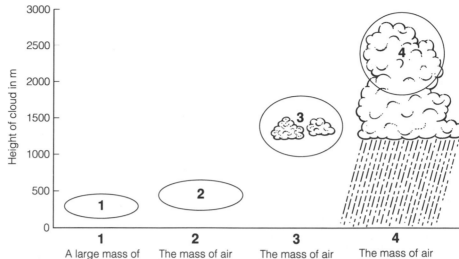

SUMMARY NOTE

Clouds form when warm air rises and cools.
The three main types of cloud are cirrus, stratus and cumulus.
Large cumulus clouds, anvil-shaped cumulonimbus clouds and anvil-shaped nimbostratus clouds produce rain.

1 A large mass of warm, damp air at ground level

2 The mass of air has reached a height where the atmosphere is cooler and the pressure is lower. The air expands and cools.

3 The mass of air has risen further and cooled. It is now saturated so water vapour condenses to form tiny droplets of water: clouds form.

4 The mass of air has risen and cooled further. So much water vapour has condensed that rain starts to fall.

Fig. 8.34   (a) Cirrus clouds (b) Stratus clouds above cumulus clouds (c) Cumulus clouds

Fronts

A **front** is a boundary between two masses of air which are at different temperatures and different humidities. (Humid air is air that contains a lot of water vapour.) As a **warm front** moves, it pushes cold air in front of it (see Fig. 8.35a). As a **cold front** moves, it pushes warm air upward (see Fig. 8.35b).

On weather maps, warm and cold fronts are shown by symbols as in Fig. 8.36.

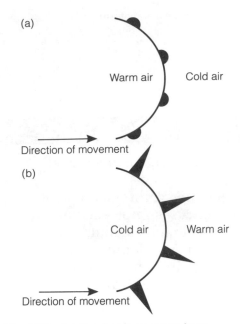

Fig. 8.36 (a) Symbol for a warm front
(b) Symbol for cold front

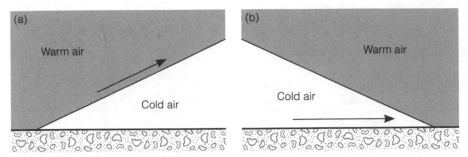

Fig. 8.35 (a) A warm front in cross-section (gradient = 1 in 100)
(b) A cold front in cross-section (gradient = 1 in 50 to 1 in 100)

Figure 8.37 shows how rain can be produced at a warm front. On days when the air rises very quickly, the picture is different. Big cumulonimbus clouds form. They produce heavy rain and sometimes thunderstorms.

Fig. 8.37 Rain from a warm front

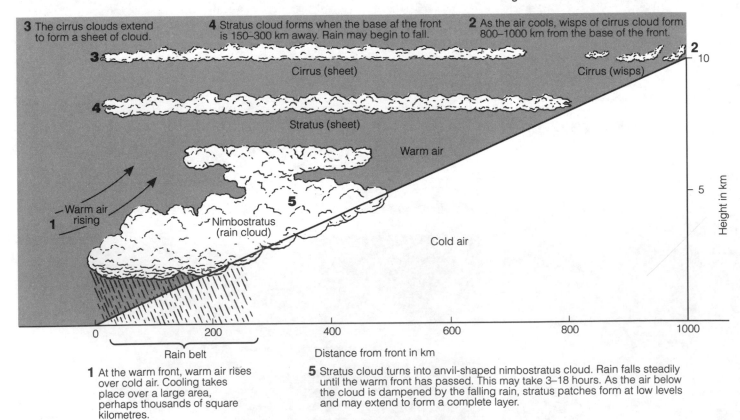

3 The cirrus clouds extend to form a sheet of cloud.

4 Stratus cloud forms when the base of the front is 150–300 km away. Rain may begin to fall.

2 As the air cools, wisps of cirrus cloud form 800–1000 km from the base of the front.

Cirrus (sheet)

Cirrus (wisps)

Stratus (sheet)

Warm air

Warm air rising

1

Nimbostratus (rain cloud)

5

Cold air

Rain belt

Distance from front in km

Height in km

1 At the warm front, warm air rises over cold air. Cooling takes place over a large area, perhaps thousands of square kilometres.

5 Stratus cloud turns into anvil-shaped nimbostratus cloud. Rain falls steadily until the warm front has passed. This may take 3–18 hours. As the air below the cloud is dampened by the falling rain, stratus patches form at low levels and may extend to form a complete layer.

Figure 8.38 shows how rain can be produced at a cold front. Cold fronts travel fast, and the rain lasts 1–2 hours. Rain stops when the front arrives.

1 As a cold front moves, it pushes warm air upwards.

2 Clouds form, usually thick stratus and nimbostratus clouds.

Cirrus

Warm air

Stratus

1

Nimbostratus

Height in km

Cold air

3

Warm air

Distance from front in km

Rain belt

3 Rain begins to fall without much warning. It lasts for 1–2 hours and stops when the front arrives.

Fig. 8.38 Rain from a cold front

Fig. 8.39 An occlusion forms.

Cold fronts travel faster than warm fronts. When a cold front catches up with a warm front, warm air is pushed upwards and an **occlusion** is formed (see Fig. 8.39). The weather produced by an occlusion is similar to that produced by a warm front.

Cold front   Warm air   Warm front
Colder air   Cold air

Cold front   Warm air   Warm front
Colder air   Cold air

Cold front   Warm air   Warm front
Colder air   Cold air

1 A warm front and a cold front are moving from left to right.

2 The cold front has caught up with the warm front.

3 The layer of cold air on the left is colder than the layer of cold air on the right and sinks beneath it. Warm air is pushed upwards, forming an occlusion.

SUMMARY NOTE

Fronts are boundaries between masses of air at different temperatures and humidities. Rain falls ahead of a warm front and stops when the front passes, after 3–18 hours. Rain falls behind a cold front and stops when the front arrives, lasting 1–4 hours. An occlusion behaves like a warm front.

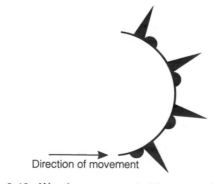

Direction of movement

Fig. 8.40 Weather map symbol for an occlusion

Weather maps use the symbols shown in Fig. 8.41. The direction of the wind is along the arrow towards the circle, from the north-west in the symbols shown. Readings of temperature in °C are also entered on maps, see Fig. 8.45.

1 Explain why clouds form at **A** but not at **B** on Fig. 8.42.

Fig. 8.42

2 On a copy of Fig. 8.43, label **a** an anticyclone, **b** a depression, **c** a warm front, **d** a cold front, **e** an occlusion. Enter arrows showing the wind direction in **f** Denmark, **g** Greenland.

Fig. 8.43

3 Refer to Fig. 8.44. For each of yachts **A** and **B**, say what kind of wind the yacht will experience **a** ahead of the front, **b** beyond the front, and **c** say when the yacht will encounter rain.

4 Study the map in Fig. 8.45. Describe the weather in each of the marked places: **A** John o'Groats, **B** Glasgow, **C** Durham, **D** Leicester, **E** Cardiff, **F** London, **G** Land's End, **H** Dublin. For each place, state the wind direction and speed in knots, the temperature in °C, the cloud cover in oktas, that is, the eighths of the sky covered by cloud, and the type of precipitation (rain, snow, etc.).

Fig. 8.41   Weather symbols

Fig. 8.44

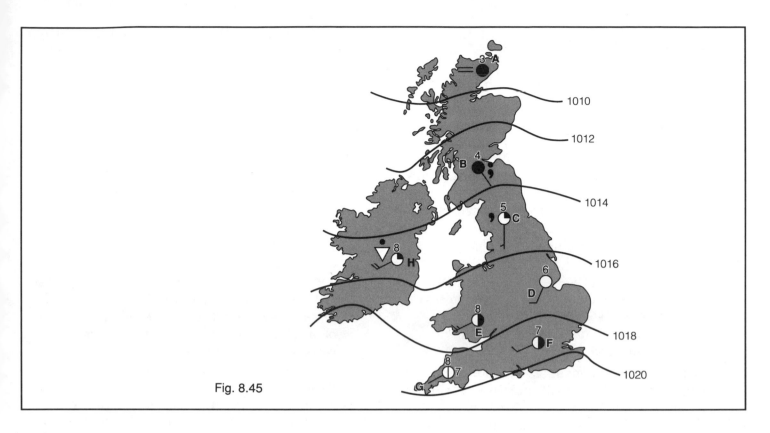

Fig. 8.45

Exercise 8

1 The boiling points of the main components of air are nitrogen, $-196\,°C$, and oxygen, $-183\,°C$.
  a Which of these two elements is the easier to liquefy?
  b Describe briefly how air is liquefied.
  c Describe how oxygen and nitrogen are obtained from liquid air.
  d Give one large-scale industrial use for each of these gases.
  e Name another gas which is obtained from liquid air, and say what it is used for.

2 A sample of air is passed slowly through sodium hydroxide solution and then over heated copper.
  a Which gas is removed by sodium hydroxide? What product is formed?
  b Which gas is removed by copper? What product is formed?
  c If 200 cm³ of air are treated in this way, what volume of gas will remain?

3 Why is carbon monoxide such a dangerous pollutant? How does it get into the air? How does nature remove it from the air?

4 When air is bubbled slowly through pure water, the pH of the water changes gradually from 7.0 to 5.7.

  a Which of the gases present in air is responsible for the change?
  b Why is the presence of this gas in air so important?

5 Why are the oxides of sulphur so unpleasant as air pollutants? How does nature remove them?

6 (i) Say whether the oxides of the following elements are acidic or basic or neutral:
     a iron, b sulphur, c carbon, d calcium, e hydrogen.
  (ii) Describe the appearance of the flame when the following burn in oxygen:
     a magnesium, b iron, c sulphur, d kerosene, e carbon.

7 A woman drives a round trip of 40 miles to work and home again on 250 days a year. Her car does 40 miles to the gallon, and the petrol contains 2 g of lead per gallon.
  a How much lead does this driver use in a year?
  b What happens to the lead?
  c What do you think should be done to reduce this source of lead in the environment?

8 The average mercury content of coal is 0.2 parts per million. Assuming all the mercury.

escapes into the air through the chimney of the power plant, calculate the mass of mercury that will be released each year by a large power plant burning 10 000 tonnes of coal per day.

9 Rush-hour traffic into and out of cities is much greater than the traffic during the rest of the day. To cope with rush-hour traffic, extra lanes must be built in the roads. Extra road maintenance is needed. Extra police are needed. The slow-moving rush-hour traffic produces massive pollution.

Bus passengers produce much less pollution per head.

Imagine that it is your job to economise on road maintenance and to cut down air pollution. What steps would you take to discourage motorists from driving and encourage them to use public transport?

10 a A power plant consumes 10 000 tonnes of coal per day. The coal contains 3% sulphur. (This is high-sulphur bituminous coal.) What mass of sulphur would be sent into the air each day in the absence of controls?

b If there were a tax on pollution, power plants would be encouraged to discharge less sulphur into the air. At a tax rate of 10p/tonne of sulphur, what would this power station have to pay?

c What tax rate do you think would be high enough to make a power station remove the sulphur from its waste gases?

d How could the power station recoup some of the expense?

11 Lead compounds are accumulating in the Arctic, far away from the cities which produce them. Figure 8.46 shows how the level of lead in Arctic ice has increased this century.

a What social change happened around the year 1750 and had the effect of increasing atmospheric lead?

b Deduce from the graph when people started adding tetraethyl lead to petrol. Why did this petrol additive cause a steep increase in the level of lead in the atmosphere? How did it cause an increase in the level of lead in Arctic ice? What advantage does the treated petrol have? Why have steps been taken to stop adding TEL to petrol?

12 A mixture of gases is produced by the combustion of petrol in a car engine. The composition of the mixture depends on the ratio of petrol vapour to air in the cylinders. Figure 8.47 shows how the relative amounts of nitrogen monoxide, hydrocarbons and carbon monoxide alter as the fuel-to-air ratio changes from a rich mixture to a lean mixture.

a Explain why the emission of nitrogen monoxide increases from left to right on the graph.

b Explain why the emission of hydrocarbons decreases from left to right on the graph.

c Explain why the emission of carbon monoxide decreases from left to right.

d What other substances are present in the exhaust gas?

Fig. 8.46 Lead content of Arctic ice

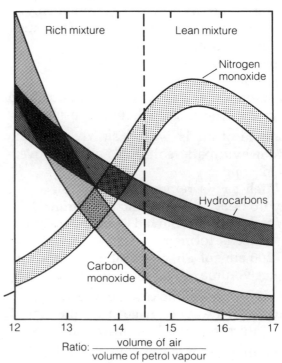

Fig. 8.47 Relative emissions of exhaust gases in rich and lean mixtures

142

CHAPTER 9 Water

Fig. 9.1 She fills her bucket from the pump

9.1 We need it

Three out of five people in Third World countries have no easy access to clean water. Women and children often spend much of their day collecting water from rivers and wells (Fig. 9.1).

Often, rivers are used for sewage disposal as well as for drinking. Many diseases are water-borne (Fig. 9.2). Four-fifths of the diseases in the Third World are linked to dirty water and lack of sanitation.

The United Nations called the 1980s the Water Decade. The UN target was clean water and sanitation for all by 1990. International aid agencies (UN, Oxfam, the World Bank and others) gave funds for pumps and irrigation channels (to provide water for agriculture) and for disinfection kits (to provide water for drinking). The target has not yet been achieved, but the work is continuing.

LYING IN WAIT

Polluted water or food washed in it can mean cholera or typhoid sweeps through a community. _____

Today river blindness and trachoma together afflict over 500 million people.

Last year diarrhoea killed 6 million children under five. _____

Billharzia will affect 200 million people worldwide this year . . .

Debilitating hookworm enters its victim through the soles of the feet.

From head to foot he is at risk.
▷ _____

Fig. 9.2 This Oxfam poster shows where water-borne diseases attack

9.2 Why is water so important?

Life began in water. The first plants and animals were aquatic (water-living). The chemical reactions that gave them life must have been reactions that could take place in water. As more complex terrestrial (land-living) creatures evolved, water kept its importance. Aqueous (in water) solutions fill the cells of the human body. Food materials and oxygen are transported round the body in an aqueous solution — blood. Digestion takes place in an aqueous solution. The body of an adult contains about 40 litres of water. In plants too, nutrients are transported round the structure in aqueous solution.

Water carries away our wastes: our sewage, our industrial grime, the waste chemicals from our factories and the waste heat from our power stations. River water decomposes some of these wastes, dilutes others until they are harmless and carries the rest out of sight, away to the sea. (See Section 9.4.)

Fig. 9.3 Water for relaxation

Fig. 9.4 Water: an eyesore and a health hazard

9.3 The water cycle

5 As clouds rise when they meet land masses, further cooling occurs. Larger drops of water fall as rain or snow.

4 Winds blow clouds towards the land.

3 As water vapour rises, it cools. Condensation produces tiny droplets of water.

2 Transpiration: the loss of water through the leaves of plants.

1 Heat from the sun makes water evaporate from the oceans.

6 Rivers flow to the sea. They receive sewage and industrial waste.

7 Rain water flows back towards the sea, completing the cycle. It dissolves chemicals from the rocks through which it passes.

Fig. 9.5 The water cycle

Did you know that there are 150 million tonnes of water in the Earth?

Yes, but only one-fiftieth of a per cent of this is on the surface of the Earth, where we can use it!

One litre of sea water contains:
- 26 g of sodium chloride (common salt)
- 7 g of magnesium sulphate (Epsom salts)
- 2 g of calcium sulphate (related to plaster of Paris)
- 1 g of potassium chloride
- 30×10^{-9} g of gold chloride.

Where can you find 23 million tonnes of gold?

Dissolved in the sea as gold salts

SUMMARY NOTE

There is a natural **water cycle**. Water vapour enters the atmosphere by **evaporation**. Water vapour leaves the atmosphere by **condensation**, followed by precipitation as rain or snow. Air dissolves in rain water. The oxygen that dissolves in water is vital to fish. If too much organic matter, e.g. sewage, is discharged into a river, the dissolved oxygen is used up in oxidising the organic matter, and the water becomes unable to support life.

Four-fifths of the world's surface is covered by water. The heat of the sun makes water evaporate from oceans, rivers and lakes. As it rises, water vapour cools and condenses to form clouds of tiny droplets. Further cooling of the clouds produces larger drops of water which fall to the ground as rain or, if it is cold enough, as snow. Rain water trickles through soil and porous rocks until eventually it finds its way back to the sea. Then the cycle begins all over again (Fig. 9.5).

As rain water falls through the air, it dissolves oxygen, nitrogen and carbon dioxide. When carbon dioxide dissolves, it forms a solution of the weak acid, carbonic acid. As rain water trickles through porous rocks, it dissolves chemicals from the rocks. The salts which rain water dissolves find their way to the sea. When water evaporates from the sea, the dissolved salts remain (Fig. 2.5).

In industrial regions, the air contains pollutant gases. These dissolve in rain water to make **acid rain** (see Section 8.13).

9.4 Dissolved oxygen

The oxygen that dissolves in water has a vital role to play. Oxygen is not very soluble: water is saturated with oxygen when the concentration of dissolved oxygen is only 10 p.p.m. (parts per million; $10^{-3}\%$). Water-living creatures and plants and all fish depend on this dissolved oxygen. When the level of dissolved oxygen falls below 5 p.p.m., aquatic plants and animals start to suffer.

Water has a natural ability to purify itself when it becomes contaminated. This ability depends on the dissolved oxygen and the bacteria present in water. When organic matter (plant and animal debris) gets into the water, **aerobic** bacteria (bacteria which need oxygen) use this matter as food. They use dissolved oxygen to oxidise debris to harmless products, such as carbon dioxide and water, with the release of energy:

oxidation reactions inside bacteria

organic pollutants + oxygen → carbon dioxide + water + energy

(plant and animal debris)   (dissolved)   (harmless products)   (needed by bacteria)

If water is to remain life-supporting, the oxygen which the bacteria use must be replaced by the dissolving of more oxygen. Sometimes rivers are overburdened with organic debris, for example, when untreated sewage is discharged into them. When this happens the dissolved oxygen is used up more rapidly than it is replaced, and the aerobic bacteria die. Then **anaerobic** bacteria (bacteria which do not need oxygen) take over. They attack the organic matter to produce unpleasant decay products, such as ammonia, hydrogen sulphide and methane.

For some synthetic materials, e.g. plastics, there are no bacteria able to oxidise them. Such materials are **non-biodegradable**, and they persist for a very long time in water.

9.5 Water treatment

The water that we use is taken mainly from lakes and rivers. It is purified to make it safe to drink. Water treatment plants use filtration and chlorination (see Fig. 9.6).

This safe drinking water is very different from the disease-carrying water which killed thousands of people in the early nineteenth century. Chlorination of drinking water is the biggest single factor that has made the difference. It is time that people in underdeveloped countries had safe water too. (For chlorine, see Section 16.5; for fluoridation of drinking water, see Section 16.11.)

In some areas, water is obtained from underground sources. As water trickles down from the surface through porous rocks, suspended matter is left behind. This **ground water** does not need the full treatment shown in Fig. 9.6. It is pumped out of the ground and chlorinated before use.

The cholera epidemic which hit London in 1831 killed more than 50 000 people.

That can't happen now in countries which chlorinate their drinking water.

2 Water is stored in a reservoir.

4 Sedimentation tank. Large lumps of solid matter settle to the bottom.

3 The 'clarifiers'. A **coagulant** is added. Small particles **coagulate** — form solid lumps.

1 Water is pumped from a river and filtered.

7 The pumping station pumps drinking water to users.

6 In the chlorination house, chlorine is added in calculated quantity to kill germs.

5 The sand beds filter out small solid particles.

Fig. 9.6 A water treatment works

9.6 Sewage works

After use, water flows into sewers which take it to a sewage works. There, it is purified sufficiently to be discharged into a river (see Fig. 9.7).

Not all sewage is treated in this way. A great deal of raw sewage is still discharged into rivers and into the sea (see Section 9.16). The reason is the cost of building new sewage works. As the population increases, some Water Authorities do not have enough equipment to treat all their area's sewage. They treat as much as they can and hope that rivers and the sea will break down the rest. With the volume of sewage increasing, this solution to the problem is becoming less and less satisfactory.

Fig. 9.7 A sewage works ▷

5 A second set of filter beds.

4 A second set of settling tanks.

6 A final set of settling tanks. Clean water flows from these into the river.

3 Filter beds filled with lumps of coke or stone. Water from the settling tanks is sprayed on to the stones through travelling metal tubes. Bacteria grow in the slime and break down harmful chemicals in it. They are **aerobic** bacteria: they need air.

7 Sludge digestion tanks. **Anaerobic** bacteria (which do not need air) in these tanks feed on the sludge. Methane is formed. This gas can be burned as a fuel. The digested sludge is no longer smelly. It is squeezed dry and sold as manure, or dumped at sea.

1 Sewer water flows in.

2 Settling tanks. The muddy part of the sewage, the **sludge**, sinks to the bottom. It is pumped to the sludge digestion tanks (7).

147

9.7 What do we use it for?

The uses shown in Fig. 9.8 represent only 10% of our total use of water. The other 90% is used:

- in agriculture to grow food
- by manufacturing industries (used as a solvent, for cleaning and for cooling)
- by power stations to generate electricity (used for cleaning and for cooling).

In industrialised countries, the total water consumption amounts to around 80 000 litres (80 tonnes) a year per person. The manufacture of

- 1 tonne of steel uses 75 tonnes of water
- 1 tonne of paper uses 2500 tonnes of water
- 1 motor car uses 45 tonnes of water.

This water is used, purified and recycled.

9.8 Chemically speaking

What is water, chemically speaking? You can split up water by passing a direct electric current through it; that is, by **electrolysis** (see Section 5.9). The gases hydrogen and oxygen are the only products you obtain. The volume of hydrogen is twice that of oxygen. This shows (see Section 12.3) that the formula is H_2O:

$$\text{water} \xrightarrow{\text{electrolyse}} \text{hydrogen} + \text{oxygen}$$
$$2H_2O(l) \longrightarrow 2H_2(g) \quad + \quad O_2(g)$$

Figure 9.9 shows what happens when you burn hydrogen in air and collect the products of combustion. The only product

Fig. 9.8 Water: 160 litres a day

3 Dry hydrogen burning.

4 Suction pump draws a stream of gas through the apparatus.

1 Stream of hydrogen from a cylinder

2 The U-tube contains anhydrous calcium chloride (a drying agent).

5 Side-arm tube in ice-water. A colourless liquid collects here.

Fig. 9.9 What is formed when hydrogen burns in air?

formed when hydrogen burns is a colourless, odourless liquid. You can test it to see whether it is water.

Tests for water

There are two quick tests that will show whether a liquid *contains* water.

Test 1 Water will turn white anhydrous copper(II) sulphate blue:

copper(II) sulphate + water $\rightarrow$ copper(II) sulphate-5-water
$$CuSO_4(s) \qquad + 5H_2O(l) \rightarrow CuSO_4 \cdot 5H_2O(s)$$
white solid   *blue solid*

Test 2 Water will turn blue anhydrous cobalt(II) chloride pink:

cobalt(II) chloride + water $\rightarrow$ cobalt(II) chloride-6-water
$$CoCl_2(s) \qquad + 6H_2O(l) \rightarrow CoCl_2 \cdot 6H_2O(s)$$
blue solid   *pink solid*

These two tests will show that the liquid *contains* water. To test whether it is *pure* water, you can find its boiling and freezing points (see Figs. 2.23 and 2.24). Pure water boils at 100 °C and freezes at 0 °C. The tests show that the liquid is in fact water. Hydrogen burns to form water:

hydrogen + oxygen $\rightarrow$ water
$$2H_2(g) \quad + O_2(g) \quad \rightarrow 2H_2O(l)$$

9.9 Water as a solvent

Almost all substances dissolve in water to some extent. Solubility was covered in Section 1.5. For most solids, solubility *increases* with temperature. The solubility of gases often *decreases* with temperature (see Thermal pollution, Section 9.16).

Aqueous solutions freeze below 0 °C and boil above 100 °C (see Section 2.8. A saturated solution of sodium chloride (common salt) freezes at −18 °C.

Since water is such a good solvent, it is difficult to obtain pure water. Distillation is one method of purifying water (see Fig. 2.9). Ion exchange is another method (see Section 9.13). By **pure** water, a chemist means water that contains no dissolved material. This is different from what the public health authority means by **pure** water. Safe drinking water contains dissolved salts: it is not pure water in the chemical sense. Water which contains substances that are harmful to life is **polluted** water.

9.10 Water in limestone regions

In limestone regions, rain water trickles over rocks composed of calcium carbonate (limestone) and magnesium carbonate. These minerals do not dissolve in pure water. Since rain water contains dissolved carbon dioxide, it is weakly acidic. It reacts with the carbonate rocks to form the soluble salts, calcium hydrogencarbonate and magnesium hydrogencarbonate:

calcium carbonate + water + carbon dioxide → calcium hydrogencarbonate solution

$$CaCO_3(s) + H_2O(l) + CO_2(g) \rightarrow Ca(HCO_3)_2(aq)$$

Gradually, over thousands of years, underground caverns and potholes have been hollowed out as rocks have been converted by acidic rain water into soluble salts (Fig. 9.10).

The process can be reversed. Sometimes, in an underground cavern, a drop of water becomes isolated. With air all round it, water will evaporate. The dissolved calcium hydrogencarbonate changes into a grain of solid calcium carbonate:

calcium hydrogencarbonate → calcium carbonate + water + carbon dioxide

$$Ca(HCO_3)_2(aq) \rightarrow CaCO_3(s) + H_2O(l) + CO_2(g)$$

Day by day, more grains of calcium carbonate are deposited. Over a century or two, enough calcium carbonate can build up to form a cone hanging from the roof of the cavern. This is called a **stalactite**. The same process can lead to the formation of a **stalagmite** on the floor of the cavern (see Fig. 9.10).

9.11 Soaps and detergents

Oil and grease do not dissolve in water. To wash oil and grease off your hands or clothes, you need a **detergent** (cleaning agent). There are two kinds of detergent: **soaps**, which are made from animal fats and vegetable oils, and **soapless detergents**, which are made from petroleum oil. Both are able to **emulsify** oil and grease (make them miscible with water). Soaps and soapless detergents are sodium salts.

One soap is sodium hexadecanoate, $C_{15}H_{31}CO_2Na$. A model of the soap is shown in Fig. 9.11. It consists of a sodium ion and a hexadecanoate ion, which we will call a *soap* ion for short. The *soap* ion has two parts, shown in Fig. 9.12 as a head and a tail.

Fig. 9.10 Underground cavern with stalactites and stalagmites

SUMMARY NOTE

In limestone regions, acidic rain water reacts with calcium carbonate to form soluble calcium hydrogencarbonate. The reverse process leads to the formation of stalactites and stalagmites.

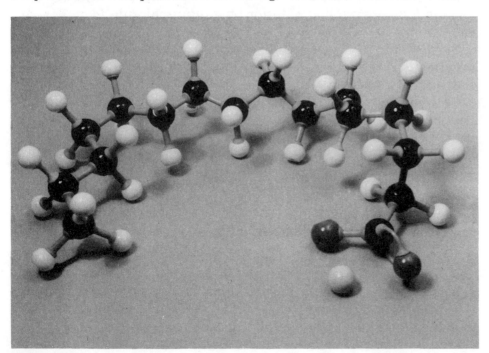

Fig. 9.11 Model of the soap, sodium hexadecanoate

Head is water-loving and fat-hating.

Tail is water-hating and fat-loving.

Fig. 9.12 The soap ion

(a) The tails of the *soap* ions are attracted to grease.

(b) The heads of the *soap* ions are attracted to water.

Fig. 9.13 Soap removes grease from cloth ▷

(c) As the heads of the *soap* ions become surrounded by water molecules, the blob of grease is squeezed away from the cloth.

(d) Droplets of grease do not join because their surfaces are negatively charged. The droplets spread through the water. The dirty water must be removed by thorough rinsing.

The tail is a long chain of —CH_2— groups. This is water-hating and fat-loving. The head is a —CO_2^- group. This group is called a **carboxylate** group (see Chapter 19). It is water-loving and fat-hating. Figure 9.13 shows how *soap* ions wash grease from cloth.

The head of each *soap* ion is attracted to the water. The tail of each *soap* ion is attracted to grease. Thus, the *soap* ions form a bridge between the blob of grease and the water. As the dirty clothes are swirled around during washing, the blob of grease surrounded by *soap* ions is dislodged from the cloth to float off into the water. Repulsion between the charges on the —CO_2^- groups keeps the droplets apart. They remain spread through the water — **emulsified**.

Soapless detergents are sodium salts of sulphonic acids. The tail of the detergent ion is a chain of fat-loving —CH_2— groups. The water-loving head is an —SO_3^- group.

9.12 Hard and soft water

Soap lathers easily in distilled water. With some types of tap water, it is *hard* to get a lather, and such water is described as **hard**. Water in which soap lathers easily is **soft** water. Hard water contains substances which combine with *soap* ions to prevent them from doing their job. Experiment shows (see Experiment 9.2) that it is the calcium and magnesium ions in water that make it hard. They combine with *soap* ions to form insoluble calcium and magnesium compounds. These compounds are the **scum** that you see floating on your bath water. The *soap* ions are no longer free, and the soap has little effect.

soap ions + calcium ions → scum

2 *soap*⁻(aq) + Ca^{2+}(aq)   → Ca(*soap*)₂(s)

Soapless detergents will still work in hard water because their calcium and magnesium salts are soluble. Soapless detergents have taken over from soaps to a large extent. Of the cleaning market, 80 per cent is held by soapless detergents.

9.13 Methods of softening hard water

If you go on adding soap to hard water for long enough, all the calcium and magnesium ions will be precipitated as scum. After that, the soap will be able to work. This is an expensive method of softening water!

Temporary hardness

If the cause of hardness is the presence of dissolved calcium hydrogencarbonate and magnesium hydrogencarbonate, then the water can be softened simply by boiling. These compounds decompose when water is boiled:

$$\text{calcium hydrogencarbonate} \rightarrow \text{calcium carbonate} + \text{carbon dioxide} + \text{water}$$

$$Ca(HCO_3)_2(aq) \rightarrow CaCO_3(s) + CO_2(g) + H_2O(l)$$

The scale which you see on the inside of kettles is calcium carbonate (see Fig. 9.14 and Experiment 9.3). Hardness which can be removed by boiling is called **temporary hardness**.

Permanent hardness

Hardness which cannot be removed by boiling is called **permanent hardness**. It is due to the presence of dissolved calcium and magnesium chlorides and sulphates. These compounds are not decomposed by heat.

Washing soda

One method of softening both temporary and permanent hardness is to add washing soda, sodium carbonate-10-water. Calcium ions and magnesium ions are precipitated as insoluble carbonates:

$$\text{calcium ions} + \text{carbonate ions} \rightarrow \text{calcium carbonate}$$

$$Ca^{2+}(aq) + CO_3{}^{2-}(aq) \rightarrow CaCO_3(s)$$

*Exchange resins

Ion exchange resins will take ions of one element out of aqueous solution and replace them with ions of another element. Permutits are manufactured ion exchange resins which will take calcium and magnesium ions out of water and replace them with sodium ions:

$$\text{calcium ions} + \text{sodium permutit} \rightarrow \text{sodium ions} + \text{calcium permutit}$$

Figure 9.15 shows how a permutit water softener works.

A permutit cannot go on softening water indefinitely. When the sodium ions in the permutit have been replaced by calcium and magnesium ions, the column must be regenerated. Brine (sodium chloride solution) is passed through the column. It converts calcium permutit back to sodium permutit.

SUMMARY NOTE

Soaps and detergents have ions which form a bridge between grease and water. Hard water contains calcium ions and magnesium ions. They combine to form an insoluble **scum**. Detergents work well even in hard water because their calcium and magnesium salts are soluble.

Fig. 9.14 Scale in a hot water cylinder after only 5 years of use

Hard water (containing Ca²⁺ ions)	Brine (sodium chloride solution)
Sodium permutit puts Na⁺(aq) ions into water in exchange for Ca²⁺(aq) ions and becomes calcium permutit	Calcium permutit takes Na⁺(aq) ions from brine, replaces them with Ca²⁺(aq) ions and becomes sodium permutit
Soft water (containing Na⁺ ions). This is how the column softens hard water.	Spent brine (containing calcium chloride) This is how brine regenerates the column.

Fig. 9.15 A permutit water softener

9.14 Advantages of hard water

For health reasons, hard water is preferable to soft water. The calcium content strengthens bones and teeth. It is also beneficial to people with a tendency to develop heart disease.

A number of industries prefer hard water. Brewers like the taste of the dissolved salts in their beer. Tanners find that leather cures better in hard water.

9.15 Pure water

All types of water can be distilled to give pure water. The apparatus shown in Fig. 2.9 could be used.

9.16 Pollution of water

Industrial pollution

Minamata is a fishing village on the shores of Minamata Bay in Japan. In 1953, a mysterious disease began to strike the villagers. Some were crippled, some became mentally deranged, some became blind and some died. A team of scientists traced the cause of the disease to the fish in the bay. The fish contained a high level of mercury compounds. This was a mystery. Although a plastics factory was discharging mercury compounds into the bay, the level was so low at 2 p.p.b. (parts per billion) that the

Plastics factory discharges mercury compounds into Minamata Bay. The water in the bay contains 2 p.p.b. of mercury, and is still safe to drink.

Plankton take in mercury compounds from the water. They cannot excrete mercury compounds.

Small fish feed on plankton. Fish cannot excrete mercury compounds. The level of mercury in their flesh builds up to 100 times that in the bay water.

Large fish feed on small fish. Mercury compounds are stored in their flesh.

At the end of this food chain is the human family. They eat fish containing 2000 – 10 000 times the concentration of mercury in the water.

Fig. 9.16 The Minamata food chain   ▷

153

water could be drunk. The scientists found out that when fish and shellfish took in mercury compounds they did not excrete them. The level of mercury in their tissues built up to 5–20 p.p.m. (parts per million). Fish is the staple diet of the villagers. They were eating fish in which the mercury level was 4000 times that of the bay water. Mercury levels built up in their bodies. The toll was 50 dead, 100 crippled and 900 seriously affected.

The Minamata tragedy was an accident. The manufacturers were discharging a low level of pollutant, and they expected the bay to dilute it to a safe level. They did not know how the mercury could be concentrated through a **food chain** (Fig. 9.16).

Unfortunately, other countries were slow to learn from the Japanese example. In 1967, many lakes and rivers in Sweden were found to be so contaminated by mercury that fishing had to stop.

In 1970, high mercury levels were found in hundreds of lakes in Canada and the USA. Now that the danger is known, chemical plants have been able to reduce spillage of mercury. This is not the end of the danger. Mercury from years of careless practice lies in the sediment at the bottom of lakes. Slowly it is converted by bacteria into soluble mercury compounds.

Thermal pollution

Water is used as a coolant, especially by nuclear power stations. River water is circulated round the plant and returned to the river at a higher temperature. If the temperature of the river is raised by many degrees, this can have serious effects. The solubility of oxygen decreases as the temperature rises. At the same time, demands on oxygen increase. Fish are more active and need more oxygen. The bacteria which feed on decaying organic matter become more active and use oxygen faster.

Agricultural pollution

Plants need a number of elements (about 20) for their growth. The elements carbon, hydrogen, oxygen, nitrogen and phosphorus are needed in substantial amounts. Water always provides enough carbon, hydrogen and oxygen; nitrogen and phosphorus are scarcer. Lake water, being poor in the nutrients nitrogen and phosphorus, supports little plant life. Since there is no decaying vegetation to use up dissolved oxygen, lake water is saturated with oxygen. Fish can thrive.

Farmers use compounds of phosphorus and nitrogen (phosphates and nitrates) to increase their crop yields (see Section 15.3). Often, fertilisers are used in large quantities. Plants can absorb only a limited amount through their roots. If land surrounding a lake receives too much fertiliser, unabsorbed fertiliser washes out of the soil into the lake water.

There the fertiliser nourishes the growth of water plants. Weeds flourish, and thick mats of algae cover the surface (Fig. 9.17). The plant growth can snag the propellers of boats. If water is taken from the lake for use, water filters become clogged with

A large nuclear power station needs 4000 tonnes of water a minute for cooling.

That's like having a river flowing through its pipes.

The water is 10 °C hotter when it comes out than when it goes in.

g. 9.17 Lake with a strong growth of
gae

weeds. The name given to this **unintentional enrichment** of lake water and river water is **eutrophication**.

When algae die, they are decomposed by aerobic bacteria. When these bacteria run out of oxygen, they die. Anaerobic bacteria take over, and convert part of the dead matter into smelly decay products. The rest of the debris falls to the bottom. Slowly a layer of dead plant material builds up on the bottom of the lake. Deprived of oxygen, fish die. The lake becomes a dead lake. Many lakes in the USA and Canada are now empty of fish. The tourist industry centred on the lakes has suffered. If the farmers could cut back on fertilisers, they would save money and the fishermen would benefit too.

Excessive fertiliser can also find its way into the **ground water**. This is the water held underground in porous layers of rock. A third of Britain's drinking water comes from ground water. The World Health Organisation recommends that the level of nitrogen in the form of nitrates should not exceed 11 p.p.m. The level in Britain is far short of this value, but it is increasing, and people are worried that in 20 years' time it may be dangerously high.

Nitrates affect human health in two ways.

1   Nitrates are converted into nitrites (salts containing the NO_2^- ion). Nitrites oxidise the iron in haemoglobin from iron(II) ions to iron(III) ions. In its oxidised form, haemoglobin can no longer transport oxygen round the body. Babies are more at risk than adults. The lower acidity of babies' stomachs encourages the conversion of nitrates to nitrites. The extreme case of nitrite poisoning is the 'blue baby' syndrome, in which the baby turns blue from lack of oxygen.

2   Nitrosoamines have been found in a number of foods. These compounds cause cancer. Some chemists think that nitrites formed from nitrates may be responsible for the formation of nitrosoamines.

Research is being done on ways of reducing the nitrate level. Of course, farmers must use fertilisers, but more care can be taken to match the input of fertiliser to the crop's ability to use it. The correct amount applied in the right season will be used up by the plants. Agricultural chemists are advising farmers how they can make the most efficient use of fertilisers. This will save the farmers money as well as making drinking water safer.

Fertilisers are not the only source of phosphates in water. Soapless detergents contain phosphates as **brighteners**. Detergents are discharged into rivers. This source of pollution could be avoided. People might be persuaded to use detergents which left their shirts just a shade less white. Then phosphates could be omitted from the detergents and stop polluting our lakes and rivers.

Estuaries and coastal waters

Coastal zones and estuaries are only 0.1% of the ocean surface, but they produce 99% of the seafood. The sea water in coastal zones contains nutrients which have been brought in by rivers. Estuaries are among the richest biological regions on Earth. Fish and shellfish abound in them. Of all the parts of the oceans, the estuaries receive the worst pollution. Shipping lanes criss-cross these waters. Collisions and groundings result in accidental discharges of oil (Fig. 9.18). Some oil tankers wash out their tanks at sea, although it is illegal for them to do so (see Chapter 18).

Coastal waters are also favourite dumping grounds for industry's toxic wastes. Nearly all wastes are finally washed out to sea.

The Mersey is Britain's dirtiest estuary. Raw sewage from Liverpool and other towns pours straight into its waters. The Secretary of State for the Environment called the pollution 'an affront to a civilised society'. In 1983, he authorised a £200 million scheme for the construction of sewage works on the banks. These will remove solid sewage and toxic metals, which are discharged in industrial effluent, and turn them into solid sludge. Ships will dump the sludge in the Irish Sea (Fig. 9.19). This solution to the Mersey's problem will not suit everyone. The Ministry of Agriculture, Fisheries and Food is worried that fish in the Irish Sea will be poisoned by the toxic metals in the sludge. This will mean a loss in income for fishermen and workers in the fish processing industry.

Fig. 9.18 Dead cormorants being collected after the accident to the oil tanker *Braer* in Shetland, 1993

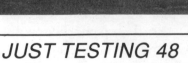

Fig. 9.19 A sludge ship carries digested sewage sludge out to sea

JUST TESTING 48

1 Water has a natural method for disposing of waste that is dumped into it. What is this method? What is wrong with dumping waste in rivers when water can cope with it in this way?
2 A layer of algae on the surface of a pond is described as **algal bloom**. Why is it undesirable?
3 What is **eutrophication**? Who loses money through eutrophication?

*4 How does lead get into our water supplies? How can contamination from these sources be reduced? (See Chapters 5, 8, 11.)

*5 What factors influence the rate of aquatic plant growth? Why is it so difficult to single out the effect of one nutrient which is present in the water as a pollutant? Design an experiment to enable you to single out the effect of one pollutant.

6 a Why are people worried about the concentration of nitrates in drinking water?

 b Could nitrates get from ground water into your body if you stopped drinking tap water? Explain your answer.

 c Why is it difficult to say exactly what concentration of nitrates in drinking water is dangerous?

9.17 Hydrogen

You have studied water, the most important compound of hydrogen. Now let us have a look at the importance of hydrogen.

Uses of hydrogen

1 **Weather balloons.** Since it is the least dense of gases, meteorologists use hydrogen to fill their weather balloons. The balloons, which are about 2 m in diameter, float up into the atmosphere, carrying a load of instruments. The instruments record information about atmospheric conditions.

2 **Making fertilisers.** A much more consuming demand for hydrogen is the manufacture of ammonia, NH_3 (see Section 15.3). Ammonium salts are used as fertilisers.

3 **Extracting metals.** Some metals are obtained from their ores with the help of hydrogen. Tungsten is the metal which is used to make electric light filaments. It is mined as tungsten oxide. Hydrogen converts heated tungsten oxide into tungsten and water:

tungsten oxide + hydrogen → tungsten + water

Hydrogen removes oxygen from tungsten oxide. Another way of saying this is: hydrogen **reduces** tungsten oxide. This reaction is a **reduction** reaction. **Reduction is the addition of hydrogen to a substance or the removal of oxygen from a substance.** Remember **oxidation** (Section 8.9): the removal of hydrogen from or the addition of oxygen to a substance. Reduction is the opposite of oxidation. Hydrogen is oxidised to water. Tungsten oxide is reduced to tungsten:

$$\overbrace{\text{tungsten oxide} + \text{hydrogen} \rightarrow \text{tungsten}}^{\text{This is reduction}} + \underbrace{\text{water}}_{}$$

This is oxidation

Hydrogen does not reduce all metal oxides (see Section 10.8). By experiment, you will find that it reduces copper(II) oxide to copper:

$$\overset{\text{Reduction}}{\text{copper(II) oxide}\; +\; \text{hydrogen} \longrightarrow \text{copper}\; +\; \text{water}}$$
$$\underset{\text{Oxidation}}{\text{CuO(s)} \qquad\quad +\; \text{H}_2\text{(g)} \quad \longrightarrow \text{Cu(s)} \;\;+\; \text{H}_2\text{O(l)}}$$

Copper(II) oxide is an oxidising agent

Hydrogen is a reducing agent

4 *Margarine*. Another industry which consumes hydrogen is the manufacture of margarine. Solid fats, such as butter and margarine, can be sold for a higher price than vegetable oils, such as groundnut oil and sunflower seed oil. Since these vegetable oils can be produced in large quantities, there is profit to be made in converting them into solid fats. Hydrogen will do this, with the help of nickel acting as a catalyst. The process is called **hydrogenation**.

$$\text{vegetable oil} \atop \text{(vapour)} \; + \; {\text{hydrogen} \atop \text{(gas)}} \; \xrightarrow{\text{Pass over heated nickel}} \; {\text{margarine} \atop \text{(solid)}}$$

See also Section 19.3 and Fig. 9.20.

Manufacture

Hydrogen is a by-product of the electrolysis of brine (sodium chloride solution); see Fig. 5.11. It is also made by a reaction between methane (natural gas) and water (see Fig. 9.21).

Fig. 9.20 Sunflower seed oil and margarine

NATURAL GAS

Desulphurised (see Chapter 13): the sulphur compounds present would 'poison' the catalyst.

Steam reformer
Methane (in natural gas) reacts with steam to form carbon monoxide and hydrogen.
Conditions: 700 °C, 30 atm, nickel catalyst
$CH_4(g) + H_2O(g) \rightarrow CO(g) + 3H_2(g)$

STEAM

Shift reactor
Carbon monoxide reacts with steam to form carbon dioxide and hydrogen.
$CO(g) + H_2O(g) \rightarrow CO_2(g) + H_2(g)$

STEAM

Absorber
The mixture of hydrogen and carbon dioxide passes through a basic solution. Carbon dioxide is removed by the base.

HYDROGEN

Fig. 9.21 The industrial manufacture of hydrogen

Test for hydrogen

Hydrogen burns in air. If it is pure, it burns quietly and steadily (see Fig. 9.9). If there is oxygen mixed with hydrogen, when you set light to the mixture there is an explosive 'pop' (see

Experiment 7.1). This reaction can be used as a test for hydrogen.

Many of the reactions of hydrogen have been mentioned in relation to its uses. You will meet hydrogen in many of the topics in this book. Figure 9.22 gives a summary of them.

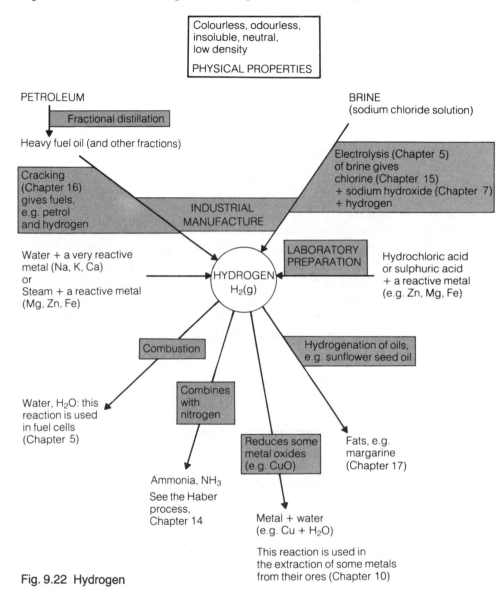

Fig. 9.22 Hydrogen

9.18 Oxidation–reduction reactions

Example 1

In Section 9.17, hydrogen was described as a **reducing agent**. Hydrogen reduces tungsten oxide to tungsten. The reaction is a **reduction**. Reduction is the addition of hydrogen to a substance or the removal of oxygen from a substance. **Oxidation** was described in Section 8.9 as the removal of hydrogen from or the addition of oxygen to a substance. Hydrogen is oxidised to water. Tungsten oxide is reduced to tungsten. Oxidation and reduction are occurring together. Hydrogen is the reducing agent and tungsten oxide is the oxidising agent.

This is reduction

tungsten oxide + hydrogen → tungsten + water

This is oxidation

| Tungsten oxide is the oxidising agent | Hydrogen is the reducing agent |

Example 2

Zinc is obtained by the reduction of zinc oxide by carbon.

This is reduction

zinc oxide + carbon → zinc + carbon monoxide

$ZnO(s)$ + $C(s)$ → $Zn(s)$ + $CO(g)$

This is oxidation

Zinc oxide is the oxidising agent; it is reduced to zinc. Carbon is the reducing agent; it is oxidised to carbon monoxide.

Again, in this reaction oxidation and reduction are occurring together. This is always true, however many examples you consider. Since oxidation never occurs without reduction, it is better to call these reactions **oxidation–reduction** reactions or **redox reactions**. You will learn more about redox reactions in Section 16.7.

JUST TESTING 49

1 Iron is obtained by the reaction

iron(III) oxide + carbon monoxide → iron + carbon dioxide

a Which substance is oxidised? Which substance is reduced? Which substance is the oxidising agent? Which is the reducing agent? What type of reaction is this – oxidation or reduction?

2 State which is the oxidising agent and which is the reducing agent in each of these reactions:
a lead(II) oxide + hydrogen → lead + water
b aluminium + iron oxide → iron + aluminium oxide
c tin sulphide + oxygen → tin oxide + sulphur dioxide
d tin oxide + carbon → tin + carbon monoxide
e copper(II) sulphide + oxygen → copper(II) oxide + sulphur dioxide
f $CH_4(g) + H_2O(g) → CO(g) + 3H_2(g)$
g $CO(g) + H_2O(g) → CO_2(g) + H_2(g)$

*9.19 Colloids

Heterogeneous mixtures

Heterogeneous mixtures are of two kinds: **suspensions** and **colloidal dispersions** (see Section 1.5, Table 1.2).

Suspensions contain relatively large particles (over 1000 nm long) of insoluble solid or liquid suspended in (scattered throughout) a liquid. In time, the particles settle out. Solid particles suspended in a liquid can be separated from the liquid by filtration through filter paper and by centrifugation. For example, in blood, the red and white blood cells are in suspension in the plasma. If a sample of blood is left for a time, the cells settle out. The separation is accelerated by centrifuging the sample.

Colloids are heterogeneous mixtures whose particles are larger than the molecules and ions that form solutions, but smaller than the particles that form suspensions (between 1 nm and 1000 nm long). Gelatin and water form a colloid. Particles of gelatin are dispersed (spread) through the water. The two components cannot be separated by filtration through filter paper. Colloids are also called **colloidal dispersions** and **colloidal suspensions**. The solid (gelatin) is the **disperse phase**, and the liquid (water) is the **dispersion phase** or **dispersion medium**. Table 9.1 lists some types of colloid.

Table 9.1 Some types of colloid

Disperse phase	Dispersion medium	Type	Example
Liquid	Gas	Aerosol	Fog, mist from aerosol spray can, clouds
Solid	Gas	Aerosol	Smoke, dust-laden air
Gas	Liquid	Foam	Soap suds, whipped cream
Liquid	Liquid	Emulsion	Oil in water, milk, mayonnaise, protoplasm
Solid	Liquid	Sol	Clay, starch in water, protein in water, gelatin in water
Gas	Solid	Solid foam	Lava, pumice, styrofoam, marshmallows
Liquid	Solid	Solid emulsion	Pearl, opal, jellies, butter, cheese
Solid	Solid	Solid sol	Some gems, e.g. black diamond, coloured glass, some alloys

The Tyndall effect

The particles of a colloid are too small to be visible, but they are large enough to scatter light. This is what happens when light is scattered by dust-laden air. The effect is named the **Tyndall effect** after its discoverer (see Fig. 9.23)

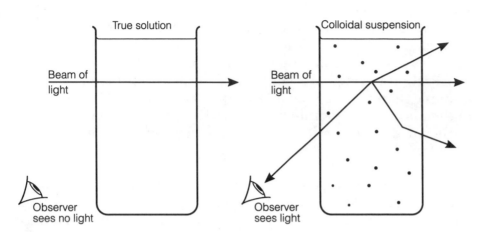

Fig. 9.23 The scattering of light by a colloid

Charge

Colloidal particles are charged. The charge is negative in some colloids and positive in others. Repulsion between the charged particles keeps them separate and dispersed. This is why colloidal particles do not clump together to form a precipitate.

Sometimes we want to precipitate colloidal particles. When water is purified for drinking, clay particles and other colloidal suspensions must be removed. This can be done by neutralising the negative charges on the clay particles. The impure water is treated with a solution containing positive ions, e.g. aluminium sulphate. Aluminium ions, Al^{3+}, are small in size and highly charged. They neutralise the negative charges on the clay particles, which are then able to clump together and settle out of solution.

The proteins in blood are colloidal and are negatively charged. In order to stop bleeding, small cuts can be treated with styptic pencils. These contain Al^{3+} or Fe^{3+} ions which neutralise the charges on the colloidal particles and help the blood to clot.

Electrostatic precipitation

When gases and air are fed into an industrial process, they often contain colloidal particles. To remove these particles, **electrostatic precipitation** is used. The charge on the particles is used to attract the particles to charged metal plates (see Fig. 8.25).

Electrophoresis

Under the influence of an electric field, colloidal particles migrate. They are attracted to one electrode and repelled by the other. This movement under the influence of an electric field is called **electrophoresis**. Since colloidal particles of different types migrate at different rates, electrophoresis can be used to separate different substances (see Fig. 9.24).

Fig. 9.24 Electrophoresis of a mixture of proteins, e.g. blood

High voltage d.c.

Electrode

Electrolyte solution

Paper soaked in electrolyte solution

(a) Apparatus for electrophoresis

Paper strip

The mixture of proteins is applied here

(b) Applying a liquid containing proteins, e.g. blood, to the paper strip

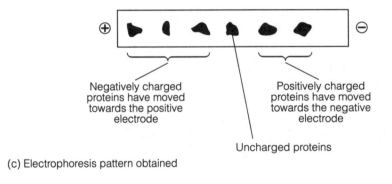

Negatively charged proteins have moved towards the positive electrode

Positively charged proteins have moved towards the negative electrode

Uncharged proteins

(c) Electrophoresis pattern obtained

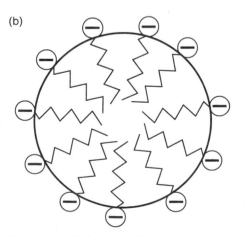

(a)

Hydrocarbon chain (fat-loving group)

Polar group (water-loving group)

(b)

Fig. 9.25 (a) An emulsifier ion
(b) A droplet of oil surrounded by emulsifier ions

Emulsifiers

An **emulsion** is a colloidal dispersion of oil in water, as we saw in Table 9.1. Examples are milk, cream, mayonnaise and many sauces. Oil and water have a natural tendency to separate, and an emulsifier is needed to keep the two together. An emulsifier ion has two parts. One is the water-loving group, a polar group with a negative charge. The other is the fat-loving group, a chain of -CH$_2$- groups which is attracted to fat and oil (see Fig. 9.25). When the emulsifier is added to a mixture of oil and water, the emulsifier ions arrange themselves so that the water-loving group dissolves in water and the fat-loving group dissolves in the oil. As emulsifier ions arrange themselves around each droplet of oil, the surface of each droplet is negatively charged. Repulsion between the drops makes them disperse through the water. Does this remind you of the emulsifying action of soaps and detergents (Section 9.11)?

Dialysis

Some membranes allow ions and small molecules to pass through them, but not large molecules or colloidal particles. They are called **dialysing membranes**. The movement of ions and small molecules through dialysing membranes is called **dialysis**. Dialysis can be used to separate colloidal particles from small molecules and ions in a solution that contains both colloids and solutes (see Fig. 9.26).

A dialysis machine called an **artificial kidney** can be used to help people with kidney disease. The kidneys remove from the blood waste products made up of small molecules, e.g. urea. If the kidneys do not function properly, these waste products build up. An artificial kidney sends blood from one of a patient's arteries through a coil of dialysis tubing immersed in a dialysis fluid, which is a solution of salts and glucose. Small molecules of waste substances such as urea pass out of the blood into the dialysis fluid. Blood cells and large molecules, e.g. protein molecules, cannot pass through and so remain in the blood. Since dialysis fluid has sugars and salts dissolved in it, sugars and salts do not diffuse out of the blood. The machine returns purified blood to the patient's body through a vein.

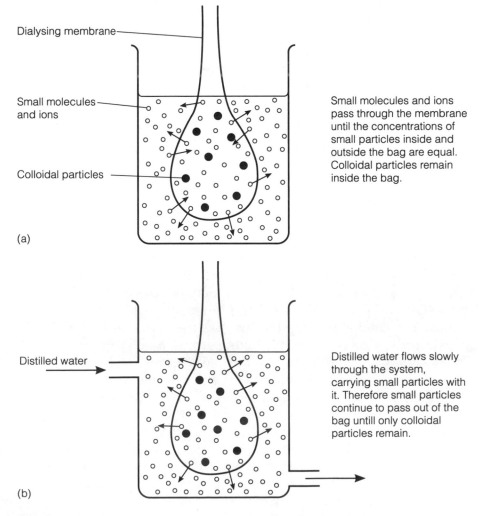

Dialysing membrane

Small molecules and ions

Colloidal particles

Small molecules and ions pass through the membrane until the concentrations of small particles inside and outside the bag are equal. Colloidal particles remain inside the bag.

(a)

Distilled water

Distilled water flows slowly through the system, carrying small particles with it. Therefore small particles continue to pass out of the bag untill only colloidal particles remain.

(b)

Fig. 9.26   Dialysis (● = colloid particle, ○ = small molecule or ion)

1 What is the difference in appearance between **a** a solution and a suspension, **b** a suspension and a colloid, **c** a solution and a colloid?

2 How can solid colloidal particles be made to separate **a** from dust-laden air, **b** from a solution of starch in water, **c** from blood?

3 **a** What is an emulsifier? **b** Explain what the emulsifier in mayonnaise does.

4 Briefly explain how an artificial kidney helps a person whose kidneys do not function properly.

Exercise 9

1 As sewage plants operate, they produce large quantities of a thick sludge which is rich in plant nutrients. What do you think should be done with it?

2 What is the purest form of water that occurs naturally?
Which ions should be present in drinking water to promote the growth of strong bones and teeth?

3 Which one of the following tests proves that a liquid is pure water?
  a The liquid is colourless and transparent.
  b It turns anhydrous copper(II) sulphate blue.
  c It boils at 100 °C at a pressure of 1 atmosphere.
  d It has a pH of 7.0.
  e It leaves no solid residue when it is evaporated.

4 Why is heat from industrial processes regarded as **thermal pollution**?

5 Many pollutants are converted into harmless impurities by bacteria in water. What harm can be done by these pollutants?
What problem arises when plastics are dumped in lakes or rivers?

6 A population of 5000 people discharges raw sewage into a river. The daily sewage from one average person takes 60 g of oxygen from the water. How many tonnes of water, containing 10 p.p.m. of oxygen, are robbed of their oxygen by the sewage from the whole town? (1 tonne = 1000 kg)

7 Explain the importance of chlorine in maintaining a safe supply of drinking water. What used to happen in Britain before water was chlorinated? Does every country now have safe drinking water?

8 A small lake (about 1.5 km across) contains 10 million tonnes of water. The lake water contains the critical level of 0.01 p.p.m. of phosphorus (as compounds). Above this level, algae start to flourish. What mass of phosphorus (as compounds) does the lake contain?

9 ● One gram of oxygen will oxidise completely about 0.25 g of petrol or oil.
  ● Water normally contains 10 p.p.m. of oxygen.
  ● A drop of oil weighs about 0.030 g.
  a Calculate the mass of oxygen in 1 tonne (1000 kg) of water.
  b How many drops of oil will this mass of oxygen oxidise?
  c What is wrong with Will Chukit's habit of pouring dirty sump oil from his car down the drain?
  d Write a letter to Mr Chukit to explain why he should stop doing this.

10 A woman on a diet decided to eat plenty of tuna fish. It is high in protein and low in fat. She ate about 350 g a day. After some months on this diet, she had difficulty in writing and talking; she had fits of shaking and difficulty in keeping her balance. These are the symptoms of mercury poisoning.

- Tuna fish contains 1 p.p.m. of mercury.
- The lowest level at which mercury has been shown to make people ill is 0.3 mg/day. (1 mg = 1×10^{-3} g)

a Calculate the woman's intake of mercury.

b How does it compare with the danger level?

11 a Explain the difference between hard and soft water.

b What makes water hard? Explain how the substances you mention get into tap water.

c Give one advantage of soft water and one advantage of hard water.

d Describe one method of softening hard water. Explain how it works.

e Compare the action of soaps and detergents in hard water.

12 Explain what hydrogen has to do with

a the tungsten filaments in electric light bulbs

b weather balloons

c margarine.

Career sketch: Animal nutrition chemist

Tony is a chemist who specialises in animal nutrition. He advises farmers on the correct rations to feed their animals. Among the animals he deals with are dairy cows, beef cows, sheep, pigs and poultry. Tony is an expert at matching the chemical composition of feedstuffs to the dietary needs of animals. Rations must meet the animals' need for energy and protein. The food they get by foraging must be supplemented with protein food, fibrous food and trace elements. Tony's work takes him into the farms. He consults with vets and with the analytical chemists who work with him. Tony has a BSc degree in chemistry.

CHAPTER 10 The Earth

10.1 The structure of the Earth

The Earth was formed as a molten mass of material cooled over a period of millions of years. The densest matter sank towards the centre, and less dense matter remained on the surface where it forms Earth's crust. This is a layer of solid rock about 50 km thick. The diameter of Earth is 12 735 km, and its average density is 5.5 g/cm³. As Earth cooled, water vapour condensed and rivers, lakes and oceans formed on its surface. No other planet has oceans and lakes, although Mars has some polar ice caps. The study of Earth is called **geology**.

Gaseous matter outside the crust forms Earth's atmosphere. During the first billion years of Earth's existence, volcanic activity was intense. The atmosphere consisted of gases which had been released from volcanoes. The gases are thought to have been mainly carbon dioxide (like the atmosphere of Venus and Mars today) with water vapour, methane and ammonia. Plants evolved and grew over much of Earth's surface, and these plants used carbon dioxide and produced oxygen in photosynthesis. The oxygen formed reacted with methane and ammonia to form nitrogen. A part of the oxygen in the atmosphere was converted into ozone, O_3. The formation of the ozone layer, which filters out

Fig. 10.1   The structure of the Earth

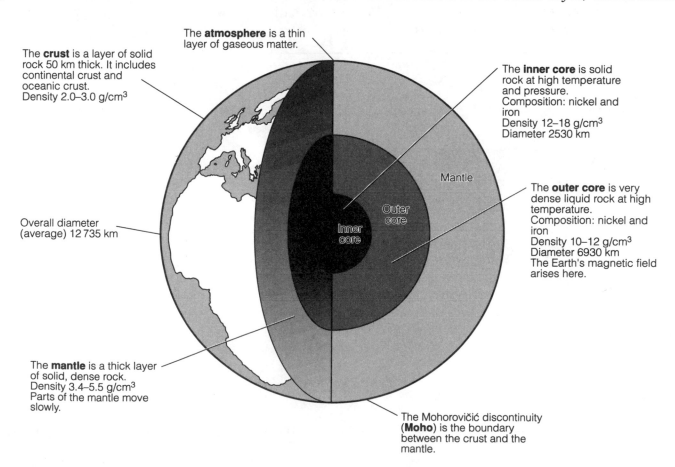

The **crust** is a layer of solid rock 50 km thick. It includes continental crust and oceanic crust. Density 2.0–3.0 g/cm³

The **atmosphere** is a thin layer of gaseous matter.

The **inner core** is solid rock at high temperature and pressure. Composition: nickel and iron Density 12–18 g/cm³ Diameter 2530 km

Mantle

Outer core

Inner core

The **outer core** is very dense liquid rock at high temperature. Composition: nickel and iron Density 10–12 g/cm³ Diameter 6930 km The Earth's magnetic field arises here.

Overall diameter (average) 12 735 km

The **mantle** is a thick layer of solid, dense rock. Density 3.4–5.5 g/cm³ Parts of the mantle move slowly.

The Mohorovičić discontinuity (**Moho**) is the boundary between the crust and the mantle.

harmful ultraviolet radiation from the Sun, made possible the evolution of a huge variety of living organisms. For 100 million years, the composition of the atmosphere has been the same as it is today (see Section 8.2).

Earth's crust is of two kinds: **continental crust**, which forms land masses, and **oceanic crust**, which lies beneath deep seas (see Table 10.1 and Fig. 10.2).

Table 10.1 Continental and oceanic crust

Continental crust	*Oceanic crust*
Forms continents and their shelves	Is beneath deep sea floors
Is between 50 km thick in lowlands and 70 km thick in mountain ranges	Is 6 km thick on average
Density 2.7 g/cm³	Density 3.0 g/cm³
Aged up to 3700 million years	Aged up to 210 million years
Has the same composition as granite rock and is often called granitic crust	Has the same composition as basalt and is often called basaltic crust
Rich in silicon and aluminium and sometimes called sial	Rich in silicon and magnesium and sometimes called sima
The deeper parts of continental crust are of denser material similar to oceanic crust.	Material similar to oceanic crust is thought to lie beneath the continents.

SUMMARY NOTE

The Earth consists of an inner core, an outer core, a mantle, a crust and an atmosphere. The boundary between the crust and the mantle is the Moho. The crust is of two types: continental (granitic) and oceanic (basaltic).

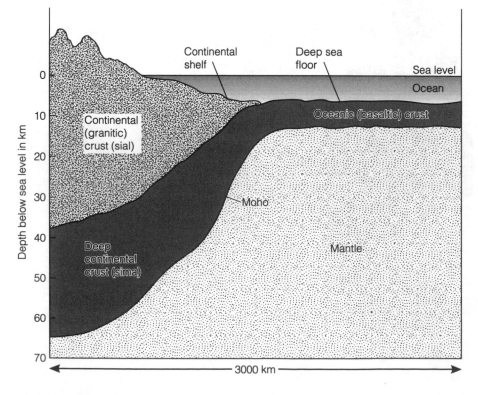

Fig. 10.2 Section showing continental crust and oceanic crust

10.2 Earthquakes and volcanoes

Earthquakes

In October 1993, an earthquake struck the state of Mahashtra in western India. A series of tremors lasted only a minute. They brought mud, stone and thatch houses tumbling down on the people sleeping inside them. In a few minutes, 10 000 people were killed and thousands more injured.

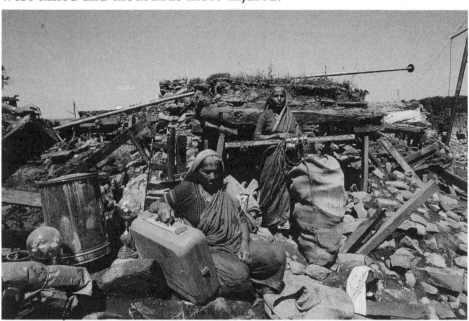

Fig. 10.3 Survivors of the earthquake in the town of Kilihari with all that is left of their homes

Every year about 500 000 earthquakes occur. Of these, about 1000 are strong enough to cause damage, and only a few are serious. Earthquakes provide us with evidence about the interior of the Earth. An earthquake occurs when forces inside the Earth become strong enough to fracture large masses of rock and make them move. Earthquakes occur in the rigid part of the Earth's crust; they cannot occur in the mantle.

Shock waves travel through the Earth from the **focus**, the point where the earthquake originates. They are felt most strongly at the **epicentre**, the point on the surface of the Earth which is directly above the focus (Fig. 10.4). Earthquake shocks are recorded with an instrument called a **seismometer**, and the study of earthquakes is called **seismometry**. The energy of earthquakes is measured on the Richter scale which ranges from 1–10. The Indian earthquake in 1993 registered 6.4. A seismogram, a recording of shock waves obtained with a seismometer, is shown in Fig. 10.5. You can see three types of shock waves: P waves – primary waves, S waves – secondary waves and L waves – long waves. The differences between P, S and L waves is shown in Fig. 10.6.

The thicknesses and densities of the core, mantle and crust have been worked out from the way shock waves pass through them. P waves can travel through liquids, while S waves cannot. Since S waves do not pass through the outer core at all, this is evidence that the outer core is liquid and at a very high temperature.

Earth's **magnetism** is evidence for the presence of iron in the core.

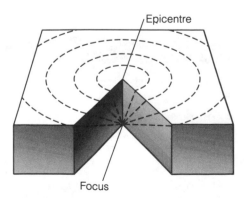

Fig. 10.4 Shock waves radiating from the focus of an earthquake

Fig. 10.5   A seismogram

First primary waves (P waves) arrive
and cause the first tremors.

Later, secondary waves (S waves)
arrive and cause a second set of
tremors.

Lastly, long waves (L waves) arrive
and cause the main shock.

End of earthquake

Time in minutes

Fig. 10.6   P, S and L waves from an
earthquake

P waves (push and pull waves)
pass through solids and liquids
and can travel through the core.
P waves travel faster than
S waves and L waves.

Epicentre of earthquake

Focus of earthquake

Mantle

Crust

S waves (shake waves)
are stopped by liquids
and therefore cannot
travel in the core.
S waves are slower than
P waves, faster than
L waves.

Shadow zone,
where no S waves
or P waves arrive

Outer core

L waves travel only in the crust
and make the ground shake.
They are slower than S waves
and P waves.

Volcanoes

Volcanoes also give us information about the structure of Earth
(see Figs. 10.14 and 10.15). The lava erupted by volcanoes is
produced in the crust and upper mantle. It does not tell us
anything about the deeper layers. A map of the places where
volcanoes and earthquakes occur gives information about the
regions of the Earth where heat is being generated and causing
eruptions (see Fig. 10.7).

SUMMARY NOTE

Evidence for the structure of
the Earth comes from
● the positions of volcanoes
  and earthquakes on the map
● material erupted by
  volcanoes
● the pattern of shock waves
  from earthquakes.

170

Do you know what meteorites are?

They're lumps of rock that gravitate towards Earth from space. Geologists think that meteorites may have been in existence ever since the planets were formed.

JUST TESTING 51

Choose the correct answers for questions **1–3**.

1 The age of Earth is estimated to be
   a 4600 years   **b** 1000 million years
   c 500 000 years   **d** 460 000 000 years

2 The average density of the whole Earth is
   a 1.0 g/cm³   **b** 3.0 g/cm³   **c** 5.5 g/cm³   **d** 12.0 g/cm³

3 The Moho lies between
   a the inner and outer core
   b the crust and the mantle
   c the oceanic and continental crust
   d the outer core and the mantle

4 Name the following parts of the Earth.
   a the solid zone made of nickel and iron
   b a zone that contains young basaltic rocks
   c a zone of granitic rocks
   d the zone of gases
   e the zone where the Earth's magnetism arises

5 a Which type of earthquake wave cannot travel through liquids?
   b Which type of shock wave causes the most damage?
   c What is the 'shadow zone'?
   d What evidence is there that the inner core of the Earth is solid?

10.3 Plate tectonics

Figure 10.7 shows where earthquakes and volcanoes occur. Some patterns can be seen in the map.

1 Earthquakes and volcanoes occur in belts of activity. The belts are hundreds of kilometres wide and thousands of kilometres long. Belts of activity run along chains of high mountains, e.g. the Alps and the Andes.

2 Belts run through the centres of the oceans. Surveys of the sea floor show that where there are mid-ocean belts, there are chains of high mountains beneath the sea. These mountain ranges are called **oceanic ridges**.

3 Belts of activity run through chains of volcanic islands, e.g. the Philippines. Surveys of the sea floor show that running close to

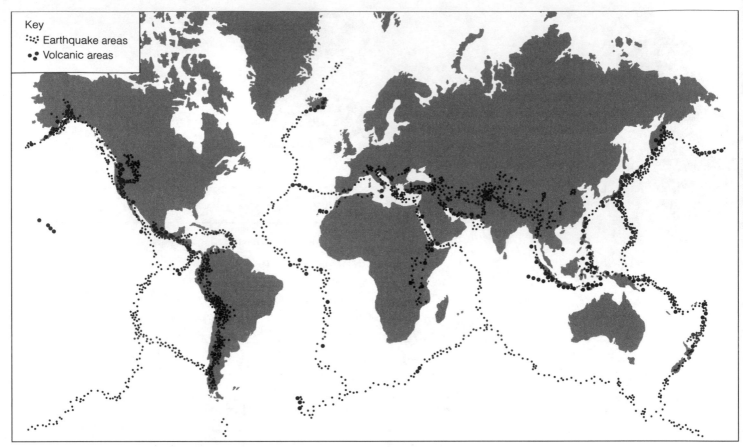

Fig. 10.7 Belts of earthquake and volcanic activity

Fig. 10.8 The plates that make up the Earth's crust

these belts there are deep **oceanic trenches** in the sea floor. Oceanic trenches also run alongside mountain ranges near the edges of continents, e.g. the Peru–Chile trench which runs parallel to the Andes.

Why do earthquakes and volcanoes occur in some parts of Earth's crust and not others? To answer this question, geologists have put forward the theory of **plate tectonics** (tectonics means construction). The outer layer of Earth is called the **lithosphere**, including the crust and uppermost layer of mantle, 80–110 km thick. According to this theory, the lithosphere is made up of a number of separate pieces or **plates** (see Fig. 10.8). Movements in the mantle make the plates move very slowly, at a rate of about 5 cm a year. As a result, plates may push against each other, creating stress. If stress builds up sufficiently, the plates may bend more and more until suddenly and violently they spring back into shape. Then the shock is felt as an earthquake. The movements of the mantle that cause all this activity must have a source of energy. It is believed that heat given out when radioactive elements decay is the source of this energy.

10.4 Plate boundaries

There are three types of boundaries between plates, **destructive boundaries**, **constructive boundaries** and **conservative boundaries**.

Destructive boundaries occur where plates are in collision. When they meet, the edge of one plate is forced to slide beneath the other and move down into the mantle. As the descending plate moves downwards into the hot mantle, it melts and becomes part of the mantle (Fig. 10.9). The process is called **subduction**. The oceanic trenches are regions where plates meet and subduction occurs. This is happening all along the west coast of South America. Some oceans are shrinking in size as subduction occurs.

Constructive boundaries occur where plates are moving apart. There are volcanoes along the oceanic ridges. When lava erupts from these volcanoes, it cools to form new oceanic crust. The new crust adds to the plates on each side and pushes them apart. As the plates move away from the ridge, the width of the ocean floor

Fig. 10.9 A destructive plate boundary. Lithosphere (crust and uppermost layer of mantle, 80–110 km thick) descends at the boundary.

An ocean and a continent meet

Ocean

Oceanic crust

Mantle

Continental crust

The edge of the denser oceanic crust sinks beneath the continental plate. It descends to a depth where the temperature is high enough to melt it, and it becomes part of the mantle.

increases. The process is called **sea-floor spreading**. It is occurring in e.g. the mid-Atlantic ridge.

Figure 10.10 shows what happens at a constructive boundary.

Conservative boundaries occur where two plates slide past one another. The San Andreas fault in California is an example (Fig. 10.11).

Fig. 10.10   A constructive plate boundary. The plates move apart as lithosphere is added between them.

Fig. 10.11   A conservative plate boundary. No lithosphere is added or lost.

10.5 The movement of plates

The conveyor belt

Material is subducted at oceanic trenches and added at oceanic ridges. As a result, lithosphere is transferred from one edge of a plate to the other edge. The amount of material subducted at one side is the same as the amount of material added at the opposite side, so the plate remains the same size. The movement of plates is described as a **conveyor belt** (Fig. 10.12). As plates ride on the mobile mantle, the continents on them move. This has been happening for thousands of millions of years. Although continents move only a few centimetres a year, they have already travelled thousands of kilometres. About 300 million years ago, northern Europe was near the equator, and tropical forests grew there. These later decayed to form coal deposits.

Fig. 10.12   The 'conveyor belt'

174

Formation of mountain ranges

A massive amount of sediment accumulates on the ocean floor (see Section 10.6). When an oceanic plate and a continental plate meet at a destructive boundary, this sediment is disturbed. As subduction of the oceanic plate occurs, sediment is scraped from the ocean floor and piled up along the edge of the continent. As more and more sediment piles up, a range of mountains is formed along the edge of the continent. The Andes mountain range was formed in this way (Fig. 10.13a).

As subduction continues, a continent carried on the subducting plate may collide with the continent on the continental plate. The continent being carried cannot subduct (being less dense than oceanic plate) so the edge buckles and folds and lifts upwards as it approaches the region of subduction. Eventually subduction stops because there is no ocean left. The two continents have joined to form a single land mass, and their edges have formed a mountain range (Fig. 10.13b). The Himalayas were formed by a collision between continental plates.

Fig. 10.13 The formation of mountain ranges (a) when oceanic and continental plates meet, (b) when two continental plates meet

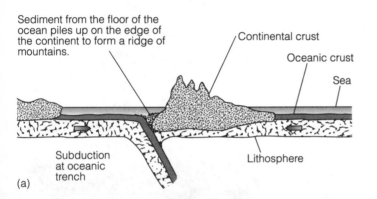

Sediment from the floor of the ocean piles up on the edge of the continent to form a ridge of mountains.

Continental crust

Oceanic crust

Sea

Subduction at oceanic trench

Lithosphere

(a)

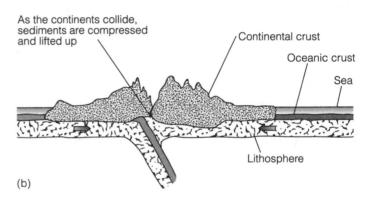

As the continents collide, sediments are compressed and lifted up

Continental crust

Oceanic crust

Sea

Lithosphere

(b)

SUMMARY NOTE

Earthquakes occur in belts of activity – along mountain ranges and along oceanic ridges and oceanic trenches. The **lithosphere** is Earth's crust and the upper part of the mantle. Geologists believe that the lithosphere consists of separate **plates**. The plates move slowly over the mantle. At oceanic ridges, the plates are moving apart. At oceanic trenches, the plates are moving together. Plate movement causes earthquakes, volcanoes and the formation of mountain ranges.

JUST TESTING 52

1 Name
   a the oceanic plate and the continental plate that were involved in the formation of the Andes
   b the two continental plates that were involved in the formation of the Himalayas
   c two plates that have no continental land
   d the plate on which the UK lies
   e the fault which runs down the west coast of the USA.

2 a Name the mountain range that runs along the west coast of South America.
   b Name the oceanic plate to the west of South America.
   c Explain how interaction between this oceanic plate and the South American plate gave rise to the range of mountains.
   d Answer this question after reading Section 10.6. Find the mid-Atlantic ridge in Fig. 10.8. Say what type of lava is erupted along this ridge. Say how this eruption of lava is related to the movement of plates on each side of the ridge.

10.6 Types of rock

Igneous rocks

Heat is generated in the Earth's crust and upper mantle. Sometimes the heat is sufficient to melt rocks. Molten rock is called **magma**, unless it reaches the Earth's surface, when it is called **lava**. Magma tends to rise, and, when cracks appear in the Earth's crust, magma is forced out from the mantle. It erupts onto the surface of the Earth as a volcano, a shower of burning lava, smoke and dust (Fig. 10.14). When volcanic lava cools, it crystallises to form rocks called **igneous rocks**. The faster the rate of cooling, the smaller are the crystals that are formed. Igneous rocks include

- basalt, formed by free-flowing mobile lava
- rhyolite, formed from slow-moving lava
- pumice, formed from a foam of lava and volcanic gases.

The types of rock erupted by a volcano are

- agglomerate, the largest fragments of rock, which settle close to the vent
- volcanic ash, finer fragments of rock
- tuff, compacted volcanic ash
- dust, which may be carried far away by the wind.

Fig. 10.15 Mount St Helens erupting

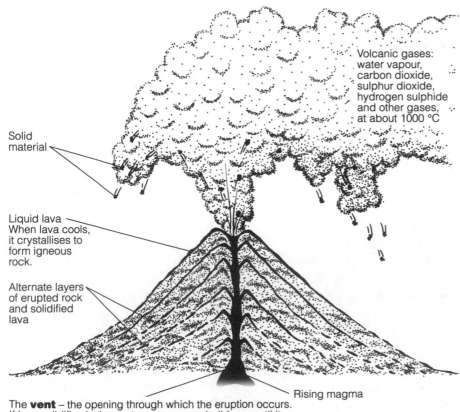

Volcanic gases: water vapour, carbon dioxide, sulphur dioxide, hydrogen sulphide and other gases, at about 1000 °C

Solid material

Liquid lava
When lava cools, it crystallises to form igneous rock.

Alternate layers of erupted rock and solidified lava

Rising magma

The **vent** – the opening through which the eruption occurs. If lava solidifies in the vent, gas pressure builds up until it causes a violent eruption of lava, rock and gas. The mixture can travel rapidly down the side of the volcano, destroying everything in its path.

Fig. 10.14 A volcano

Fig. 10.16 The Giant's Causeway in Northern Ireland consists of basalt.

176

Sedimentary rocks

When solid particles settle out of a liquid or an air stream, a **sediment** is formed. All the rocks on Earth's surface are exposed to forces which wear them down by weathering and by erosion (see Section 10.8). They are worn down to fragments of rock, pebbles, grains of sand and salts that dissolve in water. Plants and animals die and also form particulate material. All these particles are carried by gravity, winds, ice, rivers and seas. Eventually the transported material is deposited as a layer of sediment. A bed of sediment may form on a sea shore, on an ocean floor or in a desert. As more material is deposited on top, beds of sediment are slowly compacted by the pressure. Over a period of millions of years, the particles join (lithify) to form a **sedimentary rock**. Sedimentary rocks include:

- limestone, formed from the shells of dead animals
- coal, formed from the remains of dead plants
- sandstone, compacted grains of sand.

Metamorphic rocks

Metamorphic rocks are formed from either igneous or sedimentary rocks. High temperature or high pressure changes these rocks into the harder metamorphic rocks. Included among metamorphic rocks are:

- marble, formed from limestone at high temperature
- slate, formed from clay, mud and shale at high pressure
- metaquartzite, formed from sandstone at high pressure and temperature.

Earth's crust is composed of 65% igneous rocks, 8% sedimentary rocks and 27% metamorphic rocks (see Table 10.2 and Fig. 10.17).

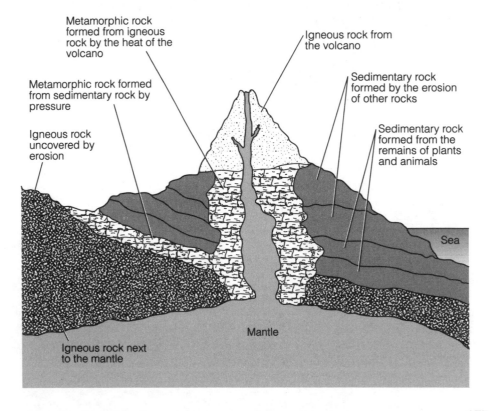

Fig. 10.17 Types of rock

	Igneous	*Sedimentary*	*Metamorphic*	
Examples	Granite, basalt, rhyolite, pumice	Limestone, clay, sandstone, mudstone	Marble, slate, hornfels, schist	**Table 10.2 Types of rock**
Method of formation	Crystallisation of magma	Deposition of particles	Recrystallisation of other rocks	
Structure	Crystalline	The grains do not usually interlock	Crystalline	
Direction of grain	Grains usually not lined up	Grains usually not lined up	Grains usually lined up	
Ease of breaking	Hard, not easy to split, may crumble on weathering	Some are soft and crumble. Some are hard to break.	Hard. May split in layers or crumble if weathered	
Appearance when broken	Shiny	Usually dull	Shiny	
Fossils	Absent	May be present	Absent	

The rock cycle

When new material is brought from the mantle into the crust, it forms igneous rocks. Igneous rocks are weathered to form rock particles. Particles are deposited and compacted to form sedimentary rocks. Both igneous rocks and sedimentary rocks are converted by slow geological processes into metamorphic rocks. Over a very long period of time, other rocks melt to reform igneous rocks. This sequence of events is called the **rock cycle**.

SUMMARY NOTE

A volcanic eruption emits lava, gases, pieces of solid rock and ash. Lava cools and solidifies to form **igneous rock**. Pieces of solid rock settle as agglomerate. Ash is compacted to form tuff.

Rocks are broken into smaller particles by weathering. These particles may be deposited as a sediment which is compacted to form **sedimentary rock**.

At high temperature and pressure, igneous rock and sedimentary rock change into **metamorphic rock**.

The **rock cycle** is the chain of slow processes that change rocks.

Fig. 10.18   The rock cycle

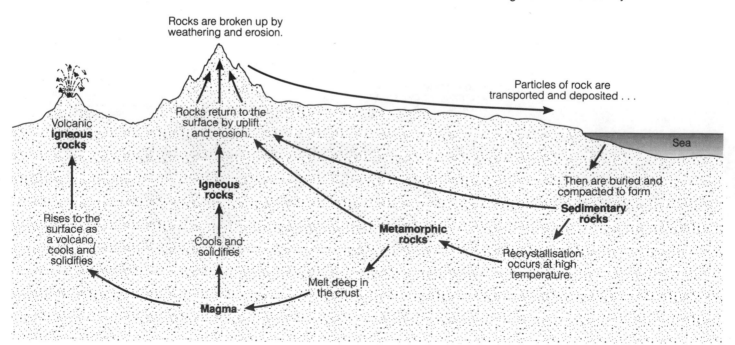

Rocks are broken up by weathering and erosion.

Particles of rock are transported and deposited . . .

Volcanic **igneous rocks**

Rocks return to the surface by uplift and erosion.

Sea

Igneous rocks

Rises to the surface as a volcano, cools and solidifies

Cools and solidifies

Metamorphic rocks

Then are buried and compacted to form **Sedimentary rocks**

Recrystallisation occurs at high temperature.

Melt deep in the crust

Magma

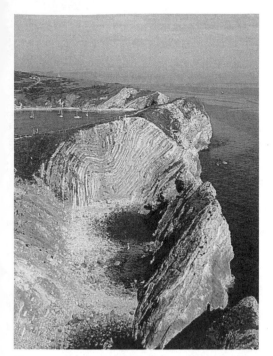
Fig. 10.19 Folding in a rock

10.7 Deformation of rocks

Although rocks are laid down in parallel layers (Fig. 10.14), the rocks you see rarely look like this (Figs. 10.19 and 10.22). Forces act on rocks and deform them. The result may be a fold, a fault, a cleavage or a joint. The deformation that results from a force depends on the type of rock. A certain force may produce a fold in a soft rock or a fault in a brittle rock.

Folding

When rocks are compressed by a large enough force, the layers **fold**. This often happens with sedimentary rocks. The rocks have been laid down in horizontal layers. When they are compressed in a horizontal direction, the layers fold. They bulge upwards in an **anticline** or downwards in a **syncline** (see Fig. 10.20).

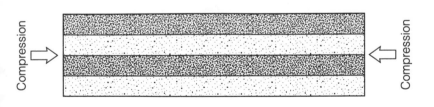
Original horizontal beds of rock

Fig. 10.20 Folding in a sedimentary rock

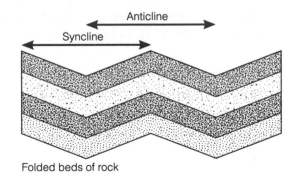
Folded beds of rock

Cleavage

Rocks may split into thin sheets under pressure. This is called **cleavage**. Slate is easily broken along **cleavage planes**. Slate is a metamorphic rock formed from shales. Under pressure, clay minerals and flaky minerals, such as mica, recrystallise so that the mica flakes lie perpendicular to the direction of maximum stress. Between the parallel layers of mica flakes are planes of weakness, the cleavage planes, and the slate formed can be easily broken along these planes.

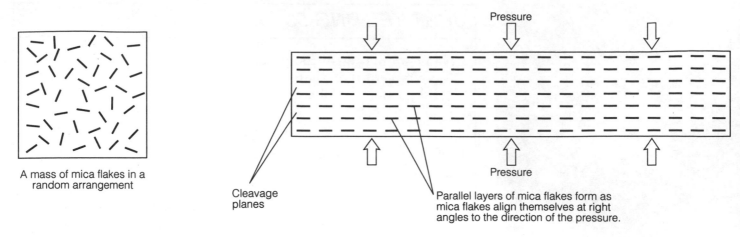

A mass of mica flakes in a random arrangement

Pressure

Cleavage planes

Parallel layers of mica flakes form as mica flakes align themselves at right angles to the direction of the pressure.

Pressure

Fig. 10.21 The formation of slate

Faults

If the forces acting on a rock are strong enough, they can break the rock to cause a **fault**. The break allows rocks on one side of the fault to move in the opposite direction to rocks on the other side of the fault. The movement takes place in jerks because of the friction between the edges of the rocks. One of these sudden jerks can cause an earthquake.

A horizontal displacement can occur at a fault where two of the Earth's plates slide past each other. A famous fault is the San Andreas fault which lies beneath the state of California, USA. California suffers from frequent slight earthquakes and some severe quakes. In 1906, an earthquake which registered 8.3 on the Richter scale killed 700 people and destroyed most of San Francisco. When the city was rebuilt, the buildings were designed to withstand earthquakes. In 1989 an earthquake measuring 6.9 hit the city and killed 300 people. The damage to the buildings was limited. In 1994 an earthquake measuring 6.6 and lasting 30 seconds killed 55 people.

Fig. 10.22 A fault in a rock

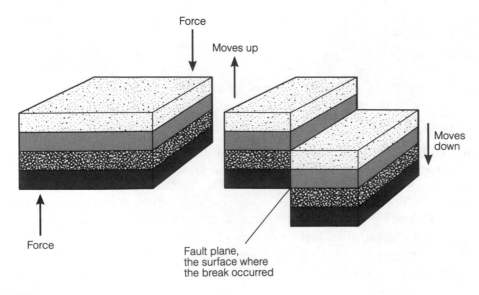

Force

Moves up

Moves down

Force

Fault plane, the surface where the break occurred

Fig. 10.23 How a vertical fault develops

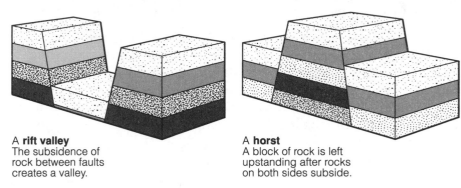

Fig. 10.24   The San Andreas fault

SUMMARY NOTE

Rocks may be deformed by
- **folding** to form synclines and anticlines
- **cleavage** – splitting into sheets
- **faulting** – developing breaks which allow slabs of rock to move against one another
- **jointing** – developing breaks without any movement of rock.

A **rift valley**
The subsidence of rock between faults creates a valley.

A **horst**
A block of rock is left upstanding after rocks on both sides subside.

Fig. 10.25   Some consequences of faults developing

Joints

Sometimes a fracture occurs without the rocks on each side of it moving relative to one another. There is no displacement of the rocks as there is in a fault, and such a break is called a **joint**. A joint in igneous rock may be caused by shrinking as a result of cooling. In sedimentary rocks, the cause may be a loss of water. Once joints have been formed, they can be penetrated by water and enlarged by weathering.

Fig. 10.26   Joints in the limestone rock at Ballynahowan, Ireland

Joints in folded rock

Fig. 10.27   Joints in folded rock

10.8 The landscape

Rocks are constantly being slowly broken down into smaller particles by forces in the environment. The forces are **physical forces**, e.g. wind, and **chemical reactions** which attack rocks. These processes are called **weathering**. When rocks are broken down and the particles are carried away by an agent such as water or wind, the process is called **erosion**.

Rain

Water is a weathering agent. Water can enter cracks in a rock. When it freezes, water expands and the cracks are opened wider. When the ice thaws, water penetrates further into the rock. After many cycles of freezing and thawing, pieces of rock may split off.

Chemical reactions occur between water and some minerals, e.g. mica. As a result, tiny particles are produced and carried away. Later they are deposited as a sediment of mud or clay.

Rivers and streams

The water cycle (Fig. 9.5) shows how rivers and streams carry water back to the oceans. All streams carry material in solution: the **solution load**. A fast-flowing stream can carry a large load of fine particles in suspension: the **suspension load**. A slow-flowing stream is more likely to deposit its load. A very fast stream can push sand and pebbles along the stream bed: the **bed load** (see Fig. 10.28).

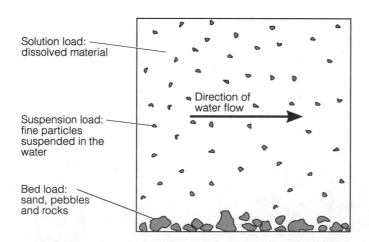

Fig. 10.28 The load carried by a stream

Erosion.   Rivers and streams cause erosion. Some minerals, e.g. calcium sulphate, dissolve slightly in water. Some, e.g. mica, are slowly broken up into small particles by water. Chemical reactions occur between acidic water and limestone rocks. In addition, the suspension load and the bed load slowly wear away the bed and the sides of the river channel.

Deposition.   Rivers and streams deposit the suspension load and the bed load that they carry. This deposition happens when the rivers slow down, for example on the inside curve of a bend and also where rivers flow into the sea or a lake.

Underground water

Some kinds of rock allow water to pass through them. Water can seep through joints in beds of sedimentary rock, e.g. limestone. Such rocks are described as **permeable**. Other rocks, e.g. sandstone, consist of mineral grains with tiny spaces between them, which water can enter. Such rocks are described as **porous**. The water held in rocks below the surface is called **ground water**. Some of it seeps upwards to the surface as a **spring**. Some of it remains as an underground reserve from which water can be drawn for consumption (see Section 9.5).

Weathering of rocks goes on below ground. As rain water permeates the ground, it dissolves some minerals. Calcium sulphate (gypsum) is slightly soluble. Rain water dissolves carbon dioxide from the air and becomes acidic. It can then react with limestone to form soluble calcium hydrogencarbonate. As limestone is removed, small openings in the rock enlarge and in time – over millions of years – form large underground passages through which flow underground rivers and streams. If the streams dry up, **underground caves** are formed (see Section 9.10).

The sea erodes rocks, as shown in Fig. 10.29. The caves have been formed where waves attack a weak point in the cliff, e.g. a joint. The arch has been formed by two caves meeting back to back and joining up. The sea stack has been left where the top of an arch has fallen away.

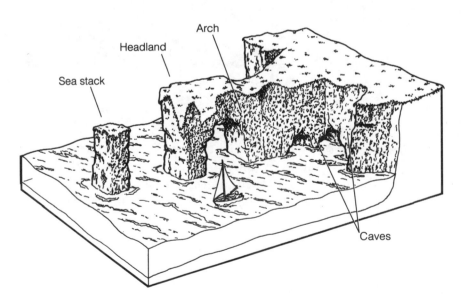

Fig. 10.29 Landscaping by the sea

Glaciers

Some parts of the world have snow all the year round. As layers of snow are added, they compress lower layers to form a mass of ice. If the ice begins to slide downhill under the influence of gravity, a **glacier** develops. Glaciers move at a rate of less than 1 metre a day. As glacial ice moves over a landscape, it wears down rocks by two methods

- **plucking** – freezing round pieces of rock and carrying them along
- **grinding** – wearing down of rocks by the sharp rocks attached to the bottom of the glacier.

When a glacier melts, it deposits all the material it has been carrying.

Fig. 10.30 A glacier

Wind

The landscaping effect of wind is most evident in desert areas. Sand dunes are easily shaped by the wind. Soil is more difficult for the wind to shape as moisture holds the particles together. In regions where plants grow, their roots bind the soil and make it difficult to erode.

Soil

Soil is formed when grains of broken-down rock become mixed with **humus** (the decayed remains of plants and animals). Between the grains are air spaces, and water can soak into the spaces. Soil which allows water to pass through easily is described as **permeable**. **Sandy soils** have large particles, with large air spaces between them so these soils are permeable, and drainage is rapid. **Clay soils** have small particles, with small air spaces between them, and drainage is slow. In sandy soils, plants may lack water; in clay soils plants may become waterlogged and lack oxygen. The best soil is a mixture of particles of different sizes with humus. Such a mixture is called **loam** and provides the best growing medium for plants.

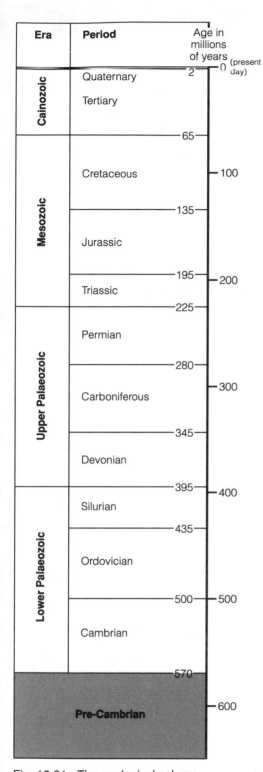

Era	Period	Age in millions of years
Cainozoic	Quaternary	2 — 0 (present day)
Cainozoic	Tertiary	
		65 —
Mesozoic	Cretaceous	— 100
		135 —
Mesozoic	Jurassic	
		195 — — 200
Mesozoic	Triassic	
		225 —
Upper Palaeozoic	Permian	
		280 —
Upper Palaeozoic	Carboniferous	— 300
		345 —
Upper Palaeozoic	Devonian	
		395 — — 400
Lower Palaeozoic	Silurian	
		435 —
Lower Palaeozoic	Ordovician	
		500 — — 500
Lower Palaeozoic	Cambrian	
		570 —
	Pre-Cambrian	— 600

Fig. 10.31 The geological column

10.9 The geological time scale

The geological column shown in Fig. 10.31 divides Earth's history into **eras**. Each era is divided into **periods**. During the Pre-Cambrian period the Earth's crust solidified, oceans and atmospheres developed and the first living organisms appeared. Human life evolved in the Quaternary period.

Relative dating

Without knowing the age of rocks, you may be able to classify them in order of age. If one sedimentary rock lies on top of another, it is likely that the upper rock was laid down after the lower one. Complications occur, however, if folding reverses the order. When fragments of rock are found embedded in another rock, the fragments must be older than the surrounding rock.

Fig. 10.32 Fossil of a sea scorpion that lived 400 million years ago

*Fossils

Fossils are the preserved remains of or marks made by dead plants and animals (see Fig. 10.32). If a Permian rock contains the mark of certain creatures, then they would have been alive 250 million years ago.

*Radioactive dating

Rocks contain radioactive isotopes (see Section 4.10). Take the case of a rock which contains the radioactive isotope uranium-238, which decays slowly through a chain of intermediates to form lead-206. The ratio of lead-206 to uranium-238 in a sample of the rock shows how long decay has been taking place, that is, the age of the rock. Radioactive dating gives the age of the Earth as 4600 million years.

185

1 Refer to Fig. 10.33.
  a Name the type of rock folds shown at **i A**, and **ii B**.
  b To which of the three types of rock does granite belong?
  c What difference would you expect to find between rock found at **E** and rock found at **F**?
  d Which is older, the rock at **C** or the rock at **D**? Explain your answer.

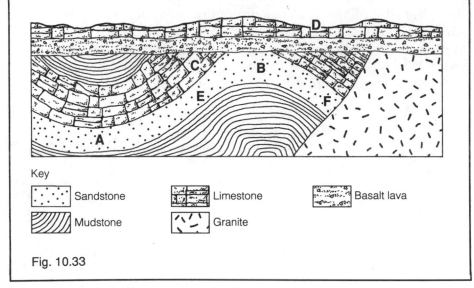

Key

Sandstone	Limestone	Basalt lava
Mudstone	Granite	

Fig. 10.33

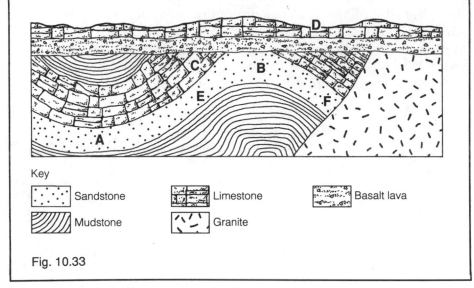

SUMMARY NOTE

Geologists can date layers of rocks
● from the order in which layers were deposited
● by identifying fossils in the rocks
● by radioactive dating.

*10.10 Evidence for the theory of plate tectonics

Continental drift

The Earth is thought to have originated from a cloud of hot gas which condensed to form a ball of hot liquid. As the liquid cooled, the densest materials sank into the core and the least dense rose to the surface, where they solidified to form the crust. Why the crust is folded into mountain ranges was a question to which scientists wanted an answer. They theorised that, as the Earth continued to cool, the core contracted and the crust folded to fit it. They compared this with the wrinkling of the skin of an old apple as the inner part dries out and shrinks.

This concept did not explain some discoveries about the Earth. Mountains occur in ranges, not in isolated peaks. Earthquakes and volcanoes occur in belts of activity, not at random over the Earth (see Fig. 10.7). Northern countries, such as the UK, contain rocks and fossils which can be formed only in desert conditions.

There is a similarity between the east coastline of South America and the west coastline of Africa (see Fig. 10.35). This led scientists to suggest that geological ages ago, the two continents were joined together and had later split up and slowly drifted apart. In 1915, a German meteorologist called Alfred Wegener gathered together the evidence in favour of the theory of **continental drift**.

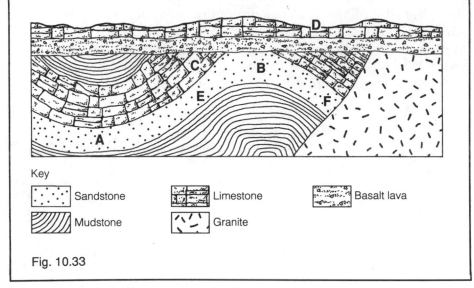

As evidence that the continents were once joined, Wegener described how mountain belts and types of rock match up on both sides of the Atlantic as though they had once been continuous. He pointed out that similar plant and animal populations are found on both sides of the Atlantic. Fossils of the same species are found on both coastlines. A particular example was the extinct reptile *Mesosaurus*. Fossils of this reptile are found in areas on both sides of the ocean (see Figs. 10.34 and 10.35).

Wegener advanced a theory to explain how continents could have drifted apart. He suggested that beneath the continents is a fluid layer of the Earth's crust, on which the continental land masses float. According to this theory, continents move horizontally because forces act on them, forces which last for geological eras. According to the theory of continental drift, South America, Africa and the rest of the southern continents were all joined in one land mass called Gondwanaland. The northern continents were joined in a land mass called Laurasia. At a still earlier time, all the continents were part of a single land mass called Pangaea (see Fig. 10.36).

What was the nature of the force that drove the continents apart? This was a question to which Wegener was unable to suggest an answer. This is one reason why the theory was not widely accepted by Wegener's fellow scientists. Today the theory is accepted, because an explanation has been put forward for the force that drives continental drift. Geologists realised the enormous magnitude of the heat produced by radioactive decay inside the Earth. The heat is more than sufficient to power all volcanic activity. The excess of heat must be used or the Earth

Fig. 10.34 *Mesosaurus*

Key

▨ Continental shelf

▮ Ancient Pre-Cambrian rocks (over 2000 million years)

⌇ Areas where fossils of Mesosaurus (a Permian reptile) are found

≣ Old mountain belt

Fig. 10.35 South America and Africa – were they joined?

180 million years ago
Pangaea, the original land mass, had split into two parts.

135 million years ago
Laurasia and Gondwanaland drifted northwards.
The North Atlantic and Indian Oceans widened.
The rift between Africa and South America lengthened.

65 million years ago
Africa and South America had separated.
The Mediterranean Sea had appeared.
India was moving towards Asia.

Today
North America and South America have joined.
Australia and Antarctica have separated.
India has joined Asia.

Fig. 10.36 The formation of the continents

would heat up. In 1931, a British geologist called Arthur Holmes suggested that the excess of heat drove convection currents in the magma. These currents power the continental drift (see Fig. 10.37). It took 30 years for the theory to be accepted.

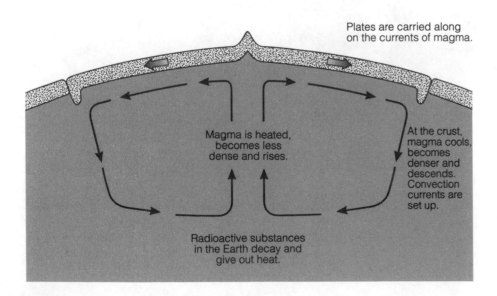

Plates are carried along on the currents of magma.

Magma is heated, becomes less dense and rises.

At the crust, magma cools, becomes denser and descends. Convection currents are set up.

Radioactive substances in the Earth decay and give out heat.

Fig. 10.37 Convection currents in magma

Evidence for the theory of continental drift

Sea floor spreading. The different parts of the sea floor can be dated. The youngest basalts on the ocean floor are at the oceanic ridges. The oldest parts of the oceanic crust are in the oceanic trenches and at the borders of continents. (See Fig. 10.38.) No oceanic basalt more than 210 million years old has been found. Continental crust, on the other hand, is over 1000 million years old.

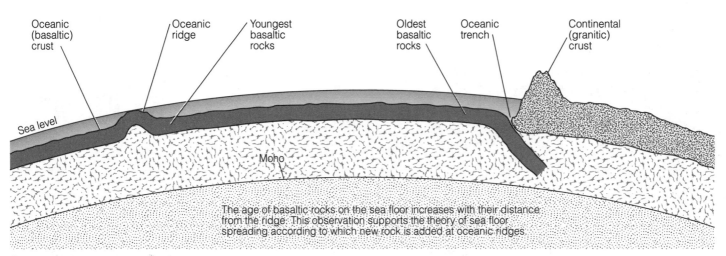

Fig. 10.38 Sea floor spreading

SUMMARY NOTE

The model of the Earth in which rigid slabs of crust rub up against each other on the surface is called **plate tectonics**.

According to the theory of **sea floor spreading**, new oceanic crust is being formed constantly along oceanic ridges. The new oceanic crust pushes the older crust away from the ridges towards the continents.

Evidence comes from the dating of basalt rocks on the ocean floor and from the pattern of 'magnetic stripes' in oceanic basalts.

Magnetic stripes. Earth's magnetism reverses its polarity every few thousand years. A reversal means that a compass needle points to the South Pole instead of the North Pole – or the other way round. Minerals which contain iron and are therefore magnetic are present in oceanic floor basalts. As they crystallise, particles of iron line up with the magnetic field in operation at the time. A study of the oceanic floor basalts shows 'magnetic stripes' as the direction of the magnetic field changes. (See Fig. 10.39.) The rate of sea floor spreading has been calculated from magnetic data as 2–10 cm per year for different oceans.

Fig. 10.39 The pattern of magnetic stripes at an oceanic ridge (Note the symmetrical pattern of bands of normally magnetised basalt and reversely magnetised basalt. Can you explain this without the theory of sea floor spreading?)

Exercise 10

1 Use the key to help you to identify some common rocks. Wear safety glasses for testing with acid.

1 Rock is made of crystals (which may be very small). Go to 2
  Rock is not made of crystals. Go to 3

2 Rock is white or pale in colour, with large crystals. **Granite**
  Rock is dark in colour, with very small crystals. **Basalt**

3 Rock splits into layers. Go to 4
  Rock does not split into layers. Go to 5

4 Rock is crumbly. **Shale**
  Rock is quite hard with definite layers. **Slate**

5 Rock fizzes when hydrochloric acid is added. Go to 6
  Rock does not fizz with acid. Go to 7

6 Rock is white in colour. **Marble**
  Rock is greyish in colour. **Limestone**

7 Rock is made of small grains, like sand. **Sandstone**
  Rock contains larger rounded pebbles. **Conglomerate**

2 Ask your teacher for a specimen of a common mineral. Work through the key in Fig. 10.40 to identify your mineral. Wear safety glasses when testing with acid.

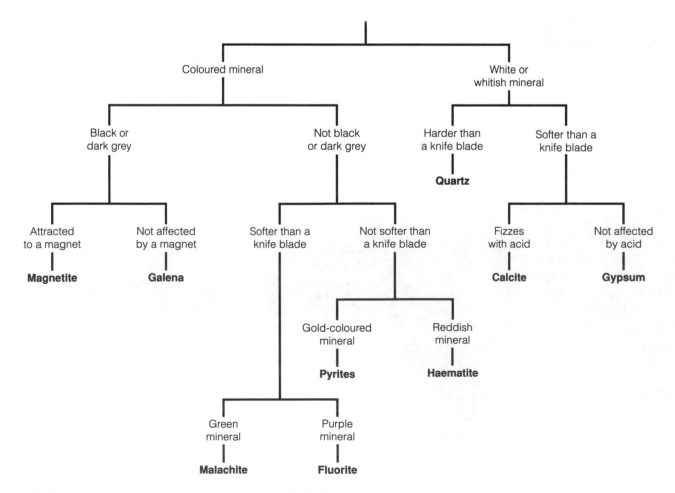

Fig. 10.40

190

3 In Fig. 10.41,
  a Name the features **D**, **E**, **F** and **G**.
  b Explain what is happening at **H**.
  c Of what kind of rock is **F** composed?
  d State the direction of movement of each of the plates **A**, **B** and **C**.
  e Explain how mountains came to be formed on the coast of **F**.

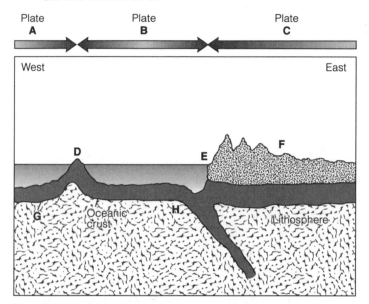

Fig. 10.41

4 Study Fig. 10.42. Give the letters of the rocks which are younger than chalk.

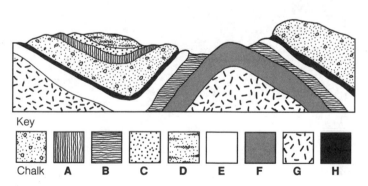

Fig. 10.42

5 Figure 10.43 shows the pattern of shock waves recorded on a seismogram after an earthquake.
  a Which point, **A** or **B** or **C**, marks the arrival of **i** the first S waves, **ii** the first L waves, and **iii** the first P waves?
  b How much time passed between the arrival of the first P wave and the first S wave?
  c If P waves travel through the crust at 8 km/s and S waves at 4 km/s, how far away is the seismometer from the epicentre of the earthquake?

Fig. 10.43

6 Study Fig. 10.44. It shows a landscape which is being altered slowly by weathering and erosion.
  a Suggest two ways in which the movement of the glacier will affect the rock with which it comes in contact.
  b Why are rock particles deposited at the foot of the glacier?
  c Mention another place where rock is being broken down, and explain how it happens.
  d Layers of rock particles are deposited on the bed of the lake. What type of rock will eventually be formed here?
  e How are rock particles carried to the sea?
  f Name two agents that may slowly break down the cliff.
  g The mountains are made of a hard igneous rock. Suggest how they have been formed.

Fig. 10.44

CHAPTER 11 _Metals_

11.1 Metals and alloys

Metals are important to us. Figure 11.1 shows one of mankind's most highly prized possessions. The car must be reliable in use, attractive in appearance and as inexpensive as possible to manufacture. To enable it to meet this description, it is made largely of **metals** and **alloys**. An alloy is a mixture of metallic elements and, in some cases, non-metallic elements also. Steel is an alloy of iron with other metallic elements and carbon. Figure 11.1 shows how the choice of a metal or alloy for a particular job depends on its properties.

Fig. 11.1   The car

1 The combined body-chassis must be strong. It may need to survive a collision or a roll-over. Steel is chosen because of its strength.
2 The cylinder block is the largest part of the engine. It contains the cylinders in which the combustion of petrol vapour in air takes place. With its complicated shape, it can be made only by pouring molten metal into a mould. Cast iron is used (see Section 11.11).
3 The pistons move up and down inside the cylinders. Pistons are usually made of aluminium, which is less dense than iron. A piston must make a gas-tight fit inside its cylinder. Each piston is encircled by a piston ring of chromium-plated cast iron. Cast iron slides easily inside the cylinder; chromium plating makes it resistant to corrosion.
4 Inlet valves allow petrol vapour and air to enter the cylinders. Exhaust valves let the combustion products escape. Valves must keep their shape at high temperatures, and must not corrode. A steel which contains chromium and nickel is chosen.
5 As each cylinder 'fires' in turn, its piston moves and gives the crankshaft a powerful jerk. To withstand a succession of powerful jerks, a crankshaft must be very tough. It is made of steel which has received special toughening treatments.

6 The gears are made of steel; the gear-box is made of cast iron.
7 The wheels are made of pressed steel or aluminium.
8 The brake discs and drums are made of cast iron.
9 The batteries are lead–acid accumulators.

10 The starter motor is wound with copper wire.
11 The springs need an unusual quality. They must be compressible. A steel containing silicon and manganese was developed for this purpose.
12 The radiator must not become corroded. Aluminium or stainless steel is used.

SUMMARY NOTE

A large number of different metals and alloys are used in making a car. No other materials have the necessary strength.

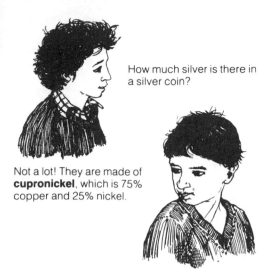

How much silver is there in a silver coin?

Not a lot! They are made of **cupronickel**, which is 75% copper and 25% nickel.

You find it fairly easy to recognise a metal when you see one (Fig. 11.2). In Experiment 3.1, you looked at the differences between metallic elements and non-metallic elements. Table 3.2 lists the differences.

Fig. 11.2 Metals in use ▷

Fig. 11.3 Concorde

Alloys

How does alloying alter the properties of metals? Many metallic elements do not have enough strength to allow them to be used for the manufacture of machines and vehicles which will have to withstand stress. Aluminium is in many ways a suitable metal from which to make aeroplanes. It has a low density and is not corroded by the atmosphere. Its drawback is that it is not strong enough. The addition of copper and a little magnesium to aluminium makes an alloy called **duralumin**. This alloy is much stronger than pure aluminium and is used for aircraft manufacture (Fig. 11.3).

Alloys have different properties from the metals (and in some cases non-metallic elements) of which they are composed. Brass differs from copper and zinc. It has a lower melting point than either of these metals. This makes it easier to *cast*. Brass makes a pleasanter, more sonorous sound than either of the two elements. It is used for making musical instruments.

Which metal or alloy would you use for electrical wiring? for making saucepans? for making drains? Before you can answer these questions, you need to study the chemical reactions of the metals.

*11.2 The metallic bond

What is it that gives metals their strength, enables them to conduct heat and electricity and allows them to be worked into different shapes without breaking? It is the type of chemical bond between the atoms: the **metallic bond**.

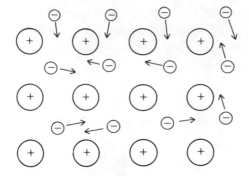

Valency electrons have separated from the atoms to leave metal cations.

Electrons move between the metal cations like a cloud of negative charge. They cancel the repulsion that would drive the cations apart.

Fig. 11.4 The metallic bond

A block of metal consists of positive metal ions and free valency electrons (Fig. 11.4). The valency electrons no longer belong to any one atom. They move between the metal ions like a cloud of negative charge. If it were not for this mobile negative charge, the metal cations would be driven apart by repulsion between their positive charges.

This structure explains the properties of metals. They conduct electricity (Fig. 11.5). Unlike ionic crystals, metals can change their shape without breaking (see Figs. 11.6 and 11.7).

Electrons are supplied at the LHS. The sea of electrons flows towards the RHS. Electrons are removed at the RHS.

Fig. 11.5 How a metal conducts electricity

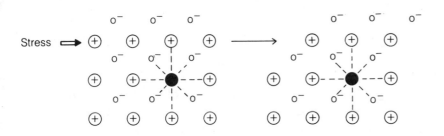

This is a metallic structure. Notice the atom shaded black. It is still bonded to the same number of other atoms after the shape of the metal has been altered.

Fig. 11.6 Metals can bend without breaking

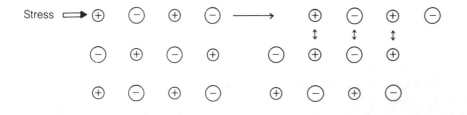

This is an ionic structure. When a force is applied, it alters the shape of the crystal. As a result, cation ↔ cation repulsion and anion ↔ anion repulsion is set up. The crystal fractures.

Fig. 11.7 Ionic compounds shatter easily

*11.3 The crystalline structure of metals

In ancient times, swordsmiths did not know about the crystalline structure of metals. By trial and error, however, they found that a sword could be hardened by rapid quenching (immersion in cold water). This was a valuable discovery for the soldiers who had to

194

Fig. 11.8   Metal grains

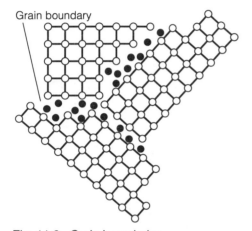

Fig. 11.9   Grain boundaries

SUMMARY NOTE

A metal consists of a mass of tiny crystals called **grains**. A piece of metal with fine grains is stronger than a piece with coarse grains.
Faults in the crystal structure, called **dislocations**, weaken a metal. They also enable metals to change shape without breaking because dislocations move when a metal is under stress.

use the swords. A soft sword would bend when it struck an enemy's shield, and while the soldiers were trying to straighten it they were easy prey for their enemies. Now the change in properties that quenching produces in a metal can be understood.

Grains

When a molten metal starts to solidify, many crystals start to grow in the liquid at the same time. Eventually the crystals meet to form a solid mass of small crystals (see Fig. 11.8). These individual crystals are called **grains**. Since each grain has grown independently, the arrangement of the atoms in one grain is not related to the arrangement in neighbouring grains (Fig. 11.9). The greater the number of grains, the stronger is the metal. A metal containing a large number of small grains is described as a 'fine-grained' metal. 'Grain-refining agents' can be added to molten metal to provide nuclei from which crystals grow, to produce a fine-grained metal.

Between the grains, at the **grain boundaries**, are atoms that have not fitted into the crystal structure. These are often atoms of impurities. Alloying is used to harden a metal, by providing additional atoms that will be trapped between the grains.

Within the grains, the crystal structure is imperfect, with faults called **dislocations** in the orderly arrangement of atoms (see Fig. 11.10).

The presence of dislocations makes a metal structure weaker and also more malleable. When the structure is stressed, e.g. when a metal is hammered, a dislocation may be forced to move. As the stress is repeated, the dislocation may travel along to the grain boundary (Fig. 11.11). This mobility of dislocations explains the malleability of metals.

There are different numbers of atoms in adjacent layers.

Fig. 11.10   A dislocation within a metal grain

Dislocation

Fig. 11.11   Dislocations moving towards a grain boundary

Work-hardening

Metals are often **worked** (reshaped) when hot, as they are then softer and easier to work. However, metals can be **cold-worked**, or forced into new shapes without being heated. Eventually cold-working makes metals **work-hardened** and difficult to reshape. The forces applied to work the metal produce large numbers of dislocations. Movement of dislocations becomes difficult because large numbers of dislocations are trying to move in different directions. The metal eventually reaches a state where the dislocations cannot move and the grains cannot change shape without risk of breaking.

Recovery.   By heating the work-hardened metal, it is possible to give its atoms enough energy to move out of their dislocations and to rearrange within the grains. This heat treatment is called **recovery** or **stress relief**.

Recrystallisation.   By heating a work-hardened metal to a high enough temperature, it can be made to recrystallise as numerous fine grains. The temperature at which this happens is called the **recrystallisation temperature**.

Annealing.   Work-hardened metals can be restored to their original state by a treatment called **annealing**. The work-hardened metal object is put into a furnace and left until both recovery and recrystallisation are complete. The metal regains its malleability and ductility and can be worked again. When a metal is shaped by cold-working, it may need to be annealed several times during the process. Each time work-hardening makes the metal too hard for further cold-working, it goes into the annealing furnace.

Hot-working

In **hot-working** or **forging**, a metal is worked at a temperature above its recrystallisation temperature. In this way, annealing is taking place while the metal is worked. Forging requires less force than cold-working because the metal is softer. It has the advantage that there is no need to break off for annealing.

Quenching and tempering.   **Quenching** is the sudden immersion of a hot metal in oil or water at room temperature. It is an important treatment for cutting tools (including the swords already mentioned!). Many crystalline materials, including metals, can change from one crystalline form into another on heating or cooling. The **austenite** form of steel, which exists at higher temperatures, can hold more carbon than the **ferrite** form, which exists at lower temperatures. When steel is quenched rapidly, the carbon atoms do not have enough time to move, and the austenite form, with its higher carbon content, persists at the lower temperature. The carbon atoms interfere with the movement of dislocations, making the metal harder, less malleable and more brittle.

Quenched steel is too brittle for many uses, and to make it less brittle, some hardness must be sacrificed. To obtain a balance between malleability and hardness, the steel is **tempered**. The metal object is heated a second time to the **tempering temperature** and then quenched again. The temperature at which the steel is worked must not be above the tempering temperature.

JUST TESTING 55

1 Explain what is meant by **a** a metal grain, **b** a dislocation.
2 Explain the following statements:
   a A metal is a polycrystalline material.
   b The malleability of a metal depends on the presence of dislocations.
3 Explain the difference between recovery, recrystallisation and annealing.
4 What is the advantage of hot-working a metal over cold-working?
5 What is quenching? Why does it make a metal harder?
6 What is tempering? What effect does it have on a metal?

11.4 The chemical reactions of metals

Reactions of metals with air

Many metals react with oxygen in the air. You studied this reaction in Experiment 8.1 (see Section 8.9). The results are summarised in Table 11.1.

Table 11.1 The reactions between metals and oxygen

Metal	Symbol	Reaction when heated in air	Reaction with cold air
Potassium	K		
Sodium	Na		
Lithium	Li		
Calcium	Ca	Burn in air to form oxides	React slowly with air to form a surface film of the metal oxide. This reaction is called **tarnishing**.
Magnesium	Mg		
Aluminium	Al		
Zinc	Zn		
Iron	Fe		
Tin	Sn	When heated in air these metals form oxides without burning.	
Lead	Pb		
Copper	Cu		
Silver	Ag		Silver tarnishes in air.
Gold	Au	Do not react.	Do not react.
Platinum	Pt		

Reactions of metals with water

You may like to start this topic by doing Experiments 10.1–10.4. The results of the experiments are summarised in Table 11.2.

Table 11.2 Reactions of metals with water and steam

Metal	Reaction with water
Potassium	Reacts violently with cold water (Fig. 11.12). Hydrogen and potassium hydroxide solution, which is a strong alkali, are formed. So much heat is given out (the reaction is so **exothermic**) that the hydrogen burns. The flame is coloured lilac by potassium atoms which have vaporised:

$$\text{potassium} + \text{water} \rightarrow \text{hydrogen} + \text{potassium hydroxide}$$

$$2K(s) + 2H_2O(l) \rightarrow H_2(g) + 2KOH(aq)$$

Potassium is kept under oil to prevent water vapour in the air from attacking it.

Sodium	Reacts with slightly less violence than potassium. Hydrogen and sodium hydroxide solution, which is a strong alkali, are formed. The hydrogen formed burns (Fig. 11.13) with a yellow flame. The flame colour is due to the presence of sodium vapour:

$$\text{sodium} + \text{water} \rightarrow \text{hydrogen} + \text{sodium hydroxide}$$

$$2Na(s) + 2H_2O(l) \rightarrow H_2(g) + 2NaOH(aq)$$

Like potassium, sodium must be kept under oil.

Lithium	Reacts similarly to sodium but less vigorously. Lithium must be kept under oil.
Calcium	Reacts readily but not violently with cold water to form hydrogen and calcium hydroxide solution, the alkali **limewater** (see Experiment 10.2 and Fig. 11.14):

$$\text{calcium} + \text{water} \rightarrow \text{hydrogen} + \text{calcium hydroxide}$$

$$Ca(s) + 2H_2O(l) \rightarrow H_2(g) + Ca(OH)_2(aq)$$

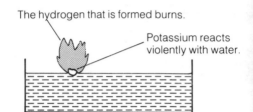

Fig. 11.12 The reaction of potassium with water (NOTE: this reaction must be done as a demonstration behind a safety screen.)

Fig. 11.13 The reaction of sodium with water (NOTE: This violent reaction must be done as a demonstration behind a safety screen.)

Fig. 11.14 The reaction of calcium with water

Fig. 11.15 The reaction of magnesium with water

Fig. 11.16 The reaction of magnesium with steam

Magnesium Reacts slowly with cold water (Fig. 11.15) to form hydrogen and magnesium hydroxide:

magnesium + water → hydrogen + magnesium hydroxide

$$Mg(s) + 2H_2O(l) \rightarrow H_2(g) + Mg(OH)_2(aq)$$

Burns in steam (Experiment 10.3 and Fig. 11.16) to form hydrogen and magnesium oxide:

magnesium + steam → hydrogen + magnesium oxide

$$Mg(s) + H_2O(g) \rightarrow H_2(g) + MgO(s)$$

Aluminium Only if the surface layer of aluminium oxide is removed will aluminium show its true reactivity (Experiment 10.12). Then it reacts to form hydrogen and aluminium oxide.

Zinc Reacts with steam to form hydrogen and zinc oxide (Experiment 10.4 and Fig. 11.17):

zinc + steam → hydrogen + zinc oxide

$$Zn(s) + H_2O(g) \rightarrow H_2(g) + ZnO(s)$$

Iron Reacts with steam to form hydrogen and the oxide, Fe_3O_4, tri-iron tetraoxide, which is blue–black in colour (Experiment 10.4 and Fig. 11.17):

iron + steam → hydrogen + tri-iron tetraoxide

$$3Fe(s) + 4H_2O(g) \rightarrow 4H_2(g) + Fe_3O_4(s)$$

Tin
Lead
Copper
Silver
Gold
Platinum
} Do not react.

Fig. 11.17 The reaction between iron (or zinc) and steam

Reactions of metals with dilute acids

You have had an introduction to this topic in Section 7.2. Experiments 7.1 and 10.1 will help you. The results are summarised in Table 11.3.

Metal	Reaction	
Potassium Sodium Lithium	The reaction is too dangerously violent for you to carry out	
Calcium Magnesium Aluminium Zinc Iron Tin Lead	Most metals react with dilute hydrochloric acid to give hydrogen and a solution of the metal chloride, e.g. zinc + hydrochloric acid → hydrogen + zinc chloride $Zn(s) + 2HCl(aq) → H_2(g) + ZnCl_2(aq)$ The speed of the reaction decreases from calcium to lead. Lead reacts very slowly. The reactions of metals with dilute sulphuric acid give hydrogen and sulphates.	
Copper Silver Gold Platinum	These metals do not react with dilute hydrochloric acid and dilute sulphuric acid. (Copper reacts with dilute nitric acid to form copper(II) nitrate.)	

Table 11.3 The reactions of metals with acids

JUST TESTING 57

1 Fruit juices are acidic. Why are food cans not made simply from iron? What metal could be used to coat iron cans to make them suitable for preserving fruit?
2 Write word and symbol equations for these reactions:
   a magnesium and hydrochloric acid
   b aluminium and hydrochloric acid
   c zinc and sulphuric acid
   d iron and sulphuric acid to form iron(II) sulphate.

Table 11.4 Reactions of metals

Metal	Reaction when heated in oxygen	Reaction with cold water	Reaction with dilute hydrochloric acid
Potassium Sodium Lithium	Burn to form the oxides.	Displace hydrogen; form alkaline hydroxides.	React dangerously fast.
Calcium Magnesium Aluminium Zinc Iron		Slow reaction No reaction, except for slow rusting of iron; all react with steam.	Displace hydrogen; form metal chlorides.
Tin Lead	Oxides form slowly without burning.	No reaction, even with steam	React very slowly.
Copper Silver Gold Platinum	No reaction		No reaction

You have studied the reactions of metals with oxygen, with water and with dilute acids.

1 Many metals react with oxygen; some metals burn in oxygen. The oxides of metals are bases.
2 The very reactive metals (e.g. sodium) react with water to give a metal hydroxide and hydrogen. Some metals react with steam to give a metal oxide and hydrogen.
3 Many metals react with dilute acids to give hydrogen and the salt of the metal.

When you look at reactions 1, 2 and 3, you find that the metals follow the same order of reactivity in all the reactions. This order is called the **reactivity series** of the metals. It is one of the important ways of classifying metals.

11.5 The reactivity series

Look at the combined results of the experiments on the reactions of metals with oxygen, water and acids. Table 11.4 summarises them. You will see that a sort of league table of metals emerges. The same metals are the most reactive in the different reactions.

Table 11.4 places the metals in order of **reactivity**, in order of their readiness to take part in chemical reactions. The table is part of the **reactivity series** of the metals. There are 70 metals in the Earth's crust. You may be surprised to see aluminium placed above zinc. Aluminium is so reactive that, when a fresh surface of aluminium meets the air, it immediately reacts with oxygen to form aluminium oxide. The surface layer of aluminium oxide prevents the metal from showing its true reactivity. If you remove the layer of aluminium oxide to expose the metal beneath it, you will see how reactive aluminium really is (Experiment 10.12).

JUST TESTING 58

1 Why does gold occur 'native' whereas zinc does not?
2 Why were silver and copper used as coinage metals?
3 Archaeologists dig up gold and silver objects made by people thousands of years ago. Why are they still in good condition? What has happened to iron objects of the same age?
4 The following metals are listed in order of reactivity:
   sodium > magnesium > zinc > copper
   Explain how this order follows from the reactions of these metals with **a** water, **b** dilute hydrochloric acid.

What predictions can be made from the reactivity series?

You see from the reactivity series that aluminium is more reactive than iron. This means that aluminium combines with oxygen more readily than iron does. What will happen when aluminium is heated with iron(III) oxide? The two metals will be in **competition for oxygen**. Which will win? Figure 11.18 shows an experiment to find out.

When the magnesium ribbon is lit, it provides enough heat to start the reaction. The reaction that follows is very exothermic. After the crucible has cooled, you can take a lump of solid iron out of the bottom:

aluminium + iron(III) oxide → iron + aluminium oxide
$$2Al(s) + Fe_2O_3(s) \rightarrow 2Fe(s) + Al_2O_3(s)$$

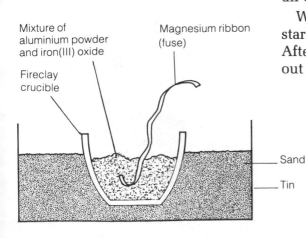

Mixture of aluminium powder and iron(III) oxide

Magnesium ribbon (fuse)

Fireclay crucible

Sand

Tin

Fig 11.18 A competition between aluminium and iron (NOTE: this experiment is a demonstration experiment. It should be done behind a safety screen.)

- What do you see that tells you that the reaction is exothermic?
- How can you prove that the metal formed is iron, not aluminium?

This reaction is called the **thermit reaction** (therm = heat). Since the iron forms in a molten state, it can be used to weld pieces of metal together (see Fig. 11.20).

Metals can **compete for anions**. Experiment 10.5 will show you what happens. Metals can displace other metals from their salts. A metal which is higher in the reactivity series will displace a metal which is lower in the reactivity series from a salt. Copper is above silver in the reactivity series. Figure 11.21 shows what happens when a piece of copper wire is left to stand in a solution of silver nitrate.

Fig. 11.19 Competition for oxygen

JUST TESTING 59

1 Which metal would you use for making saucepans: magnesium, iron or copper? Explain your choice.

2 Which metal would you use for making electrical contacts in a space capsule? (Expense is no object, and it is essential that the contacts do not tarnish.)

3 What would you expect to see if you drop a piece of magnesium ribbon into a test-tube of copper(II) sulphate solution?
Try it, and see if you are right.
Write a word equation and a chemical equation for what happens.

4 What would you expect to see if you drop a piece of zinc into a test-tube of lead(II) nitrate solution?
Try it and see if you are right.
Why is the reaction slower than in **3**?
Write a word equation and a chemical equation for what happens.

5 What would you expect to happen if you drop a piece of iron into a solution of zinc sulphate? Again, check your prediction.

6 A metal, **X**, is displaced from a solution of one of its salts by a metal, **Y**. A metal, **Z**, displaces **Y** from a solution of one of its salts. Place the metals in order of reactivity.

7 The following metals are listed in order of reactivity, with the most reactive first:
    Na, Mg, Al, Zn, Fe, Pb, Cu, Hg, Au
List the metals which will
a occur 'native'
b react with dilute acids
c displace lead from lead(II) nitrate solution
d react with cold water
e react with steam.

Fig. 11.20 Mending the line. The thermit mixture is packed into a break in a railway line. The molten iron produced will fill the gap and weld the broken ends together

Fig. 11.21 A silver tree

11.6 Metals in the Periodic Table

The reactivity series (Table 11.5) is one way of classifying metals. You have already met another important classification, the Periodic Table of the elements (see Chapter 4).

You can see from Table 11.6 that it is possible to draw a line across the Periodic Table to separate the metallic elements from the non-metallic elements. The non-metallic elements, including chlorine, oxygen and the noble gases, are on the right-hand side of the line. The metallic elements are on the left-hand side of the line.

Table 3.2 summarises the differences between the physical properties of metallic and non-metallic elements. Table 11.7 summarises the differences between the chemical properties of metallic and non-metallic elements.

Table 11.6 The Periodic Table

| | | | | | | | | | | | | | | | | ← Metals → | | ← Non-metals → | | 0 |

1	2	H												3	4	5	6	7	He
Li	Be													B	C	N	O	F	Ne
Na	Mg				Transition metals									Al	Si	P	S	Cl	Ar
K	Ca	Sc	Ti	V	Cr	Mn	Fe	Co	Ni	Cu	Zn	Ga	Ge	As	Se	Br	Kr
Rb	Sr	Y	Zr	Nb	Mo	Tc	Ru	Rh	Pd	Ag	Cd	In	Sn	Sb	Te	I	Xe
Cs	Ba	La	Hf	Ta	W	Re	Os	Ir	Pt	Au	Hg	Ti	Pb	Bi	Po	At	Rn

(For symbols, see p. 411)

Table 11.5 A section of the reactivity series

Potassium	K
Sodium	Na
Lithium	Li
Calcium	Ca
Magnesium	Mg
Aluminium	Al
Zinc	Zn
Iron	Fe
Tin	Sn
Lead	Pb
Copper	Cu
Silver	Ag
Gold	Au
Platinum	Pt

Table 11.7 Chemical properties of metallic and non-metallic elements

Metallic elements	*Non-metallic elements*
1 Metals which are high in the reactivity series react with dilute acids to give hydrogen and a salt of the metal.	Non-metallic elements do not react with dilute acids.
2 Metallic elements form cations, e.g. Na^+, Mg^{2+}, Al^{3+}.	Non-metallic elements form anions, e.g. Cl^-, O^{2-}.
3 The oxides and hydroxides are bases (Section 7.3), e.g. Na_2O, CaO. If they dissolve in water, they give alkaline solutions, e.g. NaOH.	Many oxides are acids and dissolve in water to give acidic solutions, e.g. CO_2, SO_2. Some oxides are neutral and insoluble, e.g. CO.
4 The chlorides of metals are ionic crystalline solids, e.g. NaCl.	The chlorides of non-metals are covalent liquids or gases, e.g. HCl(g), CCl_4(l).

The alkali metals

The elements in Group 1 – lithium, sodium, potassium, rubidium and caesium – are all very reactive metals. They have strongly basic oxides and hydroxides of general formulae M_2O and MOH (where M is the symbol of the metallic element). The oxides and hydroxides dissolve in water to give strongly alkaline solutions. This characteristic gives the alkali metals their name. The reactivity of the alkali metals increases as you pass down the group.

The alkaline earths

The metals in Group 2 are less reactive than those in Group 1. They form basic oxides and hydroxides with the general formulae MO and $M(OH)_2$. Their oxides and hydroxides are either sparingly soluble or insoluble. These elements are called the **alkaline earths**. Their reactivity increases as you pass down the group.

The transition metals

The metals in the block between Group 2 and Group 3 are a set of similar metallic elements. They are less reactive than those in Groups 1 and 2. Their oxides and hydroxides are less strongly basic and are insoluble. These metals are called the **transition metals**.

Transition metals are hard and dense (e.g. iron). They are good conductors of heat and electricity (e.g. copper). They have higher melting points, boiling points and heats of melting than do Group 1 and Group 2 metals. All these properties indicate the strength of the metallic bond in transition metals. Iron, cobalt and nickel are strongly magnetic, and some of the other transition metals are weakly magnetic.

Transition metals are less reactive than those in Groups 1 and 2. They can be extracted from their ores by means of chemical reducing agents. Iron oxide is reduced to iron by carbon monoxide (see Section 11.9), and zinc oxide is reduced to zinc by carbon (see Section 11.9).

Transition metals show more than one valency (see Table 11.8). They have coloured ions, except for zinc (see Table 11.9). In addition to forming simple cations, transition metals form oxo-ions in combination with oxygen. Examples are:

- chromate(VI), CrO_4^{2-} (yellow)
- dichromate(VI), $Cr_2O_7^{2-}$ (orange)
- manganate(VII), MnO_4^- (purple)
- zincate, ZnO_2^{2-} (colourless).

Many transition metals and their compounds are important catalysts. Examples are:

- Iron and iron(III) oxide in the Haber process for making ammonia (Section 15.4)
- Platinum in the oxidation of ammonia during the manufacture of nitric acid (Section 15.5)
- Vanadium(V) oxide in the Contact process for making sulphuric acid (Section 14.6)
- Nickel in the hydrogenation of oils to form fats (Section 9.17).

Table 11.8 Some transition metal ions

Metal	Ions
Copper	Cu^+, Cu^{2+}
Iron	Fe^{2+}, Fe^{3+}
Cobalt	Co^{2+}, Co^{3+}
Chromium	Cr^{2+}, Cr^{3+}, $Cr_2O_7^{2-}$, CrO_4^{2-}
Manganese	Mn^{2+}, MnO_4^-

Table 11.9 Colours of transition metal ions

Copper(II) ions	Blue
Iron(II) ions	Green
Iron(III) ions	Rust-coloured
Nickel(II) ions	Green
Cobalt(II) ions	Pink

Metalloids

Silicon and germanium are on the borderline between metals and non-metals (see Table 11.6). They are **semiconductors** – they are intermediate between metals, which are electrical conductors, and non-metals, which are non-conductors of electricity. They are often called **metalloids**. As semiconductors, these elements are vital to the computer industry (see Section 3.4).

Career sketch: Medical laboratory technician

Fiona works in a medical laboratory. She analyses blood samples. She measures cholesterol levels and examines blood under a microscope to detect the presence of diseases. She makes cultures of body fluids to find out whether bacteria or other micro-organisms are present.

Fiona has A-levels in chemistry and biology. Senior people in the same laboratory have degrees in biochemistry.

Comparison of metals

Table 11.10 summarises the differences between alkali metals, alkaline earths and transition metals. (M stands for the symbol of a metallic element.)

Table 11.10 Some reactions of metals

	Reaction with air	Reaction with water	Reaction with dilute acids	Trend
Group 1 Lithium Sodium Potassium Rubidium Caesium	Burn vigorously to form the strongly basic oxide, M_2O	React vigorously to form hydrogen and a solution of the strong alkali, MOH	The reaction is dangerously violent	The vigour of all these reactions increases down the group
Group 2 Beryllium Magnesium Calcium Strontium Barium	All burn to form the strongly basic oxide, MO	Reacts very slowly Burns in steam React readily to form hydrogen and the alkali $M(OH)_2$	All react readily to give hydrogen and a salt, e.g. MCl_2	The vigour of all these reactions increases down the group
Transition metals Iron	When heated, all form oxides without burning	Rusts slowly, reacts with steam to form hydrogen and iron oxide	Reacts to give hydrogen and a salt	
Copper		Does not react	Does not react	

11.7 Uses of metals and alloys

We find plenty of uses for metals and alloys. Sometimes an industrialist wants a material to do a particular job and there is no metal or alloy which fits the bill. Then metallurgists set to work to invent a new alloy with the right characteristics. The uses of a metal are related to its physical properties and its position in the reactivity series. Table 11.11 gives some examples.

SUMMARY NOTE

The chemical reactions of metals and non-metallic elements are different. Many metals react with acids. Metals form cations. Their oxides are bases, and their chlorides are crystalline solids.

Table 11.11 What are metals and alloys used for?

Metal/Alloy	Characteristics	Uses
Aluminium (**Duralumin** is an important alloy)	Low density	Aircraft manufacture (Duralumin)
	Never corroded	Food wrapping
	Good electrical conductor	Electrical cable
	Good thermal conductor	Saucepans
	Reflector of light	Car headlamps
Brass (alloy of copper and zinc)	Not corroded	Ships' propellers
	Easy to work with	Taps, screws
	Sonorous	Trumpets
	Yellow colour	Ornaments
Bronze (alloy of copper and tin)	Harder than copper	Coins, medals
	Not corroded	Statues, springs
	Sonorous	Church bells
Copper	Good electrical conductor	Electrical circuits
	Not corroded	Water pipes and tanks
Gold	Beautiful colour	Jewellery
	Never tarnishes	Filling teeth
		Electrical contacts
Iron	Hard, strong	Construction, transport
	Inexpensive, rusts	See Tables 11.14 and 11.15
Lead	Dense	Protection from radioactivity
	Unreactive	Lead is no longer used for water pipes now that we know that it reacts very slowly with water.
Magnesium	Bright flame	Flares and flash bulbs
Mercury	Liquid at room temperature	Thermometers
		Electrical contacts
		Dental amalgam for filling teeth
Silver	Beautiful colour and shine	Jewellery
	Good electrical conductor (Tarnishes in city air)	Electrical contacts in telephones, computers etc.
	Good reflector of light	Mirrors
Sodium	High thermal capacity	Coolant in nuclear reactors
Solder (alloy of tin and lead)	Low melting point	Joining metals, e.g. in an electrical circuit

How many miles of copper wire are there in your school buildings?

Ten miles, would you believe?

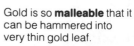

Gold is so **malleable** that it can be hammered into very thin gold leaf.

One cm³ of gold will make 10 square metres of gold leaf!

Steel (alloy of iron etc.)	Strong	See Tables 11.14 and 11.15
Tin	Low in reactivity series	Coating 'tin cans'
Zinc	High in reactivity series	Protection of iron and steel; see Table 11.16

11.8 Compounds and the reactivity series

How stable are metal oxides?

- The more reactive a metal is, the more readily it forms compounds.
- The more reactive a metal is, the more difficult it is to split up its compounds.

Copper is an unreactive metal. Copper(II) oxide is easily reduced to copper (reduction; see Section 9.18). Hydrogen will reduce hot copper(II) oxide to copper (see Experiment 10.7):

$$\text{copper(II) oxide} + \text{hydrogen} \xrightarrow{\text{heat}} \text{copper} + \text{water}$$
$$\text{CuO(s)} + \text{H}_2\text{(g)} \rightarrow \text{Cu(s)} + \text{H}_2\text{O(l)}$$

Carbon is another reducing agent. When heated, it will reduce the oxides of metals which are low in the reactivity series (see Experiment 10.14):

$$\text{lead(II) oxide} + \text{carbon} \xrightarrow{\text{heat}} \text{lead} + \text{carbon monoxide}$$
$$\text{PbO(s)} + \text{C(s)} \rightarrow \text{Pb(s)} + \text{CO(g)}$$

Metals which are low in the reactivity series are often obtained from their ores by reduction with carbon:

$$\text{zinc oxide} + \text{carbon} \xrightarrow{\text{heat}} \text{zinc} + \text{carbon monoxide}$$
$$\text{ZnO(s)} + \text{C(s)} \rightarrow \text{Zn(s)} + \text{CO(g)}$$

The oxides of metals which are high in the reactivity series are not reduced by hydrogen or carbon. Aluminium is high in the reactivity series; its oxide is difficult to reduce. The method used to obtain aluminium from aluminium oxide is electrolysis (see Section 11.12).

If a metal is very low in the reactivity series, its oxide will decompose when heated. The oxides of silver and mercury decompose when heated (see Fig. 3.10):

$$\text{mercury(II) oxide} \xrightarrow{\text{heat}} \text{mercury} + \text{oxygen}$$
$$\text{2HgO(s)} \rightarrow \text{2Hg(l)} + \text{O}_2\text{(g)}$$

The stability of other compounds

Some compounds are more **stable** than others. This means that they are more difficult to decompose (split up) by heat than others. Table 11.12 shows how the stability of the compounds of a metal ties in with the position of the metal in the reactivity series.

Why do they call titanium 'the aerospace metal'?

It's low in density. And it stays strong at the high and low temperatures that supersonic aircraft have to stand up to.

Table 11.12 Action of heat on compounds

Cation	Anion				
	Oxide	Chloride	Sulphate	Carbonate	Hydroxide
Potassium Sodium	No decomposition	No decomposition	No decomposition		
Calcium Magnesium Aluminium Zinc Iron Lead Copper			Oxide + sulphur trioxide, $MO + SO_3$	Oxide + carbon dioxide, $MO + CO_2$	Oxide + water, $MO + H_2O$
Silver Gold	Metal + oxygen		Metal + $O_2 + SO_3$	Metal + $O_2 + CO_2$	Metal + $O_2 + H_2O$

The sulphates and carbonates and hydroxides of the most reactive metals are not decomposed by heat. Those of other metals decompose to give oxides, e.g.

$$\text{calcium carbonate} \xrightarrow{\text{heat}} \text{calcium oxide} + \text{carbon dioxide}$$
$$CaCO_3(s) \xrightarrow{} CaO(s) + CO_2(g)$$

$$\text{copper(II) hydroxide} \xrightarrow{\text{heat}} \text{copper(II) oxide} + \text{water}$$
$$Cu(OH)_2(s) \xrightarrow{} CuO(s) + H_2O(l)$$

$$\text{lead(II) sulphate} \xrightarrow{\text{heat}} \text{lead(II) oxide} + \text{sulphur trioxide}$$
$$PbSO_4(s) \xrightarrow{} PbO(s) + SO_3(g)$$

SUMMARY NOTE

The oxides of the less reactive metals (e.g. Cu) are easily reduced (e.g. by carbon or hydrogen). The oxides of reactive metals at the top of the reactivity series are difficult to reduce.

Compounds of the less reactive metals (e.g. hydroxides, sulphates and carbonates) are decomposed by heat. Compounds of the very reactive metals do not undergo thermal decomposition.

11.9 Extraction of metals from their ores

Metals occur in rocks in the Earth's crust. Some metals, such as gold, occur as the free metal, uncombined. They are said to occur 'native'. This is unusual: only metals which are very unreactive can withstand the action of air and water for thousands of years without being converted into compounds. Most metals are mined as compounds.

The business of obtaining metals from deposits of their compounds is expensive. Rock containing the metal compound is mined. Lumps of rock are crushed and ground by heavy machinery. Then a chemical method must be found for extracting the metal. All these stages cost money. If the rock contains enough of the metal compound to make it pay to extract the metal, the rock is called an **ore**.

Fig. 11.22 Open-cast mining: the surface is removed in layers

The method used to extract a metal from its ore depends on the position of the metal in the reactivity series. The compounds of reactive metals are difficult to reduce to the metals. (See Table 11.13.)

Table 11.13 Methods used for the extraction of metals

Potassium Sodium Calcium Magnesium	The anhydrous chloride is melted and electrolysed.
Aluminium	The molten anhydrous oxide is electrolysed.
Zinc Iron Copper Lead	Found as sulphides and oxides. Sulphides are roasted to give oxides; oxides are reduced with carbon.
Silver Gold	Found 'native' (as the free metals).

Sodium

Sodium is mined as sodium chloride (rock salt) in Cheshire (see Section 16.1). Electrolysis is the method used to obtain sodium. Molten anhydrous sodium chloride (not brine, which is aqueous sodium chloride) is electrolysed to give sodium at the negative electrode and chlorine at the positive electrode.

Cathode: sodium ion + electron → sodium atom
$$Na^+(l) + e^- \rightarrow Na(s)$$

The electrolysis of the molten anhydrous chloride is used to obtain other reactive metals, e.g. potassium, calcium and magnesium. It is an expensive method of obtaining metals because of the cost of the electricity consumed.

Aluminium

Aluminium is mined as **bauxite**, an ore which contains aluminium oxide, $Al_2O_3 \cdot 2H_2O$. This ore is very plentiful, yet aluminium was not extracted from it until 1827. In 1886, a commercial method of obtaining aluminium was invented. First, anhydrous pure aluminium oxide is obtained from the ore. The oxide must be melted before it can be electrolysed. This is difficult because aluminium oxide melts at 2050 °C. The big breakthrough in 1886 came when Charles Martin Hall and Paul Héroult discovered that the electrolysis of aluminium oxide could be carried out in molten **cryolite**, Na_3AlF_6, at 700 °C. Their invention, the Hall–Héroult cell, is shown in Fig. 11.23.

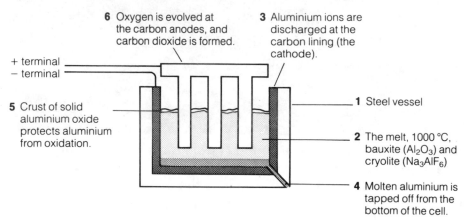

6 Oxygen is evolved at the carbon anodes, and carbon dioxide is formed.

3 Aluminium ions are discharged at the carbon lining (the cathode).

+ terminal
− terminal

5 Crust of solid aluminium oxide protects aluminium from oxidation.

1 Steel vessel

2 The melt, 1000 °C, bauxite (Al_2O_3) and cryolite (Na_3AlF_6)

4 Molten aluminium is tapped off from the bottom of the cell.

◁ Fig. 11.23 Electrolysis of aluminium oxide

Aluminium is the third commonest element in the Earth's crust, coming after oxygen and silicon (Fig. 11.24). It occurs mainly in clays. No economic method of extraction from clays has yet been found, although chemists are working on the problem.

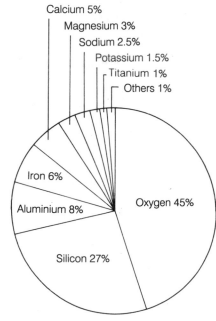

Calcium 5%
Magnesium 3%
Sodium 2.5%
Potassium 1.5%
Titanium 1%
Others 1%
Iron 6%
Aluminium 8%
Oxygen 45%
Silicon 27%

Fig. 11.24 Elements in the Earth's crust

Iron

Iron is mined as the oxides **haematite**, Fe_2O_3, and **magnetite**, Fe_3O_4, and as the sulphide **iron pyrites**, FeS_2. The sulphide ore is roasted in air to convert it into an oxide. The oxide ores are reduced to iron in a **blast furnace** (Fig. 11.25). A blast furnace is about 50 metres high. It is a tower made of steel plates and lined with heat-resisting bricks. It costs about £1 million. A blast of hot air is sent in near the bottom. Iron ore, coke and limestone are fed in at the top. Iron ores and limestone are plentiful resources. Coke is made by heating coal.

A number of chemical reactions take place in the blast furnace.

1 Coke burns in the blast of air at the bottom of the furnace. Carbon dioxide is formed:

$$\text{carbon (coke)} + \text{oxygen} \xrightarrow{\text{heat}} \text{carbon dioxide}$$
$$C(s) + O_2(g) \rightarrow CO_2(g)$$

2 Higher up the furnace, carbon dioxide reacts with coke to form carbon monoxide:

$$\text{carbon dioxide} + \text{carbon (coke)} \xrightarrow{\text{heat}} \text{carbon monoxide}$$
$$CO_2(g) + C(s) \rightarrow 2CO(g)$$

A load of iron oxide, limestone and coke is fed in. The small 'bell' lowers to let the load fall on to the large 'bell'. Then the large bell lowers to let the load fall into the furnace.

Exhaust gases

In the blast furnace, iron oxide is reduced to iron.

A hot blast of air enters through this circular pipe.

Molten slag is run off.

Molten iron is run off.

Fig. 11.25 A blast furnace

3 Carbon monoxide is the reducing agent in the blast furnace. It reduces iron oxides to iron:

$$\text{iron(III) oxide} + \text{carbon monoxide} \xrightarrow{\text{heat}} \text{iron} + \text{carbon dioxide}$$
$$\text{Fe}_2\text{O}_3(s) + 3\text{CO}(g) \rightarrow 2\text{Fe}(s) + 3\text{CO}_2(g)$$

As a result, molten iron trickles to the bottom of the furnace.

4 Limestone decomposes in the blast furnace:

$$\begin{matrix}\text{calcium carbonate} \\ \text{(limestone)}\end{matrix} \xrightarrow{\text{heat}} \text{calcium oxide} + \text{carbon dioxide}$$
$$\text{CaCO}_3(s) \rightarrow \text{CaO}(s) + \text{CO}_2(g)$$

The calcium oxide produced combines with acidic impurities, e.g. silicon(IV) oxide (sand), SiO_2, in the iron ore. A molten mixture of compounds called a **slag** is formed:

$$\text{calcium oxide} + \begin{matrix}\text{silicon(IV) oxide} \\ \text{(sand)}\end{matrix} \xrightarrow{\text{heat}} \begin{matrix}\text{calcium silicate} \\ \text{(slag)}\end{matrix}$$
$$\text{CaO}(s) + \text{SiO}_2(s) \rightarrow \text{CaSiO}_3(l)$$

The process runs continuously. The raw materials are fed in at the top, and molten iron and molten slag are run off separately at the bottom. The slag goes to builders and road-makers, who use it to lay foundations. The process is much cheaper to run than an electrolytic method. The availability of the raw materials and the low cost of extraction make iron cheaper than other metals.

Copper

Copper is far down the reactivity series. It is found 'native' (uncombined) in some parts of the world. It is also mined as the sulphide. This is roasted in air to give impure copper. Pure copper is obtained from this by the electrolytic method shown in Figs. 11.26 and 11.27.

Flow of electrons

2 The negative electrode is a strip of pure copper. Copper ions are discharged:

$$Cu^{2+}(aq) + 2e^- \rightarrow Cu(s)$$

The strip of pure copper becomes thicker.

1 The electrolyte is copper(II) sulphate solution.

3 The positive electrode is a lump of impure copper. When a current flows, this electrode takes electrons from copper atoms. These go into solution as copper ions:

$$Cu(s) \rightarrow Cu^{2+}(aq) + 2e^-$$

The electrons flow through the external circuit from the positive electrode to the negative electrode.

4 Anode sludge

Fig. 11.26 Purifying copper by electrolysis

Fig. 11.27 'Electrowinning' of copper

After the cell has operated for a week, the negative electrode becomes very thick. It is lifted out of the cell, and a new thin sheet of copper is put in its place. When all the copper has been removed from the impure slab of metal which forms the positive electrode (the anode), a new piece of impure copper is substituted. Undissolved matter from the old anode lies on the bottom of the cell as **anode sludge**.

Any impurities in the copper are likely to be metals such as iron and zinc, which are more reactive than copper. Their ions stay in solution while copper ions are discharged. Metals which are less reactive than copper, that is, silver and gold, accumulate in the anode sludge. They can be extracted from this material.

Silver and gold

The unreactive metals, silver and gold, are found 'native'. Figure 11.28 shows a prospector 'panning' for gold in Northern Ireland, where a new deposit was discovered in 1982.

JUST TESTING 60

1 Refer to the electrolytic method of purifying copper in Fig. 11.26.
  Impure copper contains other metals, such as iron. Why do iron ions remain in solution while copper ions are discharged?
  Write the equations for the processes which occur at the electrodes. (See Section 5.10 for help.)

Fig. 11.28 Panning for gold

2 Why has the human race been using copper, silver and gold for longer than other metals?

3 Suggest what A, B, C and D might be.
A is a metal which reacts violently with water to form an alkaline solution.
B is a metal which does not react with steam or with dilute hydrochloric acid.
C is a metal which, when exposed to air, immediately becomes coated with a layer of oxide.
D is a metal which is easily worked and which reacts only very very slowly with water.

4 Copy and complete the following equations. Be careful! Some of the suggested reactions do not happen. In these cases write 'no reaction'.
a calcium + dilute hydrochloric acid →
b copper + dilute sulphuric acid →
c copper + oxygen →
d gold + dilute sulphuric acid →
e aluminium + iron(III) oxide →
f tin + iron(III) oxide →
g carbon monoxide + iron(III) oxide →
h carbon monoxide + aluminium oxide →
i zinc + copper(II) sulphate solution →
j lead + dilute sulphuric acid →

Magnesium

The oceans are a vast reserve of magnesium compounds. The percentage of magnesium in sea water is 0.14%. Figure 11.29 illustrates the Dow process for extracting magnesium from sea water.

How much magnesium can you get from a cubic kilometre of sea water?

About one million million million million tonnes of magnesium!

Sea water

Solution of Ca(OH)$_2$(aq) ⟶ Precipitate of Mg(OH)$_2$(s)
(Magnesium is the only common ion in sea water that forms an insoluble hydroxide.)

Hydrochloric acid ⟶ The precipitate is filtered and dissolved in HCl(aq) as MgCl$_2$(aq).

The solution is evaporated to give MgCl$_2$(s).

Magnesium + chlorine ⟵ The MgCl$_2$(s) is melted and electrolysed.

Fig. 11.29 The Dow process: magnesium from sea water

Zinc

Zinc is found chiefly as the sulphide, ZnS, **zinc blende**, and as the carbonate, $ZnCO_3$, **calamine** (also called **smithsonite**). These ores are converted into zinc oxide which can be reduced to zinc. The four steps in the process are as follows.

1 *Concentration.* The ore is concentrated by **froth flotation**. Powdered ore is tipped into a vat of water. A stream of air causes the mixture to foam. The foam carries small particles of ore to the surface. Froth is allowed to overflow from the vat, and powdered ore is collected from it. Waste rock falls to the bottom of the vat.

2 *Roasting.* The zinc ore is roasted in air. This converts both the carbonate and the sulphide into zinc oxide.

zinc carbonate → zinc oxide + carbon dioxide
$$ZnCO_3(s) \rightarrow ZnO(s) + CO_2(g)$$

zinc sulphide + oxygen → zinc oxide + sulphur dioxide
$$2ZnS(s) + 2O_2(g) \rightarrow 2ZnO(s) + 2SO_2(g)$$

3 *Reduction.* The oxide is heated with powdered carbon (as coke or coal).

zinc oxide + carbon → zinc + carbon monoxide
$$ZnO(s) + C(s) \rightarrow Zn(s) + CO(g)$$

4 *Purification.* Zinc is usually purified by distillation. Alternatively, it is converted into zinc sulphate which is electrolysed.

Tin

Tin is mined as the ore SnO_2, **cassiterite** or **tinstone**. The extraction of tin involves the following four steps.

1 *Washing.* The ore is pulverised and washed with water so that particles of less dense materials float away.

2 *Roasting.* This removes sulphur and arsenic as volatile oxides.

3 *Reduction.* The ore is heated with anthracite (carbon). Limestone is added to produce a slag with the impurities.

tin(IV) oxide + carbon → tin + carbon monoxide
$$SnO_2(s) + 2C(s) \rightarrow Sn(s) + 2CO(g)$$

4 *Purification.* The impure tin is heated just enough to melt it and poured off from a solid residue. This residue contains iron and other metals which have higher melting points.

Lead

Lead is found chiefly as the sulphide PbS, **galena**. The metal is extracted as follows.

1 *Roasting of galena.*

lead(II) sulphide + oxygen → lead(II) oxide + sulphur dioxide
$$2PbS(s) + 3O_2(g) \rightarrow 2PbO(s) + 2SO_2(g)$$

2 *Reduction of lead(II) oxide by coke.*

lead(II) oxide + coke → lead + carbon monoxide
$$PbO(s) + C(s) \rightarrow Pb(s) + CO(g)$$

3 *Purification.* The metal is treated by a process that removes copper, silver and other metals.

SUMMARY NOTE

Magnesium can be extracted from sea water because it forms an insoluble hydroxide.
Zinc is mined as the sulphide and the carbonate. These are roasted to form the oxide, which is reduced by carbon.
Tin is mined as the oxide which is reduced by carbon.
Lead is mined as lead sulphide. This is roasted to form lead oxide, which is reduced by carbon.

JUST TESTING 61

1 a What is the source of the calcium hydroxide used in the precipitation of magnesium from sea water?
  b What other product is formed? What can this product be used for?
2 a Suggest a use for the sulphur dioxide produced by roasting zinc blende.
  b When zinc sulphate is electrolysed, what is discharged at the anode? What change takes place in the nature of the electrolyte? What use can be made of the changed electrolyte in the purification process?
3 Limestone is added in the reduction of tin(IV) oxide to form a slag with the impurities. Silicon(IV) oxide, SiO_2, is one of these. Explain how a slag is formed.

11.10 Focus on iron and steel

The iron that comes out of the blast furnace is called **pig iron** or **cast iron** (see Section 11.1). It contains 3% to 4% carbon. The carbon content lowers the melting point and makes cast iron easier to melt and mould than pure iron. Cast iron expands slightly as it solidifies. This makes it flow into all the corners of a mould and reproduce the shape exactly. By casting, objects with complicated shapes can be made, e.g. engine blocks (see Fig. 11.1).

The carbon atoms in cast iron interfere with the metallic bonding (see Section 11.2) and make the metal brittle. Cast iron cannot be bent without snapping. It cannot be used for the bodywork of a car (Fig. 11.1).

Iron which contains less than 0.25% carbon is called **wrought iron**. Wrought iron is tough, is easily worked and resists corrosion well (Fig. 11.30). Ornamental gates and horse shoes used to be made from wrought iron. Nowadays, mild steel is used.

Steel

The high carbon content of cast iron makes it brittle. Fortunately, carbon can be burnt off as its oxides, the gases carbon monoxide, CO, and carbon dioxide, CO_2. Iron is less easily oxidised. Other impurities (e.g. sulphur, phosphorus and silicon) are also converted into acidic oxides. These are not gases, and something must be added to remove them. A base, such as calcium oxide, will do this. It combines with acidic oxides to form a mixture of compounds of

Fig. 11.30 Cannon from the Mary Rose: the cannon is made of bronze

Fig. 11.31 A basic oxygen furnace holding 150–300 tonnes of steel

low melting point called a **slag**. When the percentage of carbon is less than 1%, the iron–carbon alloy is a **steel**. Other elements may be alloyed with steel to give alloys with different properties.

Figure 11.31 shows a **basic oxygen furnace**. In it, cast iron is converted into steel. One converter can produce 150–300 tonnes of steel in an hour.

There are various types of steel. They differ in their carbon content and are used for different purposes.

Table 11.14 Cast iron and types of steel and their uses

Type of steel	Properties	Uses
Mild steel (<0.25% carbon)	Pliable (can be bent without breaking).	Chains and pylons
Medium steel (0.25–0.45% carbon)	Tougher than mild steel, more springy than high carbon steel	Nuts and bolts Car springs and axles Bridges
High carbon steel (0.45–1.5% carbon)	The carbon content makes it both tough and brittle.	Chisels, files, razor blades, saws, cutting tools
Cast iron (2.5–4.5% carbon)	Cheaper than steel, easily moulded into complicated shapes	Drain pipes, fire grates, engine blocks (these articles will break if they are hammered or dropped)

Alloy steels

Metallurgists are constantly designing new alloys suited to different uses. Many elements are used for alloying with steel. The different alloy steels have different properties which fit them for different uses.

Table 11.15 Different alloy steels

Element	Properties of alloy	Uses
Chromium	Prevents rusting if > 10%.	Stainless steels, acid-resisting steels, cutlery, car accessories, tools
Cobalt	Takes a sharp cutting edge. Can be strongly magnetised.	High-speed cutting tools Permanent magnets
Manganese	Increases strength and toughness.	Some is used in all steels; steel in railway points and safes contains a high percentage of manganese.
Molybdenum	Strong even at high temperatures	Rifle barrels, propeller shafts
Nickel	Resists heat and acids.	Stainless steel cutlery, industrial plants which must withstand acidic conditions
Tungsten	Stays hard and tough at high temperatures.	High-speed cutting tools
Vanadium	Increases springiness.	Springs, machinery

Figure 11.32 illustrates the relationship between iron and steel.

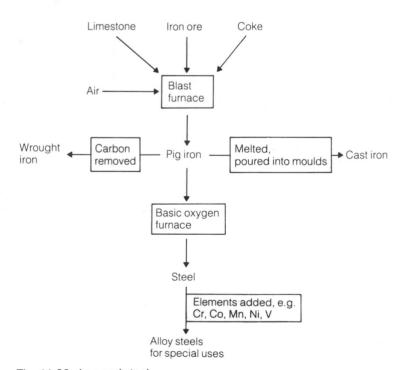

Fig. 11.32 Iron and steel

SUMMARY NOTE

- Cast iron contains up to 4% carbon. It is easy to mould, but it is brittle.
- Wrought iron is the purest form of iron. It is easily worked without breaking.
- Steels contain carbon. Mild (low carbon) steel is pliable; high carbon steel is hard; medium steel is intermediate. The steels are suited to different uses.
- Alloy steels contain other elements. The other elements are added to give a steel with the right characteristics for a particular job. You should know a few examples of steels and their uses.

11.11 Rusting of iron and steel

Experiments 8.2, 8.3, 10.9 and 10.10 will introduce you to this topic. Iron and steel rust. Rust is hydrated iron(III) oxide, $Fe_2O_3 \cdot nH_2O$. The number n of water molecules in the formula varies. The conditions iron needs to rust are water and air and acidity. (See Fig. 11.33 and Question **8** of Just Testing 63.) The carbon dioxide present in air provides sufficient acidity. The presence of salts increases the speed at which iron rusts.

The rusting of iron is a serious problem. Replacing rusted iron and steel structures costs the UK £500 million a year. Car engines have a very long life, but the average British car lasts only ten years.

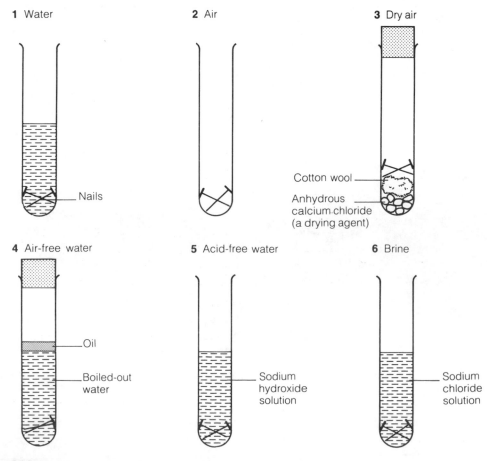

Fig. 11.33 Experiments on rusting

218

Table 11.16 Rust prevention

Method	Where it is used	Comment
1 A coat of paint	Large objects, e.g. ships and bridges	If the paint is scratched, the iron beneath it starts to rust. Corrosion can spread under parts of the paintwork which are still sound.
2 A film of oil or grease	Moving parts of machinery, e.g. a bicycle chain	The protective film must be renewed.
3 A coat of metal		
Chromium plating	Car bumpers, cycle handlebars	Applied by electroplating (see Chapter 5). Gives a decorative finish as well as protection.
Galvanising (zinc plating)	Galvanised steel girders are used in the construction of buildings and bridges.	Even if the layer of zinc is scratched, the iron underneath does not rust. Zinc is above iron in the reactivity series: as long as some zinc remains, zinc will corrode in preference to iron.
Tin plating	Food cans	Steel cans are coated with tin by electroplating them or by dipping them into molten tin. Tin is below iron in the reactivity series. If the layer of tin is scratched, the iron beneath it rusts. Zinc cannot be used for food cans because zinc and its compounds are poisonous.
4 Stainless steel	Cutlery, car accessories (e.g. radiator grilles)	Steels containing chromium (10%–25%) or nickel (10%–20%) do not rust.
5 Sacrificial protection	Ships	Bars of zinc are attached to the hull of the ship. Being above iron in the reactivity series, zinc is corroded. As long as the zinc bars remain, they protect the ship from rusting. When they have corroded, they must be replaced.
	Underground pipes	Bags of magnesium scrap are attached to underground pipes. Magnesium corrodes in preference to the pipes. From time to time, the magnesium must be replaced.

Corrosion of the bodywork is the factor that limits the life of the car. Table 11.16 lists some of the methods which are used to protect iron and steel against rusting. Some of them use a protective coating to exclude water and air, while others work by sacrificing a more reactive metal.

The Earth contains vast deposits of metal ores. During the twentieth century we have used more metal than in all the previous centuries together. We need our machinery and our means of transport. The Earth's resources are not inexhaustible. If we keep on mining iron ore and allowing tonnes of iron and steel to rust every year, we may one day run short of iron. We throw tonnes of used iron and steel objects on the scrap heap (Fig. 11.34). It makes better sense to collect scrap iron and steel and recycle it, that is, melt it down and re-use it.

SUMMARY NOTE

Iron and steel rust when exposed to air and water in slightly acidic conditions. Many different treatments are used to protect iron and steel from rusting:
- a protective coat of oil or grease or another metal (e.g. chromium, zinc or tin)
- alloying with nickel and chromium
- the sacrifice of a more reactive metal (e.g. magnesium or zinc).

Fig. 11.34 Car dump

JUST TESTING 63

1 In what ways is steel better than iron?
   What chemical reaction occurs when iron is converted into steel?
   Briefly describe one industrial method of converting iron into steel.

2 What are **a** cast iron, **b** wrought iron, **c** steel?
   Give one use for each metal.

3 Describe how the rusting of iron is prevented
   a on the moving parts of a bicycle
   b on a food can
   c on parts of a ship above the water-line
   d on parts of a ship below the water-line.

4 Galvanised iron is used for roofing. Explain why this is a weatherproof material.

5 Why did the Bronze Age come before the Iron Age? Give two examples of things which were made during the Industrial Revolution and which needed iron or steel for their manufacture.

6 Cars are spray painted. The paint reaches some areas more easily than others. On which parts of a car body is the paint layer likely to be thinnest? Which parts of a car body are the most likely to be affected by the salt that is spread on roads in winter?

*7 A number of metals are used in making a car. A solution of salt is an electrolyte. What happens when two different metals are in contact with an electrolyte solution? (See Section 5.11 if you need help.)

8 Refer to Fig. 11.33.
  a In which tubes do the iron nails rust?
  b Explain the difference between tubes 2 and 3. Are the times taken for the nails to rust different?
  c What has been boiled out of the water in tube 4? What does the layer of oil do?
  d The nails in tube 5 do not rust. What does this show about rusting?
  e Why is experiment 6 important? Where does iron come into contact with sodium chloride solution?

11.12 Focus on aluminium

Uses of aluminium

Aluminium is a versatile metal with thousands of applications. It is not a very strong metal. Its alloys, such as duralumin (which contains copper and magnesium), are used when strength is needed (see Table 11.17).

The Audi A8, unveiled at the 1994 Geneva Motor Show, has a lightweight aluminium body, giving improved performance and reduced fuel consumption. The 'space frame' provides a safety cage and the passenger cell is more rigid than that of steel-bodied cars. The 2.8 litre V6 engine accelerates the car from 0 to 100 km/h in 9.1 seconds.

Fig 11.35 The Audi A8

Table 11.17 Some uses of aluminium and its alloys

Property	Use for aluminium which depends on this property
1 Low density	Aircraft manufacture: the alloy **duralumin** is used because it is stronger than aluminium.
2 Good electrical conductor	Used for overhead cables. It is replacing copper because cables of aluminium are lighter and need less massive pylons to carry them.
3 Never corroded (except by bases)	Door-frames and window-frames are often made of aluminium. **Anodised aluminium** is used. The thickness of the protective layer of aluminium oxide has been increased by **anodising** (see Experiment 5.10).
4 Non-toxic	Packaging food: milk bottle tops, cases for frozen foods etc., baking foil
5 Reflects light when polished	Car headlamp reflectors
6 Good thermal conductor	Saucepans etc.
7 When highly polished, insulates by reflecting heat	Aluminium can also be used as a thermal insulator. It reflects heat when it is highly polished. Aluminium blankets are used to wrap premature babies. They keep the baby warm by reflecting heat back to the body. Firefighters wear aluminium fabric suits to reflect heat away from their bodies.

Aluminium wire can be pulled out *really* fine. Guess how much aluminium you'd need to make a wire that would go right round the world!

Only 10 kilograms. Am I right?

Some problems

Bauxite is found near the surface in Australia, Guinea, Brazil and other countries. It is extracted by open-cast mining (Fig. 11.36). A surface layer 1 m to 60 m thick is excavated, and an ugly scar is left on the landscape. In some places, mining companies have taken measures to restore the landscape after a mine has been exhausted.

Often bauxite is converted into pure aluminium oxide at the mine. An impurity which is always found in bauxite is iron(III) oxide, which is red. After it has been separated from the ore, iron(III) oxide is pumped into vast ponds which become the unsightly **red mud ponds**. Near Quebec in Canada is a vast area (many square kilometres) of red mud ponds. The mud cannot be pumped into the sea because it would harm the fish.

After purification, aluminium oxide is shipped to an aluminium **smelter** (a plant for extracting aluminium). The high consumption of electricity makes the electrolytic method of obtaining aluminium expensive. Aluminium smelters are often built in areas which have **hydroelectric power** (electricity from water-driven generators). This is relatively cheap electricity. Waterfalls and fast-flowing rivers provide hydroelectric power. They are found in areas of outstanding

Fig. 11.36 Open-cast mining for bauxite

SUMMARY NOTE

Aluminium is a metal with a multitude of uses. With its low density and its resistance to corrosion, it has advantages over other metals.

Both the mining and the smelting of aluminium create environmental problems. Open-cast mines and red mud pools spoil the landscape. Fluoride emission has harmed cattle.

Before a decision is made on a site for a new aluminium smelter, various factors are weighed up. They include
- the cost of electricity
- transport costs
- the availability of a workforce.

natural beauty, such as the highlands of Scotland and Norwegian fiords. Conservationists often object to the siting of aluminium smelters in such beauty spots.

Sometimes there are other objections. There is the cost of carrying ore to a remote area and then transporting aluminium away for sale. There is the problem of either finding a workforce locally or bringing workers into the area and providing housing. It is often more cost-effective to build an aluminium plant in an area which has a bigger population and better transport, and to pay more for electricity from a coal-fired power station.

The exhaust gases from aluminium smelters are 'scrubbed' with water. The waste water contains fluoride from the electrolyte. It is discharged into rivers. The remaining exhaust gases are discharged into the atmosphere through tall chimneys. Fluoride emissions have been known to kill grass and cause tooth decay and lameness in cattle. In the past, farmers in the USA successfully sued aluminium smelters for damage to their cattle. Smelters now take more care to control fluoride emission. Chemists are working on the possibility of replacing the fluoride in the electrolysis cell with a chloride.

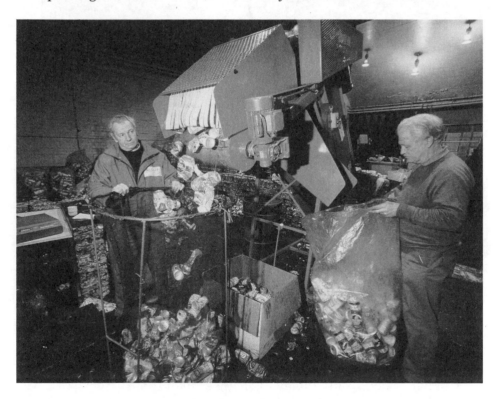

Fig. 11.37 Sorting steel and aluminium cans for recycling

JUST TESTING 64

1 The needs of an aluminium plant are
  - raw materials, purified bauxite and cryolite imported by sea
  - electric power (from coal-fired or gas-fired or hydroelectric power stations)
  - transport to bring raw materials to the site and take away the product by rail and sea
  - a workforce.

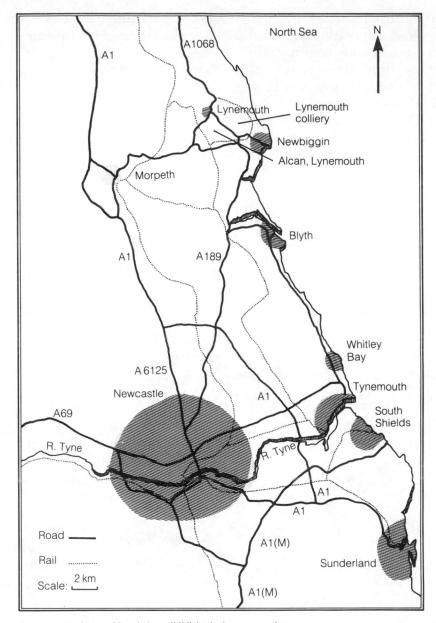

Fig. 11.38 Alcan Aluminium (UK) Ltd., Lynemouth

Study the map in Fig. 11.38. Explain how the choice of the Lynemouth site satisfies these needs.

2 Why was aluminium smelting carried out at Niagara Falls? What is the disadvantage of siting a plant there?

3 Emperor Napoleon III gave money to finance research on the extraction of aluminium. He was interested in the possibility of aluminium armour for his troops. What advantages over iron would aluminium have for armour?

4 Copy this passage, and fill in the gaps.
Aluminium is extracted from the ore _____. The ore is purified by removing _____, which is pumped away to form ugly _____. After purification, _____ aluminium oxide is dissolved in molten _____ and electrolysed. The electrodes are made of _____. Aluminium is deposited at the _____. At the other electrode, _____ is formed.

Some of this reacts with the electrode to form the gas _____. The exhaust gas from an aluminium smelter is scrubbed to remove the pollutant _____. This pollutant is discharged into _____.

*5 Find the percentage of aluminium in bauxite, $Al_2O_3 \cdot 2H_2O$ (after studying Chapter 12).

6 What advantages does aluminium have over steel? Give three examples of objects which are made from aluminium. Point out why aluminium is chosen for their manufacture.

11.13 Some problems metallurgists have solved

Which metal can be used as the filament in an electric light bulb?

The filament of an electric light bulb glows when it is heated. The filament must be made of metal because metals are the only good electrical conductors. Cost is not of great importance in selecting a metal for the job because the mass of metal needed is small. The colour of light emitted depends on the temperature: at 2500 °C, white light is emitted. To heat the filament to this temperature, an electric current is passed through it. More heat is generated when an electric current passes through a thin wire than through a thick wire. A thin filament must be used.

The filament metal must fit this description:
● It must not melt or evaporate at 2500 °C.
● It must be able to withstand the thermal shock of being switched on and off.
● It must not break when it is drawn into very fine wire: it must be ductile.

The only metal which combines the properties of high melting point (3410 °C) and high ductility is tungsten.

If tungsten came into contact with air at 2500 °C, it would burn. The filament is therefore enclosed in a glass bulb filled with a noble gas, usually argon (Fig. 11.39).

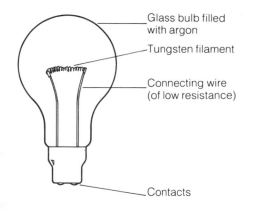

Glass bulb filled with argon
Tungsten filament
Connecting wire (of low resistance)
Contacts

Fig. 11.39 An electric light bulb

Which metal can be used as the 'element' in an electric fire?

Heat is radiated by a wire glowing red hot at 800 °C. The wire must have a high resistance if it is to give out much heat when an electric current is passed through it. It must not be oxidised in air at 800 °C. An alloy of nickel and chromium (80% Ni, 20% Cr) is used. It can operate at the working temperature without melting or becoming deformed or corroded.

The wire for the 'element' is wound on a ceramic rod. Ceramics are thermal and electrical insulators. A reflecting surface is placed behind the element. Stainless steel is used for this purpose. It can be polished to give a shiny surface, and it does not tarnish (Fig. 11.40).

Guard (could be chromium-plated steel)
Curved reflecting surface
'Nichrome' wire (nickel–chromium alloy)
Ceramic rod

Fig. 11.40 An electric fire

Which metal can be used for water pipes?

Water pipes are needed in such large quantities that they must be made from a reasonably inexpensive material. The material must be strong and hard wearing. It must be easily worked when the pipes are being installed and during later repairs. Only metals have the strength and the ease of working needed for the purpose. It is essential that the metal used does not become corroded by constant contact with water, and that it is completely non-toxic. The metals available in quantity are iron, copper, lead, aluminium and stainless steel.

Lead is easy to work, even when cold. It was the traditional metal to use for water pipes. It gave its name to plumbing (plumbum = lead in Latin; plwm = lead in Welsh). Over a period of many years, lead reacts very slowly with water to form lead compounds. These are poisonous, and lead is no longer used for water pipes.

Copper is the next easiest metal to work with at room temperature. Joints are easy to make by soldering.

Stainless steel pipes are an alternative. Joining stainless steel pipes is more difficult. Stainless steel contains chromium. A layer of chromium oxide forms on the surface of the metal. This layer protects the metal beneath it from attack by air or water. It does, however, make soldering difficult. The oxide layer must be removed before a soldered joint can be made. A **flux**, containing phosphoric acid, is used to remove the chromium oxide so that the metal beneath it can alloy with the solder, and soldered joints can be made.

Aluminium also has a surface film of the oxide. This layer of oxide must be removed before the metal can alloy with solder. It is more difficult to remove the surface layer from aluminium than from stainless steel.

Stainless steel and copper are the main choices for water pipes.

Mild steel pipes are used in central heating radiators. They are less expensive than stainless steel. The same water circulates round and round through the pipes and radiators. A layer of calcium carbonate forms inside the pipes and radiators (see Section 9.13 on hard water). This layer protects the mild steel pipes from attack by water. Mild steel cannot be used for hot water tanks because the water is constantly being changed.

Cast iron is used for the large diameter pipes needed for water mains. These pipes must be very strong to withstand changes in the pressure of the ground around them.

Exercise 11

1 Which of the following are electrical conductors?
sulphur, iron, zinc, mercury, charcoal, steel, diamond, copper, brass, graphite.

2 Name
   a a metal which is liquid at room temperature
   b a metal widely used in electrical wiring
   c a metal which is soft enough to leave marks on paper
   d a metal used for reflecting light
   e a metal used in aircraft construction
   f a metal which is alloyed to form solder
   g the metal present in both brass and bronze
   h the metal other than tin in 'tin' cans.

3 Name two gases which react with heated magnesium to give magnesium oxide. Write word equations for the reactions.
  *Write chemical equations.

4 Explain why silver is found 'native', but calcium is found as its compounds.

5 The following is a list of metals in order of decreasing reactivity. **X** and **Y** are two unknown metals:
K **X** Ca Mg Al Zn **Y** Fe Cu
  a Will **X** react with cold water?
  b Will **Y** react with cold water?
  c Will **Y** react with dilute hydrochloric acid? Explain how you arrive at your answers.
  d What reaction would you expect between **Y** and copper(II) sulphate solution?
  e Which is more easily decomposed, **X** sulphate or **Y** sulphate?

6 Here are the characteristics of three types of solder:
Solder 1: 40% lead, 60% tin, melts at 180 °C
Solder 2: 70% lead, 30% tin, melts at 80–260 °C
Solder 3: 5% tin, melts at 310 °C
Which solder would you use for each of the following jobs? Explain your choice.
  a Filling a gap in a car body (after removing rust, before repainting)
  b Mending a leaking car radiator
  c Joining wires in an electric circuit.

7 Look at the following pairs of chemicals. If a reaction happens, copy the word equation and complete the right-hand side.
  a carbon + lead(II) oxide →
  b hydrogen + calcium oxide →
  c aluminium + tin(II) oxide →
  d magnesium + sulphuric acid →
  e carbon + magnesium oxide →
  f hydrogen + potassium oxide →
  g carbon monoxide + iron(III) oxide →
  h carbon monoxide + aluminium oxide →
  i lead + sulphuric acid →
  j copper + zinc sulphate →

*8 Look at the following pairs of chemicals. If a reaction takes place, copy the equation and complete the right-hand side. Balance the equation.
  a $C(s) + CuO(s) \rightarrow$
  b $Al(s) + PbO(s) \rightarrow$
  c $Au(s) + O_2(g) \rightarrow$
  d $H_2(g) + Ag_2O(s) \rightarrow$
  e $CO(g) + Fe_2O_3(s) \rightarrow$
  f $Ca(s) + HCl(aq) \rightarrow$
  g $Zn(s) + CuSO_4(aq) \rightarrow$
  h $Cu(s) + H_2SO_4(aq) \rightarrow$
  i $Na(s) + O_2(g) \rightarrow$
  j $Cu(s) + O_2(g) \rightarrow$
  k $Pb(s) + CuSO_4(aq) \rightarrow$
  l $Al(s) + CaO(s) \rightarrow$

9 Aluminium is obtained by electrolysing aluminium oxide dissolved in molten cryolite at 700 °C. Carbon electrodes are used.
  a At which electrode is aluminium discharged?
  b What is discharged at the other electrode?
  c Why are carbon electrodes used? Why are they gradually eaten away?
  d When a solution of an aluminium salt is electrolysed, aluminium is not obtained. Why is this? What is formed?
  e Where would you expect an aluminium refinery to be situated?
  *f Write the equations for the electrode processes in **a** and **b**.

*10 For centuries, alchemists tried to change other metals into gold. Why did they value gold more than other metals? If the alchemists had succeeded, and gold were a cheap metal, what uses do you think we would make of gold today? For what purposes is gold unsuitable?
(Density = 19.3 g/cm³; m.p. = 1063 °C)

11 From which metal is each of the following objects made? Explain why that metal is chosen.
a a kettle, **b** telephone wire, **c** a post box, **d** a pen nib, **e** a horse shoe, **f** a church bell, **g** a trumpet, **h** baking foil, **i** a ship's propeller.

12 Aluminium is used for the manufacture of **a** saucepans, **b** overhead cables, **c** small boats, **d** aeroplanes, **e** hospital blankets. Explain what physical property of aluminium makes it suitable for each of these uses.

13 a • The thermit reaction shows that aluminium is a reactive metal.
  • Aluminium is used for door-frames and window-frames.
How can both these statements be true?
  b • Aluminium conducts heat.
  • Aluminium is used as a thermal insulator.
How can both these statements be true?

14 a Aluminium oxide is a common mineral. Seven thousand years elapsed between the discovery of copper and the day when aluminium was first seen. What was the reason for this gap in time?

b Explain why recycling aluminium is easier than recycling scrap iron.

15 Draw a blast furnace. Name the raw materials used in it. Name the two substances produced.

16 Explain how steel is made from cast iron. What advantages does steel have over cast iron? Draw a diagram of the process used to convert cast iron into steel.

17 Explain how rusting is prevented by **a** galvanising, **b** tin plating, **c** sacrificial protection, **d** painting.

18 Explain why
a saucepans are made from aluminium
b aeroplanes are made from aluminium alloys
c bells are made from bronze
d bridges are made from steel
e solder is made from lead
f dental amalgams are made from mercury
g teeth can be capped with gold caps.

19 Write short notes to explain the meanings of the following words:

a element, **b** malleable, **c** ductile, **d** abundant, **e** alloy.

20 a Copy this table. In the gaps write a tick if a chemical reaction occurs and a cross if no reaction happens.

Metal	Reaction with cold water	Reaction with hot water	Reaction with dilute hydrochloric acid
Sodium			
Zinc			
Magnesium			
Tin			
Calcium			
Copper			

b Write a list of the metals in order of increasing reactivity.

21 The map below shows Port Talbot and its surroundings. Explain why a big iron and steel industry developed here. List the needs of the industry, and explain how Port Talbot meets these needs.

*22 Some of the metals and alloys used in spacecraft are listed below.

Metal	Density in g/cm³	Melting point in °C	Useful properties
Stainless steel	7.8	1400	Very strong
Aluminium	2.7	660	Resists corrosion. Can be strengthened by alloying
Beryllium	1.8	1280	Keeps its strength at high and low temperatures
Duralumin	2.8	600	Hard and strong
Gold	19.3	1060	Highly reflecting. Very malleable
Magnesium	1.7	650	Strong
Titanium	4.5	1670	Keeps its strength at high and low temperatures

a A Skylark research rocket is made of stainless steel and duralumin. Explain why these metals are chosen.

b A satellite carries sensitive electronic equipment. Very high temperatures could damage this equipment. The danger is avoided by covering the satellite with metal foil. Which metal do you think is used? How does it avoid high temperatures inside the satellite?

c Military aircraft reach speeds higher than that of Concorde. The engine must withstand high temperatures without being deformed. Which metal or metals in the list could be used?

d Space rockets are jet-propelled. The fuel burns to form a stream of gas at high temperature and high pressure, which passes out of a nozzle. Fuel does not burn continuously; the nozzle experiences the low temperature of space alternating with the high temperature of the exhaust gases. The metal chosen for a space rocket motor must also be of low density and high melting point. Which of the metals listed is suitable?

e The chief structural material in the Prospero spacecraft is magnesium. The exterior panels are made of glass-reinforced plastics. What is the chief advantage of magnesium over the other metals listed? Magnesium is chosen for satellites which have to orbit the Earth for many years because it can withstand irradiation by cosmic rays. What kind of space vehicle could *not* be made of magnesium? Why?

Career sketch: Food scientist

Kirstie took a degree in biochemistry last year. Now she is a member of a team which has developed a new source of protein. The team grows a bacterium on a diet of methanol, ammonia and oxygen. The bacterium can make protein from these starting materials. A culture of the bacterium is grown, harvested and dried. It is used as food for cattle.

Other food scientists work in the food processing industry. They study the chemical nature of foods and the changes which take place when foods are stored and when they are cooked. Food scientists develop new methods of processing and preserving foods. They also try to improve foods by altering their flavour and colour and texture.

CHAPTER 12 *Chemical calculations*

12.1 Relative atomic mass

The masses of atoms are very small. Some examples are

- mass of hydrogen atom, H $= 1.4 \times 10^{-24}$ g
- mass of lead atom, Pb $= 2.9 \times 10^{-22}$ g
- mass of carbon atom, C $= 1.7 \times 10^{-23}$ g.

These masses are so uncomfortable to deal with that we use **relative atomic masses**. The hydrogen atom is the lightest of atoms. Chemists had the idea of comparing the masses of other atoms with that of the hydrogen atom. On the relative atomic mass scale

- the relative atomic mass of hydrogen is 1
- the relative atomic mass of lead is 207 (a lead atom is 207 times heavier than a hydrogen atom)
- the relative atomic mass of carbon is 12 (a carbon atom is 12 times heavier than a hydrogen atom).

The symbol for relative atomic mass is A_r. Since relative atomic mass is a ratio of two masses, the mass units cancel and relative atomic mass is a number without a unit.

A complete list of relative atomic masses is given on pp. 410–11. Those of some common elements are listed in Table 12.1.

*For more advanced work, chemists take the mass of one atom of carbon-12 as the reference point for the relative atomic mass scale. On this scale

$$\text{Relative atomic mass of element} = \frac{\text{Mass of one atom of the element}}{(1/12)\ \text{Mass of one atom of carbon-12}}$$

Table 12.1 Some relative atomic masses

Element	A_r	Element	A_r
Aluminium	27	Magnesium	24
Barium	137	Mercury	200
Bromine	80	Nitrogen	14
Calcium	40	Oxygen	16
Chlorine	35.5	Phosphorus	31
Copper	63.5	Potassium	39
Hydrogen	1	Sodium	23
Iron	56	Sulphur	32
Lead	207	Zinc	65

SUMMARY NOTE

The relative atomic mass A_r of an element is the mass of one atom of the element compared with the mass of one atom of hydrogen. On the relative atomic mass scale, $A_r(\text{H}) = 1$.

JUST TESTING 65

1 Refer to Table 12.1.
  a How many times heavier is one atom of barium than one atom of hydrogen?
  b What is the ratio
  $$\frac{\text{mass of one atom of}}{\text{mercury}} \text{ to } \frac{\text{mass of one atom of}}{\text{calcium}} ?$$
  c How many atoms of nitrogen are needed to equal the mass of one atom of iron?
  d How many atoms of sodium are needed to equal the mass of one atom of lead?

12.2 Relative molecular mass

The mass of a molecule is the sum of the masses of all the atoms in it. The relative molecular mass M_r of a compound is the sum of the relative atomic masses of all the atoms in a molecule of the compound (Fig. 12.1).

4 O atoms ($A_r = 16$) = 64
1 S atom ($A_r = 32$) = 32
2 H atoms ($A_r = 1$) = 2
Total H_2SO_4 = 98

Fig. 12.1 Atoms in a molecule of sulphuric acid

You can find the relative molecular mass of sulphuric acid in this way:

Formula of compound is H_2SO_4
2 atoms of H ($A_r = 1$) = 2
1 atom of S ($A_r = 32$) = 32
4 atoms of O ($A_r = 16$) = 64
Total = 98
Relative molecular mass M_r of H_2SO_4 = 98

SUMMARY NOTE

The relative molecular mass of a covalent compound equals the sum of the relative atomic masses of all the atoms in one molecule of the compound.

$$M_r = \text{Sum of } A_r \text{ values}$$

The relative formula mass of an ionic compound equals the sum of the relative atomic masses of all the atoms in a formula unit of the compound.

12.3 Relative formula mass

Many compounds consist of ions, not molecules (see Chapter 5). For ionic compounds, the formula represents a **formula unit**, rather than a **molecule** of the compound. A formula unit of calcium chloride is $CaCl_2$. You cannot call it a molecule of calcium chloride because it consists of ions. The term **relative formula mass** is used for ionic compounds, and it can be used for covalent compounds as well. The symbol M_r can be used for both covalent compounds and ionic compounds.

JUST TESTING 66

1 Work out the relative formula masses of these compounds: CO_2, SO_2, NaOH, KCl, $Ca(OH)_2$, HNO_3, $CuCO_3$, NH_4NO_3, $CuSO_4$, $CuSO_4 \cdot 5H_2O$, $Mg(HCO_3)_2$.

12.4 Percentage composition

From the formula of a compound you can find the percentage by mass of the elements in the compound.

Example 1 Find the percentage by mass of (a) barium and (b) oxygen in barium oxide.

Method First find the relative formula mass.
The formula is BaO.
Relative formula mass = $A_r(Ba) + A_r(O)$
= 137 + 16 = 153

Percentage of barium = $\frac{137}{153} \times 100 = 89.5\%$

Percentage of oxygen = $\frac{16}{153} \times 100 = 10.5\%$

You can see that the two percentages add up to 100%.

*Example 2 Find the percentage of water in crystals of magnesium sulphate-7-water.

Method Find the relative formula mass.
The formula is $MgSO_4 \cdot 7H_2O$.

Relative formula mass = Sum of relative atomic masses

1 atom of magnesium ($A_r = 24$)	= 24
1 atom of sulphur ($A_r = 32$)	= 32
4 atoms of oxygen ($A_r = 16$)	= 64
7 molecules of water, $7 \times [(2 \times 1) + 16]$	= 126
Total = Relative formula mass	= 246

$$\text{Percentage of water} = \frac{\text{Mass of water in formula}}{\text{Relative formula mass}} \times 100\%$$

$$= \frac{126}{246} \times 100\% = 51.2\%$$

The percentage of water in magnesium sulphate crystals is 51%.

JUST TESTING 67

You do not need calculators for these problems.

1 Find the percentage by mass of beryllium, Be, in beryllium oxide, BeO.

2 Find the percentage by mass of iron in iron(III) oxide, Fe_2O_3.

3 Calculate the percentages by mass of
   a carbon and hydrogen in ethane, C_2H_6
   b nitrogen and oxygen in nitrogen monoxide, NO
   c magnesium and nitrogen in magnesium nitride, Mg_3N_2
   d sodium and iodine in sodium iodide, NaI.

4 Calculate the percentage by mass of water in
   a copper(II) sulphate-5-water, $CuSO_4 \cdot 5H_2O$ (take $A_r(Cu) = 64$)
   b sodium sulphide-9-water, $Na_2S \cdot 9H_2O$.

---

*12.5 The mole

Chemical equations tell us what products are formed when substances react. Equations can also be used to tell us *how much* product as well as *which* product, that is, *what mass* of solid product or *what volume* of gaseous product is formed. A reaction of industrial importance is

calcium carbonate → calcium oxide + carbon dioxide
$CaCO_3(s)$ → $CaO(s)$ + $CO_2(g)$

Cement manufacturers use this reaction to make calcium oxide (lime) from calcium carbonate (limestone). They sell the carbon dioxide gas produced to fizzy drink manufacturers. It is possible to calculate what mass of calcium oxide and what volume of carbon dioxide are formed when a certain mass of calcium carbonate dissociates. The key to the calculation is the idea which chemists call the **mole concept**.

We owe the reasoning behind the mole concept to a nineteenth century Italian chemist called Avogadro. This is how he argued:

We know from their relative atomic masses that one atom of magnesium is twice as heavy as one atom of carbon: $A_r(Mg) = 24$, $A_r(C) = 12$. Therefore we can say:

If 1 atom of magnesium is twice as heavy as 1 atom of carbon, then 1 hundred Mg atoms are twice as heavy as 1 hundred C atoms,
and 5 million Mg atoms are twice as heavy as 5 million C atoms,
and it follows that, if we have a piece of magnesium which has twice the mass of a piece of carbon, the two masses must contain equal numbers of atoms.

2 grams of magnesium and 1 gram of carbon contain the same number of atoms;

10 tonnes of magnesium and 5 tonnes of carbon contain the same number of atoms.

The same argument applies to the other elements. Take the relative atomic mass in grams of any element:

12 g carbon	24 g magnesium	56 g iron	40 g calcium	108 g silver	238 g uranium	207 g lead

All these masses contain the same number of atoms. The number is 6.022×10^{23}.

> The amount of an element that contains 6×10^{23} atoms (the same number of atoms as 12 g of carbon-12) is called one **mole** of that element.

The symbol for **mole** is **mol**. The ratio 6.022×10^{23}/mol is called the **Avogadro constant**. When you weigh out 12 g of carbon, you are counting out 6×10^{23} atoms of carbon. This amount of carbon is one mole (1 mol) of carbon atoms. Similarly, 80 g of calcium is two moles (2 mol) of calcium atoms. You can say that the **amount** of calcium is two moles (2 mol).

You can have a mole of carbon atoms, C, a mole of sodium ions, Na^+, a mole of sulphuric acid molecules, H_2SO_4. One mole of sulphuric acid contains 6×10^{23} molecules of H_2SO_4, that is, 98 g of H_2SO_4 (the molar mass in grams). To write 'a mole of oxygen' is imprecise: one mole of oxygen atoms, O, has a mass of 16 grams; one mole of oxygen molecules, O_2, has a mass of 32 grams.

Molar mass

The mass of one mole of a substance is called the **molar mass**, symbol M. The molar mass of carbon is 12 g/mol; the molar mass of calcium is 40 g/mol. The term molar mass applies to compounds as well as elements. The molar mass of an element is the relative atomic mass expressed in grams per mole; the

If you had 6×10^{23} pound coins and you distributed them equally between all the people on the Earth, how much would each person receive?

There are 4 billion people, so each one gets £150 million million!

molar mass of a compound is the relative formula mass expressed in grams per mole. Sulphuric acid, H_2SO_4, has a relative molecular mass of 98; its molar mass is 98 g/mol. Notice the units: relative molecular mass has no unit; molar mass has the unit g/mol.

Amount (in moles) of substance $= \dfrac{\text{Mass of substance}}{\text{Molar mass of substance}}$

Molar mass of element $= \dfrac{\text{Relative atomic mass}}{\text{in grams per mole}}$

Molar mass of compound $= \dfrac{\text{Relative formula mass}}{\text{in grams per mole}}$

Example What is the amount of lead present in 414 g of lead?
Method
A_r of lead $= 207$
Molar mass of lead $= 207$ g/mol
Amount of lead $= \dfrac{\text{Mass of lead}}{\text{Molar mass of lead}}$
                     $= \dfrac{414 \text{ g}}{207 \text{ g/mol}}$
                     $= 2.0$ mol
The amount (number of moles) of lead is 2.0 mol.

Example If you need 2.5 mol of sodium chloride, what mass of sodium chloride do you have to weigh out?
Method
Relative formula mass of NaCl $= 23 + 35.5 = 58.5$
Molar mass of NaCl $= 58.5$ g/mol
Amount of substance $= \dfrac{\text{Mass of substance}}{\text{Molar mass of substance}}$
2.5 mol $= \dfrac{\text{Mass}}{58.5 \text{ g/mol}}$
Mass $= 58.5$ g/mol $\times 2.5$ mol
                               $= 147$ g
You need to weigh out 147 g of sodium chloride.

SUMMARY NOTE

The number of atoms in 12.000 g of carbon-12 is 6.022×10^{23}. This is the number of atoms in a mass of any element equal to its relative atomic mass expressed in grams. This number of atoms is called one **mole** (1 mol) of atoms. The ratio 6.022×10^{23}/mol is called the Avogadro constant. The number of moles of a substance is called simply the **amount** of that substance. The mass of one mole of an element or compound is the **molar mass** M of that substance.
M of an element $=$
   A_r expressed in g/mol
M of a compound $=$
   M_r expressed in g/mol

JUST TESTING 68

1 State the mass of
  a 1 mol of sodium atoms
  b 3 mol of bromine molecules, Br_2
  c 0.25 mol of nitrogen atoms, N
  d 0.25 mol of nitrogen molecules, N_2
  e 0.5 mol of sulphur atoms, S
  f 0.5 mol of sulphur molecules, S_8.

2 Find the amount (moles) of each element present in
  a 46 g of sodium, Na
  b 0.6 g of magnesium, Mg
  c 32 g of oxygen, O_2
  d 127 g of copper, Cu.

3 State the mass of

    a 1.0 mol of sulphur dioxide molecules, SO_2

    b 10 mol of sulphuric acid, H_2SO_4

    c 0.50 mol of sodium hydroxide, NaOH

    d 2.0 mol of calcium carbonate, $CaCO_3$.

4 The Avogadro constant is 6×10^{23}/mol.

    a What mass of aluminium contains (i) 6×10^{23} atoms, (ii) 3×10^{25} atoms?

    b What mass of aluminium contains the same number of atoms as (i) 62 g of phosphorus, (ii) 4.0 g of carbon?

*12.6 Calculating the mass of reactant or mass of product

The reason for studying the mole concept is that it enables us to work out useful information, such as the mass of product that can be obtained from a given mass of starting material.

Example 1 What mass of quicklime (calcium oxide) is obtained when 10 tonnes of limestone (calcium carbonate) are decomposed?

Method First write the equation for the reaction:

    calcium carbonate → calcium oxide + carbon dioxide
    $CaCO_3(s)$ → $CaO(s)$ + $CO_2(g)$

The equation tells us that

    1 formula unit of calcium carbonate forms 1 formula unit of calcium oxide

    1 mole of calcium carbonate therefore forms 1 mole of calcium oxide.

Using the molar masses $M(CaCO_3)$ = 100 g/mol, $M(CaO)$ = 56 g/mol,

    100 g of calcium carbonate forms 56 g of calcium oxide.

The mass of calcium oxide from 10 tonnes of calcium carbonate is therefore given by

$$\text{Mass of CaO} = \frac{56}{100} \times (\text{Mass of CaCO}_3)$$

$$= \frac{56}{100} \times 10 \text{ tonnes} = 5.6 \text{ tonnes}$$

Example 2 What mass of tungsten(III) oxide, W_2O_3, must be reduced with hydrogen to yield 10 kilograms of tungsten?

Method The equation comes first:

    tungsten(III) oxide + hydrogen → tungsten + water
    $W_2O_3(s)$ + $3H_2(g)$ → $2W(s)$ + $3H_2O(l)$

From the equation you can see that

    1 mole of tungsten(III) oxide forms 2 moles of tungsten.

Using the molar masses $M(W_2O_3) = 416$ g/mol,
$M(W) = 184$ g/mol,

416 g of tungsten(III) oxide form 368 g of tungsten.

The mass of tungsten(III) oxide required to yield 10 kg of tungsten is therefore given by

Mass of tungsten(III) oxide $= \dfrac{416}{368} \times$ Mass of tungsten

$$= \dfrac{416}{368} \times 10 \text{ kg}$$

$$= 11.3 \text{ kg}$$

SUMMARY NOTE

The balanced equation for a chemical reaction tells you how many moles of product are formed from one mole of reactant. You can use the equation with the molar masses of the reactant and the product to find out what mass of product is formed from a certain mass of reactant.

JUST TESTING 69

You do not need calculators for these problems.

1 What mass of copper(II) oxide, CuO, is formed when 127 g of copper are completely oxidised?

2 Mercury(II) oxide, HgO, decomposes to give mercury and oxygen when heated. What mass of mercury is obtained from 54 g of mercury(II) oxide?

3 What mass of carbon dioxide can be made by decomposing 200 g of calcium carbonate?

4 When hydrochloric acid neutralises potassium hydroxide, the products of the reaction are potassium chloride and water:
$$HCl(aq) + KOH(aq) \rightarrow KCl(aq) + H_2O(l)$$
Find what mass of potassium chloride is formed when 14 g of potassium hydroxide are completely neutralised by hydrochloric acid.

5 Sodium sulphate can be made by neutralising sodium hydroxide with sulphuric acid:
$$2NaOH(aq) + H_2SO_4(aq) \rightarrow Na_2SO_4(aq) + 2H_2O(l)$$
Calculate the mass of sodium sulphate that can be made from 80 g of sodium hydroxide and an excess of sulphuric acid.

Remember: The balanced equation for the reaction is the key to each of these calculations.

*12.7 Finding the equation for a reaction

If you know the mass of each reactant taking part in a reaction, you can calculate the number of moles of each reactant taking part in the reaction. This will give you the equation for the reaction.

Example Under certain conditions, nitrogen combines with oxygen to form an oxide. Given that 0.56 g of nitrogen form 1.20 g of the oxide of nitrogen, find the equation for the reaction.

Method Relative atomic masses are $A_r(N) = 14$, $A_r(O) = 16$

Amount of nitrogen, N_2 = Mass/Molar mass
$$= 0.56 \text{ g} / 28 \text{ g/mol} = 2.0 \times 10^{-2} \text{ mol}$$
Mass of oxygen $= 1.20 \text{ g} - 0.56 \text{ g} = 0.64 \text{ g}$
Amount of oxygen, O_2 = Mass/Molar mass
$$= 0.64 \text{ g} / 32 \text{ g/mol}$$
$$= 2.0 \times 10^{-2} \text{ mol}$$

Therefore

2.0×10^{-2} mol N_2 reacts with 2.0×10^{-2} mol O_2

It follows that

1 mol N_2 reacts with 1 mol O_2.

The equation must be

$$N_2(g) + O_2(g) \rightarrow$$

Balancing the equation gives

$$N_2(g) + O_2(g) \rightarrow 2NO(g)$$

SUMMARY NOTE

If you know the mass of product that is formed from a certain mass of reactant, and you know their molar masses, you can work out the equation for the reaction.

---

* JUST TESTING 70

1 One gram of mercury reacts with iodine to form 1.635 g of an iodide of mercury.
  a What amount (how many moles) of mercury reacts?
  b What amount (how many moles) of iodine reacts?
  c What is the ratio: moles of mercury/moles of iodine?
  d Find the equation for the reaction.

2 A sample of powdered copper weighs 1.27 g. It reacts with oxygen to form 1.43 g of an oxide of copper.
  a What is the amount (mol) of copper that reacts?
  b What is the amount (mol) of oxygen that reacts?
  c Find the ratio: amount (mol) copper/amount (mol) oxygen.
  d Work out the equation for the reaction.

Crucible with lid
The lid is raised from time to time to let air in.

Pipeclay triangle which supports crucible

A known mass of magnesium ribbon

Heat

Fig. 12.2 Converting magnesium into magnesium oxide

*12.8 Finding formulas

The formula of a compound is worked out from the percentage composition by mass of the compound.

Example 1: Finding the formula of magnesium oxide

Experiment 11.1 can be done to find the mass of oxygen that combines with a weighed amount of magnesium. A certain mass of magnesium is heated as shown in Fig. 12.2.

When all the magnesium has been converted into magnesium oxide, the mass of magnesium oxide is found. The mass of oxygen that has combined with the magnesium is found by subtraction. A typical set of results is given overleaf.

(1) Mass of crucible = 16.18 g
(2) Mass of crucible + magnesium = 17.24 g
(3) **Mass of magnesium** = (2) − (1) = 1.06 g
(4) Mass of crucible + magnesium oxide = 17.95 g
(5) **Mass of oxygen combined** = (4) − (2) = 0.71 g

The results are treated in this way:

Element	Magnesium		Oxygen
Mass	1.06 g		0.71 g
A_r	24		16
Amount in moles	1.06/24		0.71/16
	= 0.044	=	0.044
Divide through by 0.044 =	1 mole Mg	to	1 mole O
Formula	MgO		

The formula MgO is the simplest formula which fits the results. Other formulas (Mg_2O_2, Mg_3O_3 etc.) also fit the results. MgO is the **empirical formula** for magnesium oxide.

The empirical formula of a compound is the simplest formula which represents the composition by mass of the compound.

Example 2: Finding the empirical formula of copper oxide

Figure 12.3 shows an apparatus for reducing copper oxide to copper (see Experiment 11.2). A set of results might look like this:

Fig. 12.3 Reducing copper oxide to copper

(1) Mass of 'boat' = 21.04 g
(2) Mass of 'boat' + copper oxide = 23.76 g
(3) Mass of 'boat' + copper = 23.21 g
(4) Mass of copper = (3) − (1) = 2.17 g
(5) Mass of oxygen = (2) − (3) = 0.55 g

The results are treated in this way:

Element	Copper		Oxygen
Mass	2.17 g		0.55 g
A_r	63.5		16
Amount in moles	2.17/63.5		0.55/16
	= 0.034		0.034
Ratio	1 mole of Cu	to	1 mole of O
Empirical formula	CuO		

The oxide is copper(II) oxide.

Example 3: Finding the formula of copper(II) sulphate crystals

When copper(II) sulphate crystals are heated gently, they lose water of crystallisation (Fig. 12.4). The result is **anhydrous** copper(II) sulphate. The mass of anhydrous copper(II) sulphate

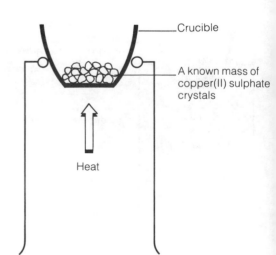

Fig. 12.4 Heating copper(II) sulphate crystals

formed from a weighed mass of crystals can be found. The results can be treated in this way:

Suppose that 4.00 g of crystals give 2.56 g of anhydrous copper(II) sulphate. Then the mass of water lost is 1.44 g.

Compound	Copper(II) sulphate	Water
Formula	$CuSO_4$	H_2O
Mass	2.56 g	1.44 g
M_r	159.5	18
Amount in moles	2.56/159.5	1.44/18
	= 0.0160	= 0.080
Divide by 0.0160	= 1 mol to	5 mol
Empirical formula	$CuSO_4 \cdot 5H_2O$	

SUMMARY NOTE

The empirical formula of a compound shows the symbols of the elements present and the ratio of the number of atoms of each element present in the compound.

---

*JUST TESTING 71

You do not need calculators for these problems.

1 Find the empirical formulas of the following compounds:
  a a compound of 25.4 g of copper and 3.2 g of oxygen
  b a compound of 24.0 g of calcium and 5.6 g of nitrogen
  c a compound of 0.31 g of phosphorus and 1.07 g of chlorine.

2 Calculate the empirical formulas of the compounds which have the following percentage compositions by mass:
  a 40% calcium, 12% carbon, 48% oxygen
  b 36% beryllium, 64% oxygen
  c 80% carbon, 20% hydrogen.

3 Find the empirical formulas of the compounds formed when
  a 4.00 g of mercury form 4.64 g of a mercury sulphide
  b 0.62 g of phosphorus form 1.10 g of a phosphorus oxide
  c 5.60 g of iron form 16.25 g of an iron chloride.

4 Find n in the empirical formulas of these hydrates:
  a barium chloride crystals, $BaCl_2 \cdot nH_2O$, given that 1.22 g of the crystals lose water of crystallisation on heating to form 1.04 g of anhydrous barium chloride
  b magnesium sulphate crystals, $MgSO_4 \cdot nH_2O$, given that 1.23 g of the crystals form 0.60 g of anhydrous magnesium sulphate.

*12.9 Molecular formula and empirical formula

The empirical formula of a compound is the simplest formula that states the composition of the compound. The empirical formula mass may not be the same as the molar mass. The formula that gives the correct molar mass is called the **molecular**

formula. The molecular formula is a multiple of the empirical formula.

Example The empirical formula of a compound is CH. The molar mass is 78 g/mol. What is the molecular formula of the compound?

Method

Empirical formula mass of CH = 12 + 1   = 13 g/mol
Molar mass   = 78 g/mol
Molar mass/Empirical formula mass   = 6
The molecular formula is 6 × the empirical formula
The molecular formula is C_6H_6.

---

*JUST TESTING 72

1 The empirical formula of a compound is CHO_2. Its molar mass is 90 g/mol. What is the molecular formula of the compound?

2 The empirical formula of a compound is C_3H_6O. If its molar mass is 58 g/mol, what is its molecular formula?

---

*12.10 The volumes of reacting gases

The volume of a fixed mass of gas depends on its temperature and pressure (see Chapter 1):

• As the temperature increases, the volume of gas increases.
• As the pressure increases, the volume of gas decreases.

We therefore have to state the temperature and pressure at which the volume of a gas is measured. We shall compare gas volumes at room temperature (20 °C) and 1 atmosphere. These conditions are called room temperature and pressure, **r.t.p.**

It has been found that one mole of gas occupies 24 litres at r.t.p. It does not make any difference what the gas is:

• 2 g of hydrogen   ⎤ All these are one mole of gas (the
• 32 g of oxygen   ⎬ molar mass expressed in grams).
• 44 g of carbon dioxide   ⎦ All occupy 24 litres at r.t.p.

This volume, 24 litres, is called the **gas molar volume**.
   The fact that different gases have the same molar volume makes calculations on the reacting volumes of gases easy. When you look at the ratio of the numbers of moles of gases reacting, you are looking at the ratio of the volumes of gases reacting. If the equation shows

$$2A(g) + 3B(g) \rightarrow C(g) + D(g)$$

you know that

2 moles of A react with 3 moles of B

and (at r.t.p.)

2 × 24 litres of A react with 3 × 24 litres of B

240

that is,

2 litres of A react with 3 litres of B

and, in general,

the volume of B is 1.5 times the volume of A.

Example 1 A car engine burns octane, C_8H_{18}:

octane   + oxygen → carbon dioxide + water
$$2C_8H_{18}(g) + 25O_2(g) → 16CO_2(g) \qquad + 18H_2O(l)$$

What volume of oxygen is needed to ensure the complete combustion of 1 litre of octane vapour?

Method From the equation, you see that

2 moles of octane burn in 25 moles of oxygen

therefore

1 mole of octane burns in 12.5 moles of oxygen

that is,

24 litres of octane vapour burn in 12.5×24 litres of oxygen

1 litre of octane vapour burns in 12.5 litres of oxygen.

Example 2 A coal-fired electric power station burns coal which contains sulphur. The sulphur burns to form sulphur dioxide, $SO_2(g)$. If the power station burns 56 tonnes of sulphur in its coal every day, what volume of sulphur dioxide does it send into the air?
(1 tonne = 1000 kg = 1 000 000 g = 10^6 g)

Method The equation for combustion of sulphur is

sulphur + oxygen → sulphur dioxide
$$S(s) \qquad + O_2(g) \quad → SO_2(g)$$

The equation tells you that

1 mol of sulphur forms 1 mol of sulphur dioxide

that is,

32 g of sulphur form 24 litres of sulphur dioxide

therefore

$$56 \text{ tonnes of sulphur form } \frac{56 \times 10^6}{32} \times 24 \text{ litres of } SO_2$$

$$= 42 \times 10^6 \text{ litres}$$

This power station gives out 42×10^6 litres (42 million litres) of sulphur dioxide in a day.

SUMMARY NOTE

One mole of any gas occupies 24 litres at room temperature and pressure: the **gas molar volume** is 24 l at r.t.p. The volumes of the gaseous reactants taking part in a chemical reaction are in the same ratio as the numbers of molecules of the different gaseous reactants shown in the equation for the reaction.

(Use gas molar volume = 24 litres at r.t.p.)

1 Calculate the volume of oxygen needed for the complete combustion of 75 cm³ of methane, $CH_4(g)$. What volume of carbon dioxide is formed?

2 What volume of carbon dioxide is formed by the complete combustion of 60 g of carbon?

3 What volume of hydrogen is formed when 6.0 g of magnesium react with an excess of sulphuric acid? The equation is

$$Mg(s) + H_2SO_4(aq) \rightarrow H_2(g) + MgSO_4(aq)$$

4 What mass of calcium carbonate would be needed to provide 120 litres of carbon dioxide? The equation for the thermal decomposition is

$$CaCO_3(s) \rightarrow CaO(s) + CO_2(g)$$

*12.11 Reactions in solution

Many reactions take place in solution. One way of stating the concentration of a solute in a solution is to state the mass of solute present in 1 litre of solution, e.g. grams per litre, g/l. A more convenient method is to state the amount in moles of a solute present in 1 litre of solution (see Fig. 12.5):

- If 1 mole of solute is present in 1 litre of solution, the concentration of solute is 1 mole per litre, 1 mol/l
- 2 moles of solute in 1 litre of solution:
  concentration = 2 mol/l
- 4 moles of solute in 10 litres of solution:
  concentration = 0.4 mol/l

One litre is 1000 cubic centimetres. A litre is also known as a cubic decimetre, dm³.

1 litre = 1000 cm³ = 1 dm³

1 mole of solute	1 mole of solute	2 moles of solute	1.5 moles of solute
in 1 litre of solution	in 500 cm³ of solution	in 250 cm³ of solution	in 250 cm³ of solution
Concentration 1 mol/l	2 mol/l	8 mol/l	6 mol/l

Fig. 12.5 Making solutions of known concentration

$$\text{Concentration in moles per litre} = \frac{\text{Amount of solute in moles}}{\text{Volume of solution in litres}}$$

Rearranging,

$$\text{Amount of solute (mol)} = \text{Volume of solution (l)} \times \text{Concentration (mol/l)}$$

Example 1 Calculate the concentration of a solution that was made by dissolving 60 g of sodium hydroxide and making the solution up to 1.00 litre.

Method

Molar mass of sodium hydroxide, $NaOH$ = 23 + 16 + 1
= 40 g/mol

Amount in moles	= Mass/Molar mass = 60 g / 40 g/mol
	= 1.5 mol
Volume of solution	= 1.0 litre
Concentration	= Amount in moles/Volume in litres
	= 1.5 mol / 1.0 l
	= 1.5 mol/l

Example 2 Calculate the amount in moles of solute present in 250 cm^3 of a solution of hydrochloric acid which has a concentration of 2.0 mol/l.

Method

Amount (mol)	= Volume (l) × Concentration (mol/l)
Amount of solute	= 250 × 10^{-3} l × 2.0 mol/l
	= 0.50 mol

Note that when you are given the volume in cm^3, you have to change it into litres. This makes the units come right:

$$\frac{\text{Amount}}{\textbf{(moles)}} = \frac{\text{Volume}}{\textbf{(litres)}} \times \frac{\text{Concentration}}{\textbf{(moles per litre)}}$$

*JUST TESTING 74

1 Calculate the concentrations of the following solutions:
   a 5.6 g of potassium hydroxide in 500 cm^3 of solution
   b 8.0 g of sodium hydroxide in 5.0 l of solution
   c 9.8 g of sulphuric acid in 2.5 l of solution
   d 7.3 g of hydrogen chloride in 250 cm^3 of solution.

2 Find the amount of solute in moles present in the following solutions:
   a 250 cm^3 of a solution of sodium hydroxide of concentration 2.0 mol/l
   b 1.00 l of hydrochloric acid of concentration 0.020 mol/l
   c 500 cm^3 of sulphuric acid of concentration 0.12 mol/l
   d 10 cm^3 of a 0.25 mol/l solution of potassium hydroxide.

Neutralisation

One of the reactions carried out in solution is neutralisation. Take the neutralisation of hydrochloric acid by sodium hydroxide solution:

$$\text{hydrochloric acid} + \text{sodium hydroxide} \rightarrow \text{sodium chloride} + \text{water}$$

$$\text{HCl(aq)} + \text{NaOH(aq)} \rightarrow \text{NaCl(aq)} + \text{H}_2\text{O(l)}$$

You see from the equation that

1 mole of HCl neutralises 1 mole of NaOH.

1 mole of HCl is present in 1 litre of solution of concentration 1 mol/l.

1 mole of NaOH is present in 1 litre of solution of concentration 1 mol/l.

Therefore

1 litre of hydrochloric acid of concentration 1 mol/l neutralises 1 litre of sodium hydroxide solution of concentration 1 mol/l.

You cannot assume that one mole of acid always neutralises one mole of base. You always have to look at the equation for the reaction. As in all the other types of calculation, the starting point is the balanced chemical equation for the reaction.

Here are some examples of other acid–base reactions.

1 $\text{hydrochloric acid} + \text{calcium hydroxide} \rightarrow \text{calcium chloride} + \text{water}$

$$2\text{HCl(aq)} + \text{Ca(OH)}_2\text{(aq)} \rightarrow \text{CaCl}_2\text{(aq)} + 2\text{H}_2\text{O(l)}$$

Here, 2 moles of acid neutralise 1 mole of base.

2 $\text{sulphuric acid} + \text{potassium hydroxide} \rightarrow \text{potassium sulphate} + \text{water}$

$$\text{H}_2\text{SO}_4\text{(aq)} + 2\text{KOH(aq)} \rightarrow \text{K}_2\text{SO}_4\text{(aq)} + 2\text{H}_2\text{O(l)}$$

Here, 1 mole of acid neutralises 2 moles of base.

Titration

A solution of known concentration is called a **standard** solution. You can use a standard solution of a base to find out the concentration of a solution of an acid. The method of doing this is **titration** (see Fig. 12.6). The idea is to find out what volume of, say, acid of unknown concentration is needed to neutralise a known volume, usually 25 cm³, of a standard solution of a base.

Example 1 A titration tells you that 18.5 cm³ of hydrochloric acid neutralise 25.0 cm³ of a 0.100 mol/l solution of sodium hydroxide. You can find out the concentration of hydrochloric acid.

Method

1 First write the equation

$$\text{hydrochloric acid} + \text{sodium hydroxide} \rightarrow \text{sodium chloride} + \text{water}$$

$$\text{HCl(aq)} + \text{NaOH(aq)} \rightarrow \text{NaCl(aq)} + \text{H}_2\text{O(l)}$$

You see that 1 mole of HCl neutralises 1 mole of NaOH.

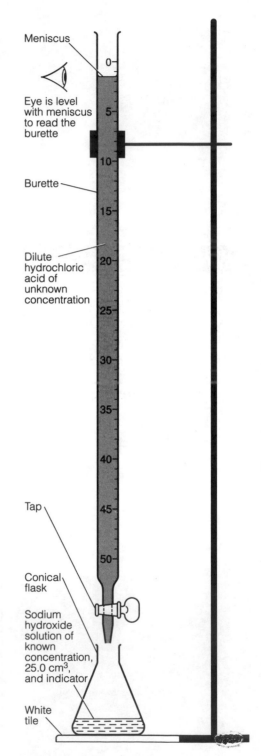

Meniscus

Eye is level with meniscus to read the burette

Burette

Dilute hydrochloric acid of unknown concentration

Tap

Conical flask

Sodium hydroxide solution of known concentration, 25.0 cm³, and indicator

White tile

Fig. 12.6 Titration. Hydrochloric acid is added to the conical flask until the indicator shows that the contents of the flask are neutral. The volume of acid added can be read off the burette

244

2 Now work out the amount in moles of base. You must start with the base because you know the concentration of base, and you do not know the concentration of acid.

Remember: Amount (mol) = Volume (l) × Concentration (mol/l)

$$\text{Amount in moles of NaOH} = \text{Volume (25.0 cm}^3\text{)} \times \text{Concentration (0.100 mol/l)}$$
$$= 25.0 \times 10^{-3} \times 0.100$$
$$= 2.50 \times 10^{-3} \text{ mol}$$

3 Now work out the concentration of acid:

$$\text{Amount in moles of HCl} = \text{Amount in moles of NaOH}$$
$$= 2.50 \times 10^{-3} \text{ mol}$$

also

$$\text{Amount (mol) of HCl} = \text{Volume of HCl(aq)} \times \text{Concentration of HCl(aq)}$$

therefore, if c mol/l is the concentration of HCl,

$$2.50 \times 10^{-3} \text{ mol} = 18.5 \times 10^{-3} \text{ l} \times c \text{ mol/l}$$
$$\text{and } c \text{ mol/l} = 2.50 \times 10^{-3} \text{ mol}/18.5 \times 10^{-3} \text{ l}$$
$$= 0.135 \text{ mol/l}$$

The concentration of hydrochloric acid is 0.135 mol/l.

Example 2 In a titration, 25.0 cm³ of sulphuric acid of concentration 0.120 mol/l neutralised 23.0 cm³ of potassium hydroxide solution. Find the concentration of the potassium hydroxide solution.

Method

1 First write the equation

$$\text{sulphuric acid} + \text{potassium hydroxide} \rightarrow \text{potassium sulphate} + \text{water}$$

$$H_2SO_4(aq) + 2KOH(aq) \rightarrow K_2SO_4(aq) + 2H_2O(l)$$

You see that 1 mole of H_2SO_4 neutralises 2 moles of KOH.

2 Now work out the amount in moles of acid. You must choose the acid because you do not know the concentration of the base:

$$\text{Amount in moles of acid} = \text{Volume (25.0 cm}^3\text{)} \times \text{Concentration (0.120 mol/l)}$$
$$= 25.0 \times 10^{-3} \times 0.120 \text{ mol}$$
$$= 3.00 \times 10^{-3} \text{ mol}$$

3 Now work out the concentration of base:

$$\text{Amount in moles of KOH} = 2 \times \text{Amount in moles of } H_2SO_4$$
$$= 6.00 \times 10^{-3} \text{ mol}$$

also

$$\text{Amount (mol) of KOH} = \text{Volume of KOH(aq)} \times \text{Concentration of KOH(aq)}$$

therefore, if c mol/l is the concentration of KOH

$$6.00 \times 10^{-3} \text{ mol} = 23.0 \times 10^{-3} \text{ l} \times c \text{ mol/l}$$
$$c \text{ mol/l} = 6.00 \times 10^{-3} \text{ mol}/23.0 \times 10^{-3} \text{ l}$$
$$= 0.261 \text{ mol/l}$$

The concentration of potassium hydroxide is 0.261 mol/l.

---

*JUST TESTING 75

1 25.0 cm³ of hydrochloric acid are neutralised by 30.0 cm³ of a solution of sodium hydroxide of concentration 0.25 mol/l. Find the concentration of the hydrochloric acid.

2 25.0 cm³ of hydrochloric acid are neutralised by 20.0 cm³ of a solution of 0.15 mol/l sodium carbonate solution. Find the concentration of the hydrochloric acid.

3 A solution of sodium hydroxide contains 20 g/l. What volume of this solution would be needed to neutralise 25.0 cm³ of 0.10 mol/l hydrochloric acid?

4 What is the volume of sulphuric acid of concentration 0.100 mol/l that will neutralise **a** 5.3 g of sodium carbonate, **b** 2.1 g of sodium hydrogencarbonate?

5 The following results were obtained in tests on antacid indigestion tablets:

Brand	Price of 100 tablets	Volume of 0.01 mol/l acid required to neutralise 1 tablet
Neutro	75p	2.5 cm³
Fixit	90p	3.3 cm³
Baso	125p	4.0 cm³
Alko	150p	4.5 cm³

Which antacid tablets offer the best value for money?

*12.12 Calculations on electrolysis

When a current passes through solution of a salt of a metal which is low in the reactivity (electrochemical) series, metal ions are discharged and metal atoms are deposited on the cathode (see Section 5.6). In the electrolysis of silver nitrate, the cathode process is

$$Ag^+(aq) + e^- \rightarrow Ag(s)$$

This equation says that one silver atom accepts one electron to form one atom of silver. Therefore one mole of silver ions accept one mole of electrons to form one mole of silver atoms (108 g).

We can measure the quantity of electric charge needed to deposit 108 g silver. Electric charge is measured in **coulombs** (C).

Positive terminal of battery
Negative terminal of battery

mA

Milliammeter

Anode

Cathode

Cell

Silver nitrate solution

Fig. 12.7 Electrolysis apparatus

One coulomb is the electric charge that passes when 1 ampere flows for 1 second.

Charge in coulombs = Current in amperes × Time in seconds

A circuit such as that in Fig. 12.7 can be used to pass a measured current through an electrolysis cell for a known time. By weighing the cathode before and after the passage of a current, the mass of silver deposited can be found. The results of such experiments show that 96 500 coulombs are needed to deposit 108 g of silver. This quantity of electricity must be the charge on one mole of electrons. The value 96 500 C/mol is called the **Faraday constant**, after Michael Faraday who did much of the early work on electrolysis.

Now in the deposition of copper in electrolysis, the cathode process is:

$$Cu^{2+}(aq) + 2e^- \rightarrow Cu(s)$$

One mole of copper ions need two moles of electrons for discharge;
One mole of copper ions need 2 × 96 500 coulombs for discharge.

When aluminium is deposited during the electrolysis of molten aluminium oxide, the cathode process is:

$$Al^{3+}(l) + 3e^- \rightarrow Al(l)$$

One mole of aluminium ions need three moles of electrons for discharge;
One mole of aluminium needs 3 × 96 500 coulombs for discharge.

$$\text{Number of moles of element discharged} = \frac{\text{Number of moles of electrons}}{\text{Number of charges on one ion of the element}}$$

$$= \frac{\text{Number of coulombs/96 500}}{\text{Number of charges on one ion of the element}}$$

Example 1 A current of 10.0 milliamps (mA) passes for 1.00 hour through a solution of copper(II) sulphate. What mass of metal is deposited?
Method

Charge in coulombs = Current in amperes × Time in seconds
Charge = 0.010 × 1.00 × 60 × 60 = 36 C
Charge = 36/96 500 moles of electrons

The equation is:

$$Cu^{2+}(aq) + 2e^- \rightarrow Cu(s)$$

1 mole of electrons deposit $\frac{1}{2}$ mol copper, therefore 36/96 500 moles of electrons deposit:

$$\frac{1}{2} \times 36/96\,500 \text{ mol copper} = \frac{1}{2} \times 36 \times 63.5/96\,500 \text{ g copper}$$
$$= 0.0119 \text{ g copper}$$

0.0119 g copper is deposited.

Example 2 Aluminium is extracted by the electrolysis of molten aluminium oxide.

How many coulombs of electricity are needed to produce 1 tonne of aluminium (1 tonne = 1000 kg)?

Method

The equation:

$$Al^{3+}(l) + 3e^- \rightarrow Al(s)$$

shows that 3 moles of electrons are needed to give 1 mole of aluminium.

$1.00 \times 10^6 \times 3/27$ mol electrons are needed to give 1 tonne of aluminium.

$$1.00 \times 10^6 \times 3/27 \text{ mol of electrons} = 96\,500 \times 1.00 \times 10^6 \times 3/27 \text{ C}$$
$$= 1.07 \times 10^{10} \text{ C}$$

1.07×10^{10} C will deposit 1 tonne of aluminium.

Example 3 A metal of relative atomic mass 27 is deposited by electrolysis. If 0.201 g of the metal is deposited when 0.150 A flow for 4.00 hours, what is the charge on the ions of this element?

Method

Charge in coulombs = Current in amperes × Time in seconds

Charge = $0.150 \times 4.00 \times 60 \times 60$ C = 2160 C

If 2160 C deposit 0.201 g of the metal,

then 96 500 C deposit $96\,500 \times 0.201/2160$ g = 8.98 g

Since 8.98 g metal are deposited by 1 mol electrons, 27.0 g of metal are deposited by 27/8.98 mol electrons

= 3 mol electrons

The charge on the metal ions is +3.

Calculate the volume of gas evolved during electrolysis

Hydrogen. When hydrogen ions are discharged at the cathode,

$$2H^+(aq) + 2e^- \rightarrow H_2(g)$$

Two electrons are needed for the evolution of each hydrogen molecule. Two moles of electrons are needed for the evolution of one mole of hydrogen, which occupies 24 l at r.t.p. (the gas molar volume).

Chlorine. When chlorine is evolved at the anode,

$$2Cl^-(aq) \rightarrow Cl_2(g) + 2e^-$$

Two moles of electrons are needed for the evolution of each mole of chlorine, which occupies 24 l at r.t.p.

Oxygen. When oxygen is evolved at the anode,

$$4OH^-(aq) \rightarrow O_2(g) + 2H_2O(l) + 4e^-$$

Thus four moles of electrons must pass with the evolution of one mole of oxygen (24 l at r.t.p.).

Example 4 Name the gases formed at each electrode when 10.0 mA of current passes for 4.00 hours through a solution of acidified water and calculate their volumes (at r.t.p.).

Method

At the cathode hydrogen is evolved,

$$2H^+(aq) + 2e^- \rightarrow H_2(g)$$

so that 2 mol electrons discharge 1 mol hydrogen gas.
At the anode oxygen is evolved,

$$4OH^-(aq) \rightarrow O_2(g) + 2H_2O(l) + 4e^-$$

so that 4 mol electrons discharge 1 mol oxygen gas.

Charge in coulombs = Current in amperes × Time in seconds
$$= 10.0 \times 10^{-3} \times 4.00 \times 60 \times 60 = 144 \text{ C}$$
Number of mol electrons = 144 C/96 500 C/mol = 1.49×10^{-3} mol
Volume of hydrogen discharged = $\frac{1}{2} \times 1.49 \times 10^{-3} \times 24.0$ l
$$= 17.9 \text{ cm}^3 \text{ at r.t.p.}$$
Volume of oxygen = $\frac{1}{4} \times 1.49 \times 10^{-3} \times 24.0$ l
$$= 8.95 \text{ cm}^3 \text{ at r.t.p.}$$

Answer

At the cathode 17.9 cm³ (at r.t.p.) of hydrogen are evolved. At the anode 8.95 cm³ (at r.t.p.) of oxygen are evolved.

JUST TESTING 76

(See relative atomic masses on pp. 410–11.)

1 Calculate the mass of each element discharged when 0.50 mol of electrons passes through each of the solutions listed.
   a iron from iron(II) sulphate solution
   b oxygen from sodium hydroxide solution
   c lead from lead(II) nitrate solution
   d bromine from potassium bromide solution
   e nickel from nickel(II) nitrate solution

2 Which one of the following requires the largest quantity of electricity for discharge at an electrode?
   a 1 mol Cd²⁺ ions   b 2 mol Fe³⁺ ions   c 3 mol OH⁻ ions
   d 4 mol Br⁻ ions   e 5 mol Ag⁺ ions

3 Two cells containing solutions of silver nitrate and copper(II) nitrate are connected in series. When a current is passed, 0.540 g of silver is deposited in the first cell. What mass of copper is deposited in the second?

4 Calculate the volume (at r.t.p.) of each gas evolved when 2.00 mol of electrons pass through a solution of **a** dilute hydrochloric acid, **b** dilute sulphuric acid.

5 A current of 2.00 A passes for 96.5 hours through molten magnesium chloride. What mass of magnesium is deposited?

6 When a current passes through a solution of copper(II) sulphate, 120 cm³ of oxygen is evolved at the anode. What mass of copper is deposited on the cathode?

7 A current passes through two cells in series. The first contains a silver nitrate solution, and 0.1080 g of silver is deposited. The second contains a solution of the nitrate of a metal, M, of relative atomic mass 195, and 0.0975 g of M is deposited. Use this information to calculate the charge on the M ion.

8 A current of 0.010 A passes through a cell containing a solution of silver nitrate. How long will the current need to flow to deposit 0.108 g of silver on the cathode?

Exercise 12

You do not need a calculator for most of these problems. Those that need a calculator say so.

1 Use Avogadro constant = 6×10^{23}/mol. If the price of one billion (10^9) mercury atoms were 1p, what would you have to pay for 1 milligram (10^{-3} g) of mercury?

2 How many carbon atoms are there in a 2-carat diamond? One carat = 0.2 g, Avogadro constant = 6×10^{23}/mol. If the diamond costs £1500, what is the price of one carbon atom?

3 Ethanol, molecular formula C_2H_6O, is found in 'alcoholic' drinks. If you have 9.2 g of ethanol, how many moles do you have of a ethanol, b carbon atoms, c hydrogen atoms, d oxygen atoms?

4 (Calculator needed.) Find the empirical formula of the compounds which analyse as
a 40.0% C, 6.7% H, 53.3% O
b 19.2% Na, 0.8% H, 26.7% S, 53.3% O.

5 Vitamin C has the empirical formula $C_3H_4O_3$, and a molar mass of 176 g/mol. What is its molecular formula?

6 Melamine is a plastic with the empirical formula CH_2N_2. Its molar mass is 126 g/mol. What is its molecular formula?

7 Aluminium is made by electrolysing aluminium oxide. What mass of pure aluminium oxide, Al_2O_3, must be electrolysed to give 54 tonnes of aluminium?

8 (Calculator needed.) In certain illnesses, the body becomes short of salt (sodium chloride). A nurse must inject a sodium chloride solution into a vein. A 0.85 per cent solution is used (0.85 g sodium chloride per 100 g of water). What is the concentration of sodium chloride in mol/l in this solution?

9 When nitrogen and oxygen combine to form an oxide of nitrogen, under certain conditions, 0.70 g of nitrogen forms 2.30 g of an oxide. By means of a calculation, find the balanced equation for the reaction.

10 The diameter of a silver atom is 2.7×10^{-8} cm. $A_r(Ag)$ = 207, Avogadro constant = 6×10^{23}/mol. Imagine the atoms in 20.7 g of silver placed in a straight line, touching each other. What distance (km) would they cover?

11 A manufacturer's chimney emits 100 000 kg of nitrogen monoxide, NO, daily. The manufacturer decides to use the clean-up reaction:

$$\text{natural gas} + \text{nitrogen monoxide} \rightarrow \text{nitrogen} + \text{carbon dioxide} + \text{water}$$

$$CH_4(g) + 4NO(g) \rightarrow 2N_2(g) + CO_2(g) + 2H_2O($$

The cost of natural gas is 0.60p per cubic metre.
a What is the cost of running the clean-up operation?
(First convert kg of NO to cubic metres of NO; use the gas molar volume to do this. Then use the reaction equation to find out how many cubic metres of CH_4 are needed.)
b The cost of setting up the cleaning plant is high. Then there is the daily running cost. Would you spend money on installing and running a clean-up operation if you were the manufacturer? Explain your answer.

12 The emission of nitrogen monoxide from motor vehicle exhausts can be reduced by injecting a stream of ammonia into the exhaust vapour:

nitrogen monoxide + ammonia → nitrogen + water vapour

$$6NO(g) + 4NH_3(g) \rightarrow 5N_2(g) + 6H_2O(g)$$

A large car emits about 5 g of nitrogen monoxide per mile. If a car is driven 10 000 miles a year, what mass of ammonia is needed to clean up the exhaust gas?

Career sketch: Dentist

Mark is a dentist. Besides filling cavities, he also takes X-rays, treats gum diseases, and straightens teeth. Before going up to university Mark got good A-levels, including chemistry. His university course in dentistry included a lot of biochemistry and biology.

Mark's brother, Gerry, is a dental technician. He makes dentures and braces for straightening teeth. Gerry took a GCSE chemistry and trained in a school for dental technicians.

Sharon works as a dental hygienist for Mark. She carries out routine cleaning, removing deposits and stains from patients' teeth. She has GCSE in chemistry and biology and has trained in a hospital.

CHAPTER 13

Limestone, chalk and sand

13.1 Concrete

The Humber Bridge is the largest single-span suspension bridge
in the world. It is a triumph of civil engineering — one of the
wonders of modern technology (Fig. 13.1). There are two traffic
lanes in both directions, as well as lanes for cyclists and
pedestrians. The main span is 1410 m, and the overall length is
2220 m. This is the world's first suspension bridge to hang from
high towers of reinforced concrete. On all the other large bridges,
the towers are of steel. The Humber Bridge contains 500 000
tonnes of concrete. The concrete pillars have foundations that
reach 40 m down into the ground beneath the estuary. Steel was
also used in vast quantities: 30 000 tonnes.

Fig. 13.1 The Humber Bridge

What is this strong construction material, concrete? How is it
made? The first stage is the manufacture of cement. The raw
materials used to make cement are

- limestone or chalk
- shale or clay
- a small percentage of calcium sulphate (**gypsum**).

Figure 13.2 shows the method for making cement, and Fig. 13.3
shows how concrete is made from cement.

Limestone or chalk

Clay or shale

1 The raw materials are crushed, ground and mixed.

Rotary kiln
2

Powdered coal

Calcium sulphate (gypsum)

CEMENT

3

2 They are heated in a rotary kiln. Coal or oil is used as fuel.

3 The kiln product is ground with calcium sulphate (gypsum) to make cement. (Calcium sulphate prevents cement from setting too quickly after water is added.)

Fig. 13.2 Making cement

1 Sand and gravel are mixed.

2 Cement powder is added.

3 Water is added. Crystals start to grow from the cement.

4 The crystals grow and interlock with the surfaces of sand and gravel, binding the mass together.

Fig. 13.3 Making concrete

Chemical reactions occur between (a) chalk or limestone ($CaCO_3$) and (b) clay or shale, which consist largely of silicon(IV) oxide (SiO_2), aluminium oxide (Al_2O_3), silicates (compounds of silicon, oxygen and a metal) and aluminates (compounds of aluminium, oxygen and another metal). Cement, which is the product of the reactions, consists chiefly of calcium silicate ($CaSiO_3$), and calcium aluminate ($CaAl_2O_4$). A little calcium sulphate is added to slow down the rate at which concrete sets.

Concrete is one of the most versatile of all the materials used in civil engineering. It is used in the construction of all kinds of homes — from cottages to skyscrapers — as well as schools and factories, power stations and reservoirs. Transport by land, sea and air depends on concrete used in roads and bridges, docks and harbours, runways and hangars. **Reinforced** concrete is strengthened by steel supports.

There are large deposits of both limestone and chalk in the UK. The UK quarries 50 million tonnes of limestone and chalk every year. Limestone is quarried by blasting a hillside with explosive charges. Chalk can be dug out by mechanical excavators. Limestone, chalk and also marble are all forms of calcium carbonate, $CaCO_3$. They differ in the way the ions are arranged in their crystals. The quarrying of vast quantities of limestone and chalk can create difficulties. These minerals often occur in regions of outstanding natural beauty (Fig. 13.4). We do not want to despoil our countryside, but we do want the useful materials which chemists can obtain from limestone and chalk. Mining companies have to take steps to restore the countryside after they finish working a deposit of limestone or chalk (Fig. 13.5). As well as the manufacture of concrete and cement, limestone is used in the manufacture of iron in blast furnaces (see Section 11.9), in the manufacture of glass (see Section 13.9) and in the manufacture of lime (see Section 13.3).

SUMMARY NOTE

Concrete is a strong construction material. It is made from chalk or limestone and clay or shale. Vast quantities of these raw materials are quarried to meet the demand for concrete.

Fig. 13.4 A limestone quarry

Fig. 13.5 Restoring the scenery

1 Before quarrying

2 Topsoil is removed and stored. Trees are planted to shield the village from the sight of the quarry. The deposit of limestone is then worked.

3 The hole left by removal of the limestone is filled. Topsoil is spread over the area.

4 The land is restored to agricultural use

*13.2 Chemical equilibrium

In the next section, you will need the concept of chemical equilibrium. It will help you if you revise what you learned in Section 1.6 about physical changes that reach equilibrium.

Thermal dissociation

When calcium carbonate is heated strongly, it decomposes:

calcium carbonate → calcium oxide + carbon dioxide
$$CaCO_3(s) \rightarrow CaO(s) + CO_2(g)$$

The products can recombine. The base calcium oxide reacts with the acidic gas carbon dioxide to form calcium carbonate.

$$CaO(s) + CO_2(g) \rightarrow CaCO_3(s)$$

The reaction is therefore **reversible**: it can go from right to left as well as from left to right. When a substance decomposes to form products that can recombine, we say that the substance **dissociates**. When the dissociation is brought about by heat, it is called **thermal dissociation**.

Think about what happens when calcium carbonate is heated inside a closed container. When heating starts, there is no carbon dioxide or calcium oxide, and the dissociation of calcium carbonate is the only reaction that takes place. As calcium oxide and carbon dioxide are formed, they begin to recombine. As the concentration of carbon dioxide builds up inside the closed container, the rate of recombination increases. Eventually the rate of recombination is equal to the rate of dissociation of calcium carbonate. Then the amounts of calcium carbonate, calcium oxide and carbon dioxide remain constant. The system is in a state of **dynamic equilibrium**. We write reverse arrows to denote an equilibrium:

calcium carbonate ⇌ calcium oxide + carbon dioxide
$$CaCO_3(s) \rightleftharpoons CaO(s) + CO_2(g)$$

The reaction from left to right (as written) is called the forward reaction. The reaction from right to left is called the backward reaction.

The equilibrium can be disturbed. If the container is opened, carbon dioxide escapes, and more calcium carbonate dissociates. We shall see in the next section how calcium carbonate (limestone) is heated in a kiln (Fig. 13.6) to make calcium oxide (quicklime) and carbon dioxide. The kiln is open. A draft of air blows through the kiln to remove carbon dioxide and prevent the system from coming to equilibrium. More and more calcium carbonate dissociates in an attempt to reach equilibrium, and more quicklime and carbon dioxide are produced.

13.3 Limestone and lime

You may like to do Experiments 12.1 and 12.3 on heating limestone and other carbonates.

When calcium carbonate is heated strongly, it dissociates (splits up) to give calcium oxide and carbon dioxide:

The thermal dissociation of calcium carbonate (limestone) is an important industrial process.

calcium carbonate $\rightleftharpoons$ calcium oxide + carbon dioxide
$$CaCO_3(s) \rightleftharpoons CaO(s) + CO_2(g)$$

The products, calcium oxide and carbon dioxide, are both important chemicals. They are made by heating limestone in towers called **lime kilns** (Fig. 13.6).

1 Limestone and coke are fed in. The two 'bells' lower to let the load fall in, then rise to close the top of the kiln.

3 Air and carbon dioxide are swept out. Carbon dioxide can be removed from the stream of gas, and sold.

2 A draught of air enters. This is needed to burn the coke and to sweep carbon dioxide out at **3**.

4 Quicklime (calcium oxide) is removed at the bottom of the kiln.

Fig. 13.6 A lime kiln

255

The draught of air which flows through the kiln plays a very important part in the process. For one thing, it enables coke to burn and heat the limestone. Also, it removes the carbon dioxide formed. This prevents the system from coming to equilibrium. If the carbon dioxide is carried off as it is formed, it cannot linger to combine with calcium oxide and reform calcium carbonate.

Calcium oxide is called **lime** or **quicklime**. It is used on building sites. It is first allowed to react with water (see Experiment 12.3). This converts it into calcium hydroxide, which is called **slaked lime**:

calcium oxide + water → calcium hydroxide

$$CaO(s) \quad + \quad H_2O(l) \rightarrow Ca(OH)_2(s)$$

Calcium oxide, slaked lime, is mixed with sand to give **mortar**. Mortar is used to hold bricks together. As it is exposed to the air, it gradually hardens as it reacts with carbon dioxide in the air to form calcium carbonate (see Experiment 12.2).

Calcium oxide, lime, is also used in large quantities as a base. Farmers spread it on fields to neutralise excessively acidic soils (Fig. 13.7).

SUMMARY NOTE

Calcium carbonate (limestone) is heated in lime kilns to give calcium oxide (called both lime and quicklime) and carbon dioxide. Calcium oxide is mixed with sand to make mortar. It is also used to neutralise acidic soils.

Fig. 13.7 Applying lime to fields

JUST TESTING 77

1 Can you remember from Experiment 12.3 why calcium oxide is called **quicklime** and why calcium hydroxide is called **slaked lime**? What is the name commonly used for a solution of calcium hydroxide in water?

13.4 Carbonates and hydrogencarbonates

You have studied carbonates in Experiments 12.1 and 12.3. Figure 13.8 gives a summary.

Most carbonates dissociate when heated to form the metal oxide and carbon dioxide (e.g. limestone; see Section 13.3). The carbonates of Group 1 metals, e.g. Na_2CO_3, K_2CO_3, do not dissociate.

Calcium carbonate (limestone, marble, chalk) is used in the manufacture of cement, concrete, glass and iron.

Heat

Carbonates, e.g. Na_2CO_3, $CaCO_3$

Acid, e.g. HCl (aq)

Sodium carbonate is sold as washing soda, $Na_2CO_3 \cdot 10H_2O$, and is used in the manufacture of glass (Section 13.10).

Metal carbonates react with acids to give a salt of the metal (e.g. $CaCl_2$, NaCl) + carbon dioxide + water. This reaction is used in the laboratory preparation of carbon dioxide (Section 13.5) and also as a TEST for a carbonate.

Fig. 13.8 Some reactions of carbonates ▷

Figure 13.9 summarises some of the reactions of hydrogencarbonates.

Hydrogencarbonates

The hydrogencarbonates of Group 1, e.g. sodium hydrogencarbonate, $NaHCO_3$, decompose when warmed to give carbon dioxide and water and the metal carbonate. This is why sodium hydrogencarbonate is used in baking powder. The carbon dioxide which it provides makes bread and cakes rise in the oven.

Calcium hydrogencarbonate, $Ca(HCO_3)_2$, and magnesium hydrogencarbonate, $Mg(HCO_3)_2$, are present in tap water. They cause **temporary hardness**. When temporarily hard water is boiled, the hydrogencarbonates decompose to form the carbonates, and the water becomes **soft**.

Fig. 13.9 Some reactions of ▷
hydrogencarbonates

SUMMARY NOTE

- Carbonates and hydrogencarbonates react with dilute acids to give carbon dioxide and a salt.
- Hydrogencarbonates decompose when heated to give carbon dioxide and a carbonate.

JUST TESTING 78

1 What are the salts present in temporarily hard water?

2 How do these salts make the water hard?

3 What is the 'scale' which forms gradually in a kettle which is used for boiling hard water?

4 Sodium hydrogencarbonate is an ingredient of baking powder. When it dissociates in the oven, the reaction which occurs is

sodium hydrogencarbonate → sodium carbonate + carbon dioxide + water

Write a balanced chemical equation for this reaction.

13.5 Carbon dioxide

Carbon dioxide is formed when many carbonates and hydrogencarbonates are heated and when carbonates and hydrogencarbonates react with acids (see Experiments 12.3 and 12.4). Figure 13.10 shows the laboratory preparation and collection of carbon dioxide.

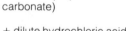

Marble chips (calcium carbonate)

+ dilute hydrochloric acid

(a) Carbon dioxide can be collected over water. It is only slightly soluble in water.

(b) Carbon dioxide, being denser than air, can be collected by downward delivery. As it is an invisible gas, it is difficult to tell when the gas jar is full.

Fig. 13.10 The preparation and collection of carbon dioxide

Fig. 13.11 Enjoying a solution of CO_2!

Properties of carbon dioxide

You have investigated the properties of carbon dioxide in Experiment 12.4. Carbon dioxide is colourless and odourless. Although it can be collected over water, it dissolves to a slight extent to give a solution of the weak acid, carbonic acid, H_2CO_3. Under pressure, the solubility of carbon dioxide increases. Dissolving carbon dioxide in water under pressure, and adding flavourings, has been turned into big business by the soft drinks industry. Many people enjoy these 'carbonated' drinks (Fig. 13.11). When the cap is taken off a bottle, the pressure is decreased, and carbon dioxide comes out of solution.

Carbon dioxide is denser than air, so it can be collected by downward delivery (Fig. 13.10b). It extinguishes a burning splint. The combination of its inability to support combustion and its high density makes carbon dioxide a suitable gas to use in fire-extinguishers (Fig. 13.12).

Some metals can burn in carbon dioxide. As you saw in Experiment 12.4, burning magnesium continues to burn in carbon dioxide. The temperature of the magnesium flame is high enough to bring about the reaction

magnesium + carbon dioxide → magnesium oxide + carbon

$$2Mg(s) \quad + \quad CO_2(g) \quad \rightarrow \quad 2MgO(s) \quad + \quad C(s)$$

Air is less dense than carbon dioxide; it stays above the blanket of carbon dioxide, and cannot reach the fire.
Being denser than air, carbon dioxide stays at ground level and keeps air away from the fire.

Fig. 13.12 Carbon dioxide as a fire-extinguisher

You can find out more about fire-extinguishers in Section 13.8.

13.6 The carbon cycle

In clean dry air the percentage by volume of carbon dioxide is 0.03%. This small percentage of carbon dioxide is essential to plants. They take in carbon dioxide through their leaves, and use it together with water taken in through their roots to **synthesise** sugars. The reaction will take place only in sunlight and only in green leaves, which possess the green pigment **chlorophyll** that catalyses the reaction. This reaction is called **photosynthesis**. (**Synthesis** means making a compound from its elements or from simpler substances; **photo** means light.)

Photosynthesis:

$$\text{sunlight} + \frac{\text{carbon}}{\text{dioxide}} + \text{water} \xrightarrow{\text{chlorophyll}} \frac{\text{glucose}}{\text{(a sugar)}} + \text{oxygen}$$

$$\text{energy} + 6CO_2(g) + 6H_2O(l) \longrightarrow C_6H_{12}O_6(aq) + 6O_2(g)$$

The energy of sunlight is transformed into the energy of the chemical bonds in glucose. In the process, oxygen is released. Glucose is converted into starch for storage in plants.

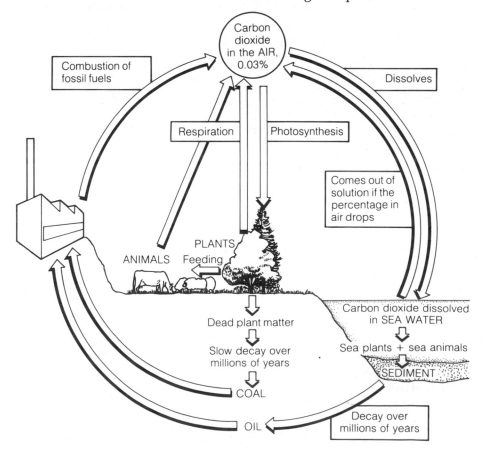

Fig. 13.13 The carbon cycle

The reverse reaction takes place in animals. In **respiration**, oxygen is used to oxidise sugars (and starches) to carbon dioxide and water with the release of energy (see Section 8.11). Plants respire to obtain energy.

————**photosynthesis** in plants: energy is stored ————→

sunlight and chlorophyll

energy + carbon dioxide + water ————→ sugars + oxygen

←—— **respiration** in animals and plants: energy is released ——

The processes which take carbon dioxide out of the air and the processes which put carbon dioxide into the air are delicately balanced. The balance is called the **carbon cycle**, and is shown in Fig. 13.13.

13.7 The greenhouse effect

The Earth's climate is affected by the levels of carbon dioxide and water vapour in the atmosphere. These gases are responsible for the **greenhouse effect**. The Earth is heated by the sun. Heat energy from the Earth is radiated back into space. The balance keeps the temperature of the planet fairly constant. If anything happens to upset the balance, the result will be a change in the world's climate. A rise in temperature could melt the ice caps at the North and South Poles. A fall could decrease the world's food production. Sunlight is radiation of wavelengths in the visible region of the spectrum. It passes unhindered through the atmosphere, unless it meets cloud cover. When the Earth sends heat energy back into space, it changes the wavelength to that of infrared radiation. Unlike sunlight, infrared radiation cannot travel freely through the air surrounding the Earth. Water vapour and carbon dioxide absorb infrared radiation. They act as 'blankets' round the Earth, hindering the escape of heat into space. Without these blankets, the Earth's surface would be $-40\,°C$, instead of a life-supporting $15\,°C$. If additional water vapour and carbon dioxide were added to the atmosphere, it would be like adding another blanket. The Earth would heat up. This blanketing by water vapour and carbon dioxide is called **the greenhouse effect** (Fig. 13.14).

The greenhouse effect was named, as you can imagine, after the way a greenhouse warms up. Sunlight enters through the glass panes, but infrared radiation has difficulty in escaping from the greenhouse through glass.

There is more water vapour than carbon dioxide in the atmosphere. Most of the greenhouse effect is due to the blanket of water vapour. There is a 'hole' in the water vapour blanket: it does not absorb radiation of certain wavelengths. Carbon dioxide covers part of the 'hole' by absorbing light at some of the wavelengths which water vapour allows to escape.

The natural carbon dioxide balance shown in Fig. 13.13 is being disturbed by the massive quantities of carbon dioxide that we send into the air by the combustion of coal and oil. The 'blanket' is getting thicker. Calculations have shown that the

Plants take carbon dioxide from the air in photosynthesis. Animals put carbon dioxide into the air in respiration. Nature maintains a balance between these processes called the **carbon cycle**.

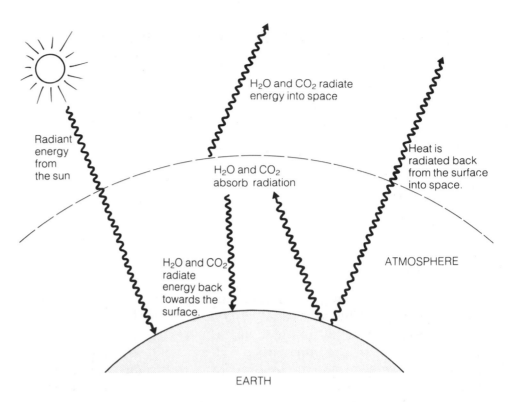

Fig. 13.14 The greenhouse effect

SUMMARY NOTE

A layer of carbon dioxide and water vapour surrounds the Earth. This layer reduces the amount of heat which the Earth radiates into space. By burning hydrocarbon fuels, we pour carbon dioxide and water vapour into the atmosphere. The layer of carbon dioxide and water vapour is growing thicker. If it becomes too thick, the Earth will warm up, and the ice caps could begin to melt.

We also put dust into the atmosphere. This has the effect of scattering some of the sun's radiation and cooling the Earth.

level of carbon dioxide could, at its present rate of increase, double in your lifetime. The result would be an increase of 2 °C in the average temperature of the Earth. This would mean that the massive ice caps of the Arctic and Antarctic regions would slowly begin to melt. The levels of oceans would begin to rise, and coastal areas would eventually be flooded.

Secondary effects would multiply the effect of carbon dioxide. The increase in temperature would make more water vaporise from the oceans. It would also drive out some of the carbon dioxide dissolved in the oceans. Thus, a still thicker greenhouse 'blanket' would be formed.

While some scientists are investigating the greenhouse effect, others are more concerned about the increasing level of particulate matter (dust etc., see Chapter 8). Sunlight which would otherwise reach the Earth is reflected into space by dust. Scientists have calculated that a fourfold increase in particulate matter would decrease the Earth's temperature by about 3 °C. They believe that such a fall in temperature would trigger a new ice age.

JUST TESTING 80

1 In the graph shown in Fig. 13.15, what could have caused the increase in temperature after 1920?

Fig. 13.15 Average temperatures this century

13.8 Fighting fire with carbon dioxide

The fire triangle

A fire needs three things: fuel, oxygen and heat. For every fuel there is an **ignition temperature**, below which the fuel will not burn. Heat is needed to raise the fuel to this temperature. The three essentials are represented by the three sides of the **fire triangle**; see Fig. 13.16. If one of the three sides is removed, the triangle will be destroyed: the fire will go out. Different fire-extinguishers attack different sides of the triangle.

Fuel. A fire can burn itself out. When fire-fighters are combating a forest fire, they cut down a band of trees in the path of the fire. Deprived of trees to burn, the fire cannot spread and gradually dies out.

Heat. The easiest way to remove heat is to throw water on to a fire (Fig. 13.17). The **soda–acid** type of extinguisher is able to provide a powerful jet of water quickly (see Fig. 13.18). There are some kinds of fires on which water cannot be used. Some metals (e.g. sodium and potassium) react with cold water. Other metals (e.g. magnesium and zinc) react with water when they are hot to produce the flammable gas hydrogen. Throwing water on to a blazing metal may therefore make the fire much worse.

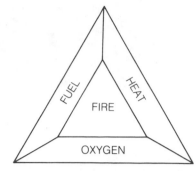

Fig. 13.16 The fire triangle

◁ Fig. 13.17 Fire-fighting

1 Strike the knob.

2 The knob smashes a bottle of concentrated sulphuric acid against a wire gauze.

3 Sulphuric acid reacts with the solution of sodium hydrogencarbonate. Carbon dioxide is formed.

4 The pressure of gas forces a jet of the aqueous solution out of the nozzle.

Fig. 13.18 A soda–acid extinguisher

Oil fires cannot be extinguished by water. Oil floats on top of water, and continues to burn. This is why fires at sea are so catastrophic.

Water should not be used on electrical fires. The firefighter could receive a shock from electricity conducted along the stream of water.

Trigger

Nozzle

Cylinder of carbon dioxide under pressure

Fig. 13.19 A pressurised carbon dioxide extinguisher

Fig. 13.20 A powder extinguisher

Why do they say you shouldn't throw water on to a blazing chip pan?

It makes burning oil splash out of the pan and spreads the fire.

What should you do then?

Switch off the gas or electricity. Wet a cloth and wring it out. Then cover the pan with the damp cloth. This will keep air out.

Oxygen. A carbon dioxide fire-extinguisher acts by starving a fire of oxygen. You may like to do Experiment 12.5 on fire-extinguishers. Figure 13.19 shows one type of carbon dioxide fire-extinguisher. It is a cylinder of carbon dioxide under pressure. When the pin is removed and the trigger is squeezed, a jet of carbon dioxide comes out of the nozzle. It lasts for about ½ minute. After use, the cylinder must be refilled ready for the next emergency.

Powder extinguishers also release carbon dioxide. They contain compounds which decompose to give carbon dioxide when thrown on to a fire, e.g. sodium hydrogencarbonate (see Experiment 12.5). Powder extinguishers are small and convenient for carrying in cars (Fig. 13.20). They can be used on oil fires and electrical fires.

Foam extinguishers use a combination of the cooling effect of water and the exclusion of air by carbon dioxide. The extinguisher is activated by striking a knob. This releases acid into a solution containing sodium hydrogencarbonate and a foam stabiliser. The acid and the hydrogencarbonate react to form carbon dioxide. The foam stabiliser prevents the bubbles of gas from escaping. A stream of foam — bubbles of carbon dioxide and aqueous solution — is propelled out of the nozzle. A layer of foam blankets the fire. It is denser than carbon dioxide alone. Foam cannot be used on the types of fires for which water is dangerous.

SUMMARY NOTE

The fire triangle:
Fuel: A fire will burn itself out if it runs out of fuel.
Heat: A fire will go out if you cool the fuel below its ignition temperature.
Oxygen: A fire will go out if it has insufficient oxygen. Many fire-extinguishers cover the fire with a dense layer of carbon dioxide to keep out oxygen.

JUST TESTING 81

1 What type of fire-extinguisher would you use on each of the following types of fire?
a a wood fire, **b** a fire in a magnesium factory, **c** a fire in a plastics factory, **d** a petrol fire, **e** a person whose clothing has caught fire, **f** a chip-pan fire, **g** a burning gas (e.g. natural gas), **h** an oil fire.

2 On which types of fire would you use each of the following types of extinguisher?
a soda–acid, **b** foam, **c** dry powder, **d** carbon dioxide under pressure.

13.9 Methods of collecting and drying gases

Collecting gases

You have noticed that different methods are used for collecting different gases. This section gives a summary of the available methods. They can be used to collect gases from the cylinders supplied by industrial manufacturers, or from laboratory apparatus.

Collecting over water.   A gas that is insoluble in water can be collected over water (see Fig. 8.13 for oxygen and Fig. 13.10a for carbon dioxide). The gas displaces the water in the gas jar. When the gas jar is full, it must be replaced by another. This method can be used for hydrogen, oxygen, chlorine, carbon dioxide and other insoluble gases. A little of the gas will dissolve in water.

Collecting by downward displacement.   A gas that is denser than air can be collected by downward displacement of air (see Fig. 13.10b for carbon dioxide). The gas displaces the air in the gas jar. This method can be used for chlorine, carbon dioxide, sulphur dioxide and other dense gases.

Collecting by upward displacement.   A gas that is less dense than air can be collected by upward displacement of air (see Fig. 13.21). This method can be used for ammonia.

Collecting in a gas syringe.   A gas supply can be connected to an empty gas syringe. As gas enters, it drives the plunger down the barrel (see Fig. 13.22). When the syringe is full, it must be replaced with another.

Fig. 13.21   Collecting by upward displacement (for a gas of low density)

SAFETY MATTERS
When collecting hydrogen, take care that there is no flame about. Hydrogen forms an explosive mixture with air.

Fig. 13.22   Collecting a gas in a gas syringe

Drying gases

Methods of drying gases are shown in Fig. 13.23. They can be used when gases are collected by upward or downward displacement of air, or in a gas syringe.

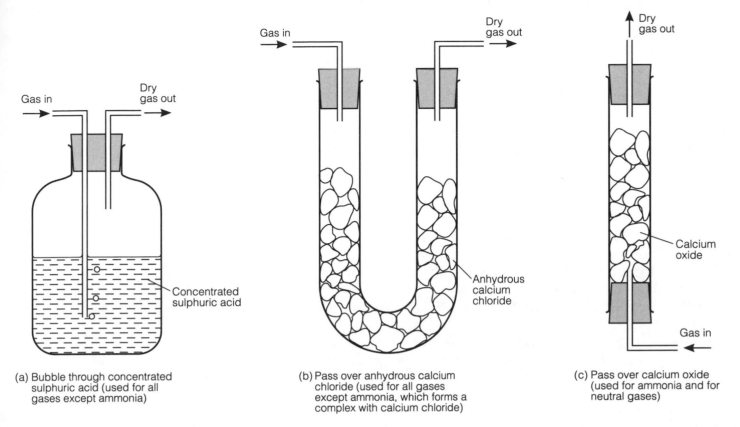

(a) Bubble through concentrated sulphuric acid (used for all gases except ammonia)

(b) Pass over anhydrous calcium chloride (used for all gases except ammonia, which forms a complex with calcium chloride)

(c) Pass over calcium oxide (used for ammonia and for neutral gases)

Fig. 13.23 Methods of drying gases

JUST TESTING 82

1 a Why is the method of Fig. 13.10a not used for collecting ammonia?
b Why is the method of Fig. 13.21 not used for collecting sulphur dioxide?

2 a Why is method (a) of Fig. 13.23 not used for drying ammonia?
b Why is method (c) of Fig. 13.23 not used for drying sulphur dioxide?

3 Rubinda was asked to fill some gas jars with dry oxygen from a cylinder of oxygen. She bubbled the gas through concentrated sulphuric acid, as in Fig. 13.23a, and then collected it as shown in Fig. 8.13.
a What did Rubinda achieve by bubbling the gas through concentrated sulphuric acid?
b Can you suggest a better method of collecting dry oxygen?

4 Carbon dioxide can be collected by either method (a) or method (b) of Fig. 13.10.
a State an advantage of method (a) over method (b).
b Sketch the apparatus you would use to collect dry carbon dioxide.

13.10 Sand and limestone:
a four-thousand-year-old combination

Seeing round corners

Mr Murray believes he has a stomach ulcer. The X-ray
photographs show nothing abnormal, and his doctor is
unconvinced. The doctor decides to take a look. He slips a thin,
flexible plastic tube about 1 metre long down Mr Murray's
throat. Mr Murray is mildly sedated but fully conscious. The
doctor peers down the tube to view the pinkish-white walls of
his patient's oesophagus. How can he see down a bent tube? The
reason is that the tube contains a bundle of **glass fibres**.

The individual glass fibres are as thin as a human hair and as
pliable. As each glass fibre is drawn out, it is sealed in a
protective coating of plastic. A bundle of glass fibres can follow
the tortuous turns of the digestive tract without snapping. Light
travelling along one bundle of glass fibres illuminates the tissues.
A second bundle of fibres carries a colour image back to the
doctor's eyes.

The tube, the doctor's **endoscope**, moves further on its way to
his patient's stomach. He is looking for ulcers, but suddenly the
endoscope shows up a patch of white tissue. It looks like the
first sign of a cancer. The X-ray photograph has not picked it up
because slight changes in colour are not detected by X-rays. An
attachment allows the doctor to take a photograph of the cancer
as he plans the operation he will have to do.

Looking through glass

Glass fibres are made from **optical** glass, a very pure kind of
glass. Optical glass is made from the same materials as ordinary
window glass: sand (silicon(IV) oxide, SiO_2), limestone (calcium
carbonate, $CaCO_3$) and sodium carbonate (Na_2CO_3). The recipe for
glass is 4500 years old. The ancient Egyptians discovered it.
When they melted sand with limestone and sodium carbonate,
they obtained a transparent material, glass. Egypt is one of the
few places where sodium carbonate occurs naturally.

Silicon(IV) oxide, SiO_2, is a crystalline substance. It has a
macromolecular structure (see Fig. 13.24). In glass, many of the
Si—O bonds have been broken, and the ordered arrangement has
been largely destroyed. Glass is a mixture of calcium silicate,
$CaSiO_3$, and sodium silicate, Na_2SiO_3. Glass is neither a liquid
nor a crystalline solid. It is a **supercooled liquid**: it appears to be
solid, but has no sharp melting point. X-rays show that the
regular, orderly packing of atoms found in other solids is not
present in glass.

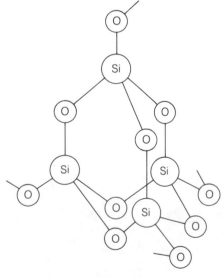

Fig. 13.24 The structure of silicon(IV)
oxide

Speaking through glass

High-grade optical glass is made from pure silicon(IV) oxide
instead of sand. Optical fibre costs about £1 per metre.

The main future of optical fibres lies in communications. A
telephone exchange needs to use thick copper cables to transmit

hundreds of telephone calls simultaneously. A pair of optical glass fibres will replace a thick copper cable. It can carry 10 000 simultaneous calls, transmitting them in the form of pulses of light. Each pattern of sound is converted into a pulse of light. The pulses of light are decoded by the receiver and converted back into sound. Optical fibres will carry a beam of light for a distance of 10 km. Fibres can be joined to cover longer distances.

Through optical fibre cables, two-way television is possible; that is, people can speak and also see each other at the same time. In the future, we shall have more sophisticated services than copper wire can provide. People will be able to communicate with shops, libraries and hospitals by two-way television.

13.11 Silicon

Silicon is the second most abundant element in the Earth's crust (see Fig. 11.24). It occurs as silicon(IV) oxide, SiO_2, in sand and quartz and as silicates (compounds of silicon, oxygen and a metal) in clays and many rocks. Many of the silicates in clays and rocks contain aluminium, and chemists are working on methods of extracting aluminium from them (see Section 11.12). Asbestos is an **aluminosilicate**.

Silicon(IV) oxide or **silica** is our source of the element silicon. Silicon is a dark-coloured shiny solid which melts at 1410 °C. It is in Group 4 of the Periodic Table, beneath carbon. The importance of silicon as a semiconductor has been described in Section 3.4. When it is heated with carbon at a high temperature, silicon(IV) oxide is reduced to silicon:

$$\text{silicon(IV) oxide} + \text{carbon} \xrightarrow{\text{heat}} \text{silicon} + \text{carbon monoxide}$$

$$SiO_2(s) + 2C(s) \rightarrow Si(s) + 2CO(g)$$

When sand is reduced, the silicon formed is not pure. Several stages of purification are needed to transform it into the very pure silicon used in silicon chips.

13.12 Some problems and their solutions

For thousands of years, craftsmen used glass without knowing anything about its chemistry. Since chemists began to study glass, they have invented many new types. Let us look at some of the problems they tackled. Glass is in the forefront of modern technology.

Problem 1 The problem was to make glass which would stand sudden changes in temperature without breaking.

Solution The solution was to add boron oxide during manufacture. The result was Pyrex® glass.

How was the problem solved? A search was made for oxides sufficiently like silicon(IV) oxide to form a glass but with somewhat different properties. From their positions in the Periodic Table, you would expect boron and silicon to have similar oxides.

Problem 2 The problem was to make plates of glass which are the same thickness all over. This is necessary for window glass.

The old solution was to grind a sheet of glass to the required thickness and smoothness. In the process, 30% of the sheet was wasted.

The new solution was found by the Pilkington Glass Company. It is the **float glass** process. A stream of molten glass flows on to a bath of molten tin. As the glass cools and solidifies, both the top and the bottom surfaces are perfectly smooth and parallel (Fig. 13.25). The speed at which the glass is drawn out of the float tank determines the thickness of the glass.

Fig. 13.25 Float glass is washed before being automatically cut and stacked

How was the problem solved? A team of chemists and engineers in St. Helens, Lancashire, worked for 7 years to perfect the process. They had to overcome enormous problems with the revolutionary new process. It is now used all over the world.

Problem 3 The problem was to make sunglasses which darken in bright light and lighten again when the light fades.

Solution The solution was to include silver chloride in the glass. The silver salt darkens on exposure to light in the same way as do the silver salts in photographic film. Photosensitive glass reverts to colourless when the light fades.

How was the problem solved? Chemists applied their knowledge of what happens in photography to a different situation.

SUMMARY NOTE

You may like to read about these examples of problem-solving in the glass industry:

- how to avoid breakage
- how to make plate glass
- how to make light-sensitive glass
- how to make glass ceramic
- how to make a soluble glass.

Fig. 13.26

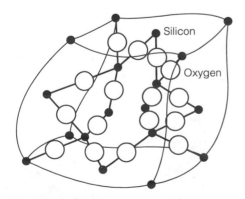

Fig. 13.27 Bonding in silica glass (a distorted silica structure, see Fig. 13.24)

Problem 4 Here the solution came before the problem! How? By accident! A researcher left some photosensitive glass in a furnace overnight. He found that the glass had become opaque. Believing that glass you cannot see through is useless, he threw it out, and found to his surprise that the glass would not break. He had made **glass ceramic**, which is almost unbreakable.

The problem of finding uses for the new material was not difficult. Makers of ovenware and electrical insulation immediately seized on glass ceramic. It is now found in the nose cones of space rockets and the tiles of space shuttles.

Problem 5 In many tropical countries, the disease **bilharzia** (or **schistosomiasis**) is a blight. It is carried by water snails. Scientists discovered that these snails can be killed by copper salts in quite low concentrations. How can health officers maintain a steady, low concentration of copper compounds in the streams and ponds where the snails live?

Solution The copper compounds can be incorporated into a **soluble glass**. To make a soluble glass, phosphorus(V) oxide, P_2O_5, is used instead of silicon(IV) oxide. When pellets of the copper-containing glass are put into the water, they dissolve slowly, releasing copper compounds gradually into the snail-infested water. This treatment is more effective than a single large dose of copper compounds.

Problem 6 A herd of sheep is grazing on land which is short of three essential **trace elements**. (These are elements which are needed in very small quantities.) The farmer wants a convenient method of adding these three elements to their diet. Can you solve his problem?

13.13 Ceramics

An important class of materials is **ceramics**. Brick and pottery are ceramics. Traditional ceramics such as these are derived from the raw materials clay and silica. They are formed on, for example, a potter's wheel and hardened in a fire kiln.

Ceramics are crystalline compounds: they consist of an ordered arrangement of atoms. Many are compounds of metallic and non-metallic elements, e.g. silicon or aluminium combined with oxygen, carbon or nitrogen. Examples of modern ceramics are: soda glass; silica glass (Fig. 13.27); aluminium oxide, Al_2O_3; zirconium oxide, ZrO_2; titanium carbide, TiC; zirconium carbide, ZrC; tungsten carbide, WC; silicon carbide, SiC; and silicon nitride, SiN. A ceramic is made by grinding the components to fine powders, mixing them and heating the mixture to a high temperature under high pressure in an electric kiln.

New uses are being found for ceramics all the time. They are used in spacecraft, in medicine, e.g. as artificial bones, in engineering, e.g. in cutting tools, engine parts and turbine blades, and in electronic components. Details of these uses are given overleaf.

The bonding in ceramics may be ionic or covalent. The bonds are directed in space, and the structure is therefore more rigid than a metallic structure. This structure makes ceramics

- crystalline
- hard (able to cut steel and glass)
- of high melting point
- poor conductors of heat and electricity because they lack free electrons
- usually opaque because light is reflected by grain boundaries in the crystal structure
- not ductile or malleable or plastic, except at high temperature
- rather brittle because the bonds are rigid, making it difficult to change the shape without breaking.

What is as hard as diamond, as strong as steel and as low in density as aluminium?

Sialon – a ceramic made of silicon, aluminium, oxygen and nitrogen.

Applications of ceramics

Vehicle components.   A ceramic coating on cast iron improves resistance to wear and tear and heat and therefore extends the life of engine parts. Ceramic bearings can operate at high speeds without lubricants. Research is going on into the use of ceramics to allow diesel engines and jet engines to run at higher temperatures. The higher the temperature at which an engine operates, the more efficiently it runs and the less fuel it consumes.

Gas turbine blades.   Blades made of ceramics, e.g. silicon nitride, can run at higher temperatures than blades made of alloys.

Machine tools.   Tools made of ceramics can rotate twice as fast as metal tools without deforming or wearing out.

Bioceramics.   Recently, chemists have been working on the possibility of using ceramics as implant materials. At present, alloys and polymers are used for replacements for e.g. hips, knees and teeth. Ceramics would be stronger and wear better than alloys or polymers and would never corrode. For replacing damaged bone, a porous ceramic implant would have the advantage that bone could grow into and bond with the implant.

Spacecraft.   When a space shuttle re-enters Earth's atmosphere, the outside temperature can reach 1500 °C. A covering of ceramic tiles protects the space shuttle. Each tile consists of very fine fibres coated with silica. The fibres are loosely packed: 95% of the tiles is air, which gives them their insulating property.

Optical materials.   Recent developments include new kinds of glass (see Section 13.12), glass fibres (see Section 13.10) and improved solar cells (see Section 20.2).

Fig. 13.28   Space-age ceramics

JUST TESTING 83

1 What is the chief difference between the methods used to fire traditional ceramics and those used for modern ceramics?
2 Explain why ceramic tiles are fitted to space shuttles.
3 Why is glass transparent and china opaque?
4 Explain why ceramics are **a** harder than metals, **b** more brittle than metals, and **c** poor electrical conductors.
5 What is the advantage of a ceramic over (i) an alloy, and (ii) a hard plastic for use as **a** a false tooth, **b** a knee implant, and **c** an artificial middle ear?

Exercise 13

1 a State the approximate percentages by volume of nitrogen and oxygen in air.
b Which of these gases is important in respiration?
c Give the names of the substances which are produced in respiration.
d Describe a test for each of these substances.
e Name the reactants and the products involved in photosynthesis.
f What other substance is needed for photosynthesis to take place?

2 a Where are the great reserves of carbon in nature?
b How does the flow of carbon dioxide into and out of the atmosphere take place (i) over land and (ii) over the sea?
c How is the burning of fossil fuels affecting the carbon cycle?
d The air near the ground in a cornfield in summer contains less carbon dioxide by day than by night. Why is this?
e The concentration of carbon dioxide in the atmosphere near the Earth increases during the winter and decreases during the summer. Why is this?
f Sea water is slightly alkaline. Fresh water is slightly acidic. In which type of water would you expect the rate of photosynthesis to be greater? Assume that the solubility of carbon dioxide in the two different kinds of water is the important factor.

3 a Why is carbon dioxide the best type of extinguisher to use on an electrical fire? Why is water not used?

b Name one type of fire which would not be extinguished by carbon dioxide. Explain why this fire would continue to burn.

4 a What is the limewater test for carbon dioxide? How does it work? What happens when you bubble carbon dioxide through limewater for a long time?
b Explain how falling on to limestone rocks makes water hard.
c Why does hard water produce 'fur' in kettles?

5 Each year, 8 million tonnes of sulphuric acid are produced in the US as a by-product of the smelting of sulphide ores. The sulphuric acid is discharged into streams.
a Calculate the mass of calcium oxide (quicklime) needed to neutralise it by means of the reaction:

$$\text{calcium oxide} + \text{sulphuric acid} \rightarrow \text{calcium sulphate} + \text{water}$$

$$CaO(s) + H_2SO_4(aq) \rightarrow CaSO_4(aq) + H_2O(l)$$

b Calculate the mass of calcium carbonate (limestone) that must be heated in a lime kiln to make the calcium oxide needed in **a**.

6

Why should I bother buying stuff in returnable bottles and then having to cart the empties back to the shop?

Go on, tell him why!

7 a What property of pure silicon crystals makes them useful as transistors?

b How can sand be reduced to silicon?

c In the manufacture of glass, what materials are added to provide (i) silicon and (ii) sodium?

d In what group of the Periodic Table are carbon and silicon?

e What type of chemical bond is present in $SiCl_4$?

f Why is silicon(IV) oxide, SiO_2, a high melting point solid, whereas carbon dioxide, CO_2, is a gas?

8 At present, scientists do not know how serious the threat from the greenhouse effect really is. Imagine that a group of scientists were to obtain new evidence that convinced everyone that the threat from the greenhouse effect is very serious. They work out that, by the year 2000, the rise in temperature will start to create deserts and to melt ice caps.

The urgent problem would be to reduce the level of carbon dioxide in the atmosphere. Discuss the ways in which nations would have to cooperate to solve this problem. Say how national aims would have to come second to world aims. Which countries would be most affected? What would happen to the developing nations' drive to industrialise? Would nuclear power help to solve the problem?

Draw up a world plan for action to reduce the level of carbon dioxide in the air. Say how you would persuade nations to follow the plan.

This is rather a big question for one person! Perhaps you should form a small group to tackle it. Or a number of groups could work out solutions and then compare notes.

Career sketch: Science editor

Selima is an editor. She works for a publisher of scientific books. Her job is to read a typescript which an author has written and prepare it for the printer. She tells the printer what size of print to use and how to arrange the headings, diagrams and photographs. She also checks the typescript very carefully for mistakes. If she finds passages which are not clear, she suggests how they can be rewritten. Selima took a degree in chemistry and biology and then did a course in publishing at a polytechnic.

CHAPTER 14   *Chemicals from sulphur*

14.1 Sulphur

General Cortes ran out of sulphur in 1521. He had set sail from Spain in 1518 to conquer Mexico. When he ran out of ammunition in 1521, he knew he would have to make his own gunpowder. Two of the ingredients were easy to find in Mexico. The third was sulphur, and the only place he could find it was in the crater of a volcano called Popocatepetl. At the bottom, a flame was burning. Yellow clouds of sulphur vapour swirled upwards, and deposited solid sulphur on the sides of the crater. A volunteer was lowered inside a large basket. He filled the basket with sulphur scraped from the sides of the crater, and was hauled up again. He descended again and again until he had collected 150 kilograms of sulphur. From this, the Spaniards were able to make enough gunpowder to keep the army of occupation supplied until a shipment could be sent from Spain.

Fig. 14.1 One way to obtain sulphur — from your neighbourhood volcano

Charles Goodyear was rather careless with sulphur in 1839. He had some lying on his laboratory bench while he was experimenting with rubber. Rubber is obtained by cutting the bark of certain tropical trees. It trickles out in the form of a liquid called latex. Latex solidifies when ethanoic acid is added. Goodyear accidentally spilt some rubber on to a mound of sulphur. When he picked up the rubber, it had turned from a soft, pliable substance into a much harder material. He quickly realised that he had made a tougher, more hard-wearing, more useful material than pure rubber. The process of **vulcanisation** was born (Fig. 14.2). In vulcanisation, rubber is mixed with sulphur, and the mixture is heated. Hard rubber, such as that used for motor tyres, contains 10% to 50% sulphur (Fig. 14.3).

The tyre industry needs enormous quantities of sulphur. What is this useful substance? Where does the industry obtain it?

Fig. 14.2 Making tyres

Fig. 14.3 Vehicle tyres

Sulphur is a non-metallic element. It does not conduct heat or electricity. It is a brittle, yellow solid, which melts at 112 °C and boils at 444 °C.

Sulphur is found **native**, that is, as free sulphur, in Sicily, Poland and the USA.

Some of the uses of sulphur are shown in Fig. 14.4, and the reactions are summarised in Fig. 14.7.

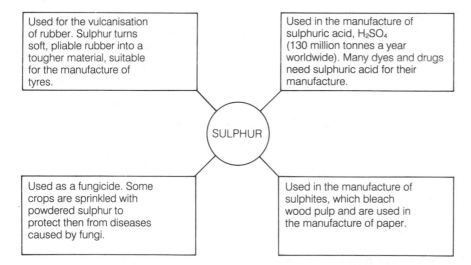

Used for the vulcanisation of rubber. Sulphur turns soft, pliable rubber into a tougher material, suitable for the manufacture of tyres.

Used in the manufacture of sulphuric acid, H_2SO_4 (130 million tonnes a year worldwide). Many dyes and drugs need sulphuric acid for their manufacture.

SULPHUR

Used as a fungicide. Some crops are sprinkled with powdered sulphur to protect then from diseases caused by fungi.

Used in the manufacture of sulphites, which bleach wood pulp and are used in the manufacture of paper.

Fig. 14.4 Some of the uses of sulphur

14.2 Allotropes of sulphur

There are two kinds of crystalline sulphur. They are called **rhombic** and **monoclinic** sulphur. Rhombic sulphur is formed when a solution of sulphur is allowed to crystallise below 96 °C (see Experiment 13.1). Methylbenzene can be used as a solvent. Monoclinic sulphur is formed when molten sulphur solidifies.

The two forms of pure sulphur have the same chemical reactions (see Fig. 14.7). They are both pure sulphur. The two forms of the element have crystals of different shapes and are called **allotropes** (see Fig. 14.5).

When solid sulphur is heated, it melts at 112 °C. On further heating, it becomes a **viscous** (treacle-like) liquid. When this

Above 96 °C, monoclinic sulphur is the stable form.

Below 96 °C, rhombic sulphur is the stable form.

Rhombic sulphur crystal (magnified 20×)

Monoclinic sulphur crystal (magnified 20×)

Fig. 14.5 The allotropes of sulphur ▷

viscous liquid is poured into cold water, it forms **plastic** sulphur (see Fig. 14.6). As plastic sulphur is not a **crystalline** form of the element, it is not an allotrope. Some of the reactions of sulphur are shown in Fig. 14.7.

Solid sulphur consists of S_8 molecules.

In molten sulphur, long chains of sulphur atoms become entangled. They make the liquid **viscous** (treacle like).
When it is poured into cold water, the liquid solidifies with the atoms in long chains. This is how plastic sulphur is made.

Fig. 14.6 Sulphur molecules

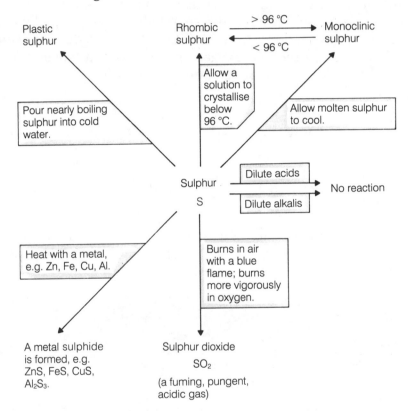

Fig. 14.7 Some reactions of sulphur

SUMMARY NOTE

- Sulphur was used in gunpowder. It is now used in **vulcanisation**, a method of toughening rubber.
- Sulphur is a non-metallic element. It exists in allotropic forms, rhombic and monoclinic. Some reactions of sulphur are shown in Fig. 14.7.

JUST TESTING 84

1 Describe and explain what happens when sulphur is
   a burned in air (see Section 8.9)
   b heated with iron (see Experiment 3.4).

2 Sulphur is a non-metallic element. Give two physical properties and two chemical properties of sulphur which back up this statement.

14.3 Sulphur dioxide

When sulphur burns, sulphur dioxide is formed (Experiment 13.2):

sulphur + oxygen → sulphur dioxide

$S(s)$ $+ O_2(g)$ → $SO_2(g)$

Fig. 14.8

Sulphur dioxide is a gas with a very unpleasant, penetrating smell. It 'fumes' in moist air. It reacts with water vapour to form a mist. It is very unpleasant to breathe, causing congestion followed by choking.

The food industry uses sulphur dioxide as a preservative. It is added in small quantities to foods such as those shown in Fig. 14.8. It prevents the growth of moulds and bacteria.

*Sulphur dioxide is also a useful bleach (see Experiment 13.2). It is mild in its action and can be used on wool and silk, as well as on paper and straw. These materials are coloured by dyes which contain oxygen. Sulphur dioxide is a **reducing agent**, that is to say, it can remove oxygen from other substances. The **reduced** form of the dye that remains is colourless:

coloured form of dye	+	solution of sulphur dioxide	→	colourless form of dye	+	oxidation product of sulphur dioxide
(dye + oxygen)	+	$SO_2(aq)$	→	(dye)	+	oxidation product of $SO_2(aq)$

The colourless substance formed is gradually oxidised by air to form the coloured dye again. This is why straw, silk and paper turn yellow with age.

Fig. 14.9 Straw boaters

Fig. 14.10 The paper industry

What happens to the solution of sulphur dioxide when it is oxidised? Sulphur dioxide is extremely soluble in water. It reacts with water to form the weak acid, sulphurous acid, H_2SO_3:

sulphur + water → sulphurous
dioxide acid

$SO_2(g)$ + $H_2O(l)$ → $H_2SO_3(aq)$

Sulphurous acid is slowly oxidised by oxygen in the air to sulphuric acid, H_2SO_4. Sulphuric acid is formed whenever sulphurous acid accepts oxygen from an oxidising agent:

sulphurous + oxygen from the air → sulphuric
acid or from an oxidising agent acid

$H_2SO_3(aq)$ + (O) → $H_2SO_4(aq)$

This reaction is the basis of two tests for sulphur dioxide. When it reduces the oxidising agents potassium dichromate(VI), $K_2Cr_2O_7$, and potassium manganate(VII), $KMnO_4$, there is a change in colour (see Fig. 14.11):

potassium dichromate(IV), orange + SO_2 → green and then blue

potassium manganate(VII), purple + SO_2 → colourless

The gas jar contains sulphur dioxide. A strip of paper spotted with potassium dichromate(VI) turns from orange to blue. A spot of potassium manganate(VII) turns from purple to colourless.

Fig. 14.11 Testing for sulphur dioxide

*14.4 Sulphites

Being an acid gas, sulphur dioxide reacts with bases. Salts of sulphurous acid called **sulphites** are formed. For example, when sulphur dioxide is bubbled into sodium hydroxide solution, sodium sulphite is formed:

sulphur + sodium → sodium + water
dioxide hydroxide sulphite

$SO_2(g)$ + $2NaOH(aq)$ → $Na_2SO_3(aq)$ + $H_2O(l)$

The weak acid, sulphurous acid, is driven out of its salts by strong acids, e.g. hydrochloric acid. This reaction is used as a method of preparing sulphur dioxide in the laboratory:

sodium + hydrochloric → sulphur + sodium + water
sulphite acid dioxide chloride

$Na_2SO_3(s)$ + $2HCl(aq)$ → $SO_2(g)$ + $2NaCl(aq)$ + $H_2O(l)$

It is also used as a **test for a sulphite**.
The reactions of sulphur dioxide are summarised in Fig. 14.12.

SUMMARY NOTE

Sulphur dioxide is a gas with a pungent smell. It is used as a food preservative and as a bleach. Sulphur dioxide is a reducing agent. It is an acidic gas, which reacts with bases to form salts called sulphites. A strong acid drives sulphur dioxide out of sulphites.

JUST TESTING 85

1 Describe two chemical tests for sulphur dioxide.

2 a Name the acid formed when sulphur dioxide dissolves in water.
  b What are the salts of this acid called?
  c What must be added to these salts to make them give sulphur dioxide?

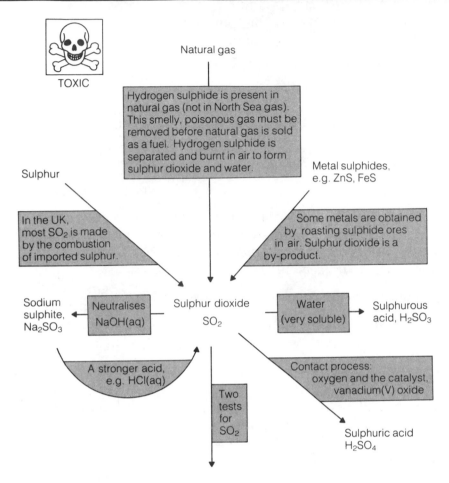

Turns potassium manganate(VII), KMnO$_4$, from purple to colourless.
Turns potassium dichromate(VI), K$_2$Cr$_2$O$_7$, from orange to blue–green.

Fig. 14.12 Some reactions of sulphur ◁ dioxide

14.5 *Sulphuric acid*

Figure 14.13 shows a phosphate fertiliser in use. The most plentiful source of phosphate is 'rock phosphate', an ore containing calcium phosphate. It has the disadvantage of being insoluble. The fertiliser industry uses it as the starting point in the manufacture of the soluble fertiliser, ammonium phosphate. Sulphuric acid is essential to the process. Calcium phosphate reacts with sulphuric acid to make phosphoric acid which is neutralised by ammonia to give ammonium phosphate. Sulphuric acid turns something we have plenty of — calcium phosphate — into something we need plenty of — fertiliser. 'Superphosphate' is another soluble phosphate fertiliser made from 'rock phosphate' and sulphuric acid. Figure 14.14 summarises the uses of sulphuric acid.

Fig. 14.13 Applying fertiliser

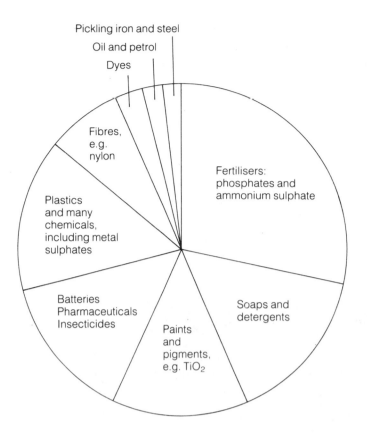

Fig. 14.14 The main uses of sulphuric acid (130 million tonnes a year worldwide)

The labels in the figure: Pickling iron and steel; Oil and petrol; Dyes; Fibres, e.g. nylon; Plastics and many chemicals, including metal sulphates; Batteries Pharmaceuticals Insecticides; Paints and pigments, e.g. TiO$_2$; Fertilisers: phosphates and ammonium sulphate; Soaps and detergents

14.6 Manufacture of sulphuric acid: the Contact Process

The Contact Process for the manufacture of sulphuric acid takes place in stages:

$$\text{sulphur} \rightarrow \begin{array}{c}\text{sulphur}\\\text{dioxide}\end{array} \rightarrow \begin{array}{c}\text{sulphur}\\\text{trioxide}\end{array} \rightarrow \begin{array}{c}\text{sulphuric}\\\text{acid}\end{array}$$

$$\text{S} \rightarrow SO_2 \rightarrow SO_3 \rightarrow H_2SO_4$$

*Conditions which give a good yield of sulphur trioxide

Sulphur dioxide and oxygen react to form sulphur trioxide:

$$2SO_2(g) + O_2(g) \rightleftharpoons 2SO_3(g)$$

The reaction is reversible: it will take place from right to left as well as from left to right. The proportion of sulphur trioxide present in the equilibrium mixture depends on the temperature and pressure.

The effect of changing the temperature or the pressure can be predicted from **Le Chatelier's Principle**. This states that: *When conditions are changed, a system in a state of equilibrium adjusts itself in such a way as to minimise the effects of the change.*

What happens when the pressure changes? How can the system minimise the effect of an increase in pressure? Well, the system can minimise the effect of an increase in pressure by decreasing in volume.

How can the system decrease in volume? It can convert
sulphur dioxide and oxygen into sulphur trioxide. It follows from
the equation that:

> 3 moles of the mixture of sulphur dioxide and oxygen form
> 2 moles of sulphur trioxide, so
> 3 volumes of the mixture form 2 volumes of sulphur trioxide
> (see Section 12.10).

Therefore if the pressure is increased, the mixture of gases will
reduce its volume by reacting to form more sulphur trioxide.

Industry. High pressure should favour the forward reaction.
However, sulphur dioxide is easily liquefied, so the Contact
Process uses a pressure of only 2 atm.

***What happens when the temperature changes? How can the
system absorb heat and minimise the effect of an increase in
temperature?***
The reaction from left to right is exothermic (gives out heat). The
reverse reaction, the dissociation of sulphur trioxide, is
endothermic (absorbs heat). The system can absorb heat by the
dissociation of sulphur trioxide. Running the process at high
temperature therefore reduces the yield.

Industry. The Contact Process uses a moderate temperature
(about 450 °C). The use of a catalyst (see Section 21.7) increases
the speed of the reaction. The original Contact Process used
platinum as the catalyst. It is easily 'poisoned' (made inactive) by
traces of impurities in the gases. Vanadium(V) oxide, V_2O_5, is now
used as the catalyst because it is cheaper and less easily
poisoned.

The industrial process

A flow diagram of the Contact Process is shown in Fig. 14.15.
The sulphur dioxide needed is obtained from

- the combustion of sulphur
- the removal of unpleasant-smelling sulphur compounds from
  petroleum oil
- the removal of hydrogen sulphide from natural gas (not North
  Sea gas)
- roasting metal sulphides in order to extract metals from their
  ores.

Sulphur dioxide and air are purified by electrostatic precipitation
(see Fig. 8.25).

A sulphuric acid plant must be sited in a place where supplies
of sulphur dioxide can reach it, that is, near a port where
cargoes of sulphur can arrive by ship, or near a gas refinery or a
metal smelter.

Fig. 14.15 Flow diagram for the Contact Process for the manufacture of sulphuric acid

Reaction of sulphur trioxide and water

Sulphur trioxide reacts with water to give sulphuric acid:

$$SO_3(g) + H_2O(l) \rightarrow H_2SO_4(l)$$

This reaction is troublesome to carry out on an industrial scale. As soon as sulphur trioxide meets water vapour, it forms a mist of sulphuric acid. Instead of water, sulphuric acid is used to absorb sulphur trioxide. Oleum is formed. On dilution with water, this gives sulphuric acid:

sulphur trioxide + sulphuric acid → oleum
$$SO_3(g) + H_2SO_4(l) \rightarrow H_2S_2O_7(l)$$

oleum + water → sulphuric acid
$$H_2S_2O_7(l) + H_2O(l) \rightarrow 2H_2SO_4(l)$$

14.7 Reactions of sulphuric acid

Dilute sulphuric acid

When concentrated sulphuric acid is mixed with water, a large amount of heat is given out. This is why making dilute sulphuric acid can be a dangerous job if it is not done properly. You must never add water to the concentrated acid. It can reach boiling point in localised regions and boil and splash out of the container. When you add the concentrated acid to water, and stir, the water can absorb the heat given out (see Fig. 14.16).

The reactions of dilute acids were covered in Chapter 7. The reactions of dilute sulphuric acid are summarised in Fig. 14.17.

281

Here lies Gillian, still and placid; she added water to the acid.
Clever Jane did as she oughter: added the acid to the water.

Anon

Fig. 14.16

A white precipitate of barium sulphate, $BaSO_4(s)$, shows that a sulphate is present.

Test for a sulphate:
Add barium chloride solution + dil. hydrochloric acid $(BaCl_2(aq) + HCl(aq))$ to a solution of a suspected sulphate.

Metals (e.g. Zn)

Metal sulphate + carbon dioxide ← Metal carbonates (e.g. Na_2CO_3) ← $H_2SO_4(aq)$ → Metal sulphate + hydrogen (e.g. $ZnSO_4 + H_2$)

DILUTE SULPHURIC ACID

REACTIONS OF A TYPICAL ACID

Metal sulphites (e.g. Na_2SO_3)

Bases (metal oxides, e.g. CuO, and hydroxides)

Alkalis, soluble bases, e.g. NaOH(aq), $NH_3(aq)$

Metal sulphate + sulphur dioxide

Metal sulphate + water (e.g. $CuSO_4 + H_2O$)

Metal sulphates e.g. Na_2SO_4, $(NH_4)_2SO_4$

Fig. 14.17 Reactions of dilute sulphuric acid

Concentrated sulphuric acid

When concentrated, sulphuric acid has other reactions (see Fig. 14.18). It acts as a drying agent and as a dehydrating agent.

Reactions as a drying agent. A **drying agent** removes water from mixtures. Gases are bubbled through concentrated sulphuric acid to dry them.

*Reactions as a dehydrating agent. A **dehydrating agent** removes the elements H_2O from compounds.

282

1 Concentrated sulphuric acid dehydrates copper(II) sulphate crystals:

copper(II) sulphate-5-water $\rightarrow$ copper(II) sulphate + water
(blue crystals)   (white, anhydrous)

$$CuSO_4 \cdot 5H_2O(s) \xrightarrow{\text{conc. } H_2SO_4} CuSO_4(s) + 5H_2O(l)$$

Heat is given out as concentrated sulphuric acid reacts with the water of crystallisation, just as it is when you add concentrated sulphuric acid to water.

2 When carbohydrates (sugars and starches) are dehydrated, carbon remains:

glucose (a sugar) $\rightarrow$ carbon (sugar charcoal) + water

$$C_6H_{12}O_6(s) \xrightarrow{\text{conc. } H_2SO_4(l)} 6C(s) + 6H_2O(l)$$

The reaction is exothermic.

Fig. 14.18 The reactions of concentrated sulphuric acid

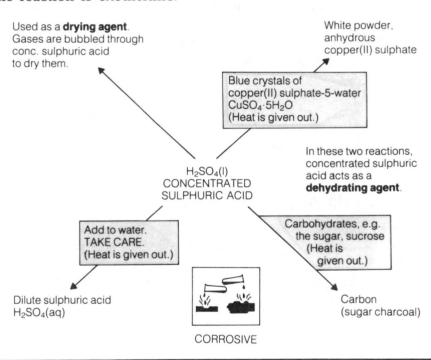

Used as a **drying agent**.
Gases are bubbled through
conc. sulphuric acid
to dry them.

White powder,
anhydrous
copper(II) sulphate

Blue crystals of
copper(II) sulphate-5-water
$CuSO_4 \cdot 5H_2O$
(Heat is given out.)

$H_2SO_4(l)$
CONCENTRATED
SULPHURIC ACID

In these two reactions,
concentrated sulphuric
acid acts as a
dehydrating agent.

Add to water.
TAKE CARE.
(Heat is given out.)

Carbohydrates, e.g.
the sugar, sucrose
(Heat is
given out.)

Dilute sulphuric acid
$H_2SO_4(aq)$

CORROSIVE

Carbon
(sugar charcoal)

SUMMARY NOTE

Concentrated sulphuric acid is a drying agent and a dehydrating agent. Heat is given out when it reacts with water.

JUST TESTING 86

1 A bottle is labelled 'dilute sulphuric acid'. How could you show that it is an acid? How could you prove that it contains sulphate ions?

2 Under what conditions does sulphuric acid react with **a** zinc, **b** copper(II) oxide, **c** copper(II) sulphate-5-water? State what products are formed in each of these reactions.

3 What is the difference between a drying agent and a dehydrating agent?

4 Describe the manufacture of sulphuric acid. How could a country which has no sulphur deposits economise on the quantity of sulphur which it imports?

14.8 Sulphates

It was the adventurers who explored the continent of South America who discovered the potato. They brought their discovery back to Europe. The potato yields more food more quickly on less land than wheat or corn or rice. After the potato was introduced into Ireland, the health of the people improved, and the population expanded rapidly. In 1845, there were 8 million people living in Ireland. For most of them, the chief item in their diet was potato.

In 1845, a mysterious disease struck the potato crop. The plants wilted, and the potato tubers rotted. Six years of potato famine followed. The potato blight was caused by a fungus which spread throughout Europe. The Irish were the worst affected because they had no other crop to fall back on. A million people died. Another million emigrated to the USA.

The Irish potato harvest was revived by an injection of new stock from South America. Today, Irish potato farmers are still growing potatoes, and they are not afraid of the blight. A simple chemical has come to the rescue. The potato blight fungus can be killed by being sprayed with **Bordeaux Mixture**. This is a very inexpensive fungicide. It is made by dissolving copper(II) sulphate and calcium oxide in water. Bordeaux Mixture is also used to combat fungal infections of apple trees, pear trees and vines. If the Irish had known in 1845 that copper(II) sulphate was a killer — as far as potato blight fungus goes — a million lives would have been saved.

14.9 Methods of preparing sulphates

Methods of making salts were covered in Chapter 7. Reactions which lead to the formation of sulphates are summarised in Fig. 14.17.
Experiments with some interesting sulphates are covered in Experiments 13.3 to 13.5.

SUMMARY NOTE

Many sulphates have important uses. The methods used for their preparation are shown in Fig. 14.17.

JUST TESTING 87

1 What chemicals, in addition to sulphuric acid, would you need in order to make **a** magnesium sulphate, **b** potassium sulphate, **c** copper(II) sulphate, **d** lead(II) sulphate? Describe how you would prepare solid samples of these four sulphates.

Exercise 14

1 An element A burned in air to give a gas B which dissolved in water to give an acid C which changed slowly into an acid D. When heated gently, the element A melted to form a brown liquid.
   a Name the element A and compounds B, C and D.
   b Is A a metallic or a non-metallic element? Give two reasons for your answer.

2 Suggest what the substances A, B, C, D and E, might be.
   a Sulphur burned in the gas A with a very bright blue flame.
   b A solution of B, on addition of barium chloride solution and dilute hydrochloric acid, gave a white precipitate.
   c A white powder C turned blue when water was added.
   d A green solid D effervesced and formed a blue solution when dilute sulphuric acid was added.
   e A black solid E reacted with dilute sulphuric acid to form a blue solution.

3 Do not write in this book. Supply words or phrases to fill the blanks.
   In the ____ process for manufacturing sulphuric acid, the gas sulphur dioxide is obtained by ____. It is mixed with ____ and purified by the method of ____. The mixture of gases is passed over a heated catalyst, ____, and the compound ____ is formed. This compound is absorbed in ____ to form ____. On dilution with water, this gives sulphuric acid.

4 Do not write in this book. State what would be observed in the tests **a** to **f**.

Test	Sodium sulphite (aq)	Sodium sulphate (aq)
Add dilute hydrochloric acid	a	b
Add barium chloride solution	c	d
Add dilute hydrochloric acid and barium chloride solution	e	f

5 Describe how you would prepare samples of **a** rhombic sulphur, **b** monoclinic sulphur, **c** plastic sulphur.

*6 How could you prove that concentrated sulphuric acid is a dehydrating agent?

7 Study this reaction scheme:
Sulphur
   ↓ A
Sulphur dioxide
   ↓ Oxygen, catalyst, heat
Gas B
   ↓ Water
Acid C ——Zinc——→ Salt D + Gas E
   ↓ Barium chloride solution
White precipitate F
   +
Hydrochloric acid
   a Give the conditions for reaction A.
   b Name gas B. Write a word equation and a symbol equation for its formation.
   c Name acid C. Give its chemical formula.
   d Name salt D, gas E and precipitate F.

8 Sulphur dioxide is released into the atmosphere by electricity power stations and sulphuric acid plants. If the sulphur dioxide were recovered from the air, it could be converted into sulphuric acid. This would reduce the need for imported sulphur.
   a Explain briefly why sulphur dioxide is regarded as a pollutant.
   b Explain why coal-fired power stations produce sulphur dioxide.
   c Explain the connection between recovering sulphur dioxide from the air and reducing imports of sulphur.
   *d The process for recovering sulphur dioxide is

   sulphur dioxide + oxygen + water → sulphuric acid

   $$2SO_2(g) + O_2(g) + 2H_2O(l) \rightarrow 2H_2SO_4(l)$$

   • Take the percentage of sulphur dioxide in the polluted air as 1% by volume.
   • Take the gas molar volume as 25 litres under the conditions of the process.

285

Calculate the mass of sulphuric acid that could be obtained from 100 000 litres of air. (The steps in the calculation are: volume of SO_2 . . . amount (mol) of SO_2 . . . amount (mol) of H_2SO_4 . . . mass of H_2SO_4. $A_r(O) = 16$, $A_r(S) = 32$, $A_r(H) = 1$.)

Find the fertiliser

To find the name of a fertiliser made from sulphuric acid, fill in the clues across. Then read the answer in 1 down.

1 This non-metallic element burns with a blue flame. (7)
2 Goodyear found out how to ___ rubber. (9)
3 Soldiers needed sulphur to make this. (9)
4 Monoclinic sulphur looks like these. (7)
5 Copper is ___ towards dilute sulphuric acid. (10)
6 The weak acid that contains sulphur. (10)
7 Concentrated sulphuric acid will ___ sugar. (9)
8 The allotrope of sulphur that crystallises at room temperature. (7)
9 The form of sulphur you get by pouring molten sulphur into water. (7)
10 Fungi do not like this sulphate. (6)
11 A measure of acidity. (2 words: 2, 6)

12 The oxide of this metal is used in the Contact Process. (8)
13 Sulphuric acid is a ___ acid. (6)
14 The number of sulphur atoms in a molecule of solid sulphur. (5)

CHAPTER 15

Nitrogen and agriculture

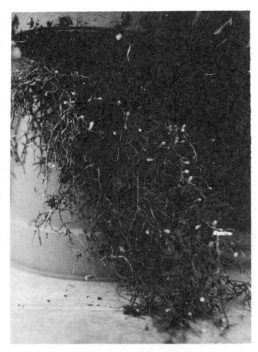

Fig. 15.1 Nodules on the roots of a leguminous plant

15.1 The nitrogen cycle

Proteins are important nitrogen compounds. They are one of the three main classes of food substances. (The others are fats and carbohydrates.) Plants can synthesise (build) proteins from simpler nitrogen-containing compounds. Animals are unable to synthesise proteins: they obtain protein by eating plants or by eating animals which have eaten plants. Some plants can synthesise proteins from the nitrogen in the air. Beans, peas and clover can do this. They have nodules on their roots which contain **nitrogen-fixing bacteria** (Fig. 15.1). These bacteria **fix** atmospheric nitrogen; that is, turn it into nitrogen compounds. Plants which cannot fix nitrogen synthesise proteins from nitrates. Ammonium salts enter the soil in the excreta of animals and through the decay of plant and animal remains. **Nitrifying bacteria** in the soil convert ammonium salts into nitrates. Another source of nitrates in the soil is rain. Nitrogen and oxygen combine in the atmosphere during a lightning storm to form oxides of nitrogen. These gases react with water to form nitric acid. A rain shower brings nitric acid to Earth, and it reacts with minerals to form nitrates. Plants take in these nitrates through their roots. Some nitrates are converted back into

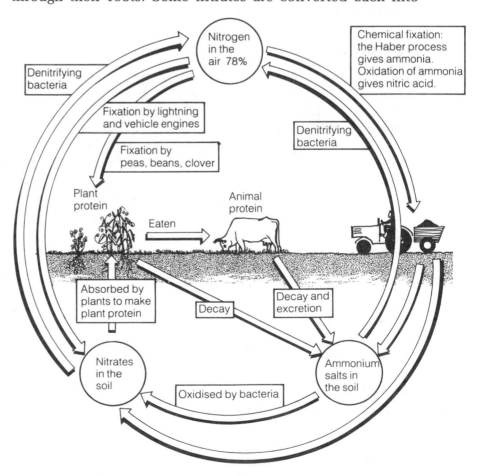

Fig. 15.2 The nitrogen cycle

gaseous nitrogen by **denitrifying bacteria**. Animals obtain proteins by eating plants or by eating other animals.

The way in which nitrogen circulates from air to soil to living things and back again is called the **nitrogen cycle** (see Fig. 15.2).

15.2 Nitrogen

You met nitrogen in Chapter 8. Figure 15.3 summarises its reactions.

Colourless, odourless, neutral gas, insoluble in water	Makes up 78% by volume of air. Obtained by fractional distillation of liquid air; see Section 8.3.	Used when an inert atmosphere is needed, e.g. for some welding jobs; see Section 8.5.

NITROGEN

Extinguishes a burning splint. Combines with burning magnesium to form magnesium nitride, Mg_3N_2.

Combines with oxygen during lightning storms. Gaseous oxides of nitrogen are formed. These react with water vapour in the air to form nitric acid. Rain containing nitric acid reacts with minerals in the soil to form nitrates. These are fertilisers. These reactions, which convert nitrogen into nitrogen compounds, are called 'atmospheric fixation' of nitrogen.

Combines with hydrogen under the conditions of the Haber process to form ammonia. This is the industrial method of 'fixing' nitrogen.

Fig. 15.3 Some reactions of nitrogen

SUMMARY NOTE

Proteins contain nitrogen. Plants synthesise proteins from nitrates. Some plants can 'fix' gaseous nitrogen. Plants can utilise the nitrogen in ammonium salts after soil bacteria convert them into nitrates. Animals rely on plants for protein.

The nitrogen cycle: This is the way nitrogen circulates from the air to the soil to living things and back again.

15.3 Fertilisers

As the world population has increased, the demand for food has increased. The world population was 3.5 billion in 1965. By 2050, it will reach 10 billion. Many people today are hungry, and many more are under-nourished. Farming has to be intensive, with large crops grown on the land available for agriculture. Crops take nutrients from the soil, and these must be replaced before the next crop is sown.

Before the nineteenth century, farmers relied on the natural fertilisers, manure and compost, to replace nutrients in the soil. When the population began to rise sharply in the nineteenth century, the need for food increased. To grow more food, farmers needed more fertilisers. They asked the chemists to make some artificial fertilisers. Before the chemists could do this, they had to find out which chemicals in manure fertilised the soil. Then they could make chemical fertilisers to do the same job. In 1842, the German chemist Justus von Liebig (of condenser fame) analysed soils to find out the differences between fertile soils (which gave good crops) and infertile soils. He found that fertile soils are richer than poor soils in

- nitrogen compounds
- phosphates
- potassium compounds
- calcium and magnesium compounds.

In Britain, in 1843, John Lawes set up the first agricultural research station in Rothamsted in Hertfordshire. He studied the effects of fertilisers on the growth of crops. His experiments showed that plants need three groups of chemicals.

1 Large quantities of carbon, hydrogen and oxygen compounds; there is no shortage of these elements. Carbon comes from carbon dioxide in the air. Hydrogen and oxygen come from water.

2 Small quantities of the **trace elements** (iron, manganese, boron, copper, cobalt, molybdenum, zinc); the quantities of these elements needed are so small that they do not normally need to be added to the soil.

3 Fairly large quantities of compounds containing nitrogen, phosphorus, potassium, calcium, magnesium, sulphur and, for some crops, sodium

Counting the cost

Most fertilisers concentrate on supplying the necessary nitrogen (N), phosphorus (P) and potassium (K). NPK fertilisers are consumed in huge quantities: in 1980, the world consumption was 19 million tonnes. In the UK, the consumption of NPK fertilisers is about 7 million tonnes a year. The fertilisers cost about £60/tonne. You can see that the fertiliser industry is very big business. The cost of fertilisers is a large item in a farmer's budget. He wants to use them as efficiently as possible. The Ministry of Agriculture, Fisheries and Food has an Agricultural Development and Advisory Service to help farmers and market gardeners. They can obtain expert advice on the type and quantity of fertiliser to apply and the best season of the year for applying it. Every farmer and grower has different probelms. The agricultural chemists must consider the type of crop and the type of soil before they can recommend the most suitable treatment. The growers want good crops, but they do not want to spend more than they need on fertilisers. It is important not to use too much fertiliser. The excessive use of fertilisers which results in the leaching of nitrates into ground water was mentioned in Section 9.16. P154

Fig. 15.4 Application of concentrated ammonia solution to a field

Fig. 15.5 Application of pellets of ammonium salts to a field

Nitrogen

Nitrogen can be absorbed by plants when it is combined as nitrates. Ammonia and ammonium salts also can be used as fertilisers because ammonium salts are converted into nitrates by organisms which live in soil. All nitrates and all ammonium salts are soluble. This makes them easily absorbed. Nitrogenous fertilisers increase both the size of the crop and the protein content of the plants. Sometimes, concentrated ammonia solution is used as a fertiliser. Usually, solid fertilisers — ammonium nitrate, ammonium sulphate and urea (CON_2H_4) — are applied in pellet form (see Figs. 15.4 and 15.5).

Phosphorus

Phosphorus is present in phosphates, the salts of phosphoric acid. Phosphates stimulate root development. Healthy roots enable the crop to take in other nutrients. The phosphates which are naturally present in soil are only slightly soluble, and are only slowly absorbed by plants. The soluble fertiliser ammonium phosphate is made from ores containing calcium phosphate (see Fig. 15.8).

Potassium

Potassium compounds are all soluble, and are therefore readily taken up by plant roots. They help plants to carry on photosynthesis. Potassium chloride is an ingredient of NPK fertilisers.

Sodium

For most crops, there is no need to add extra sodium compounds. Sugar beet is an exception: it grows better if common salt is added as a fertiliser.

The manufacture of nitrogenous fertilisers

Farmers took note of the results of the experiments on fertilisers. From 1850 onwards, European farmers started to import sodium nitrate (**Chile nitre**) from South America to fertilise their land. Vast deposits of sodium nitrate exist in Chile. Nevertheless, Europeans were not completely happy at being dependent on a remote source of fertiliser. They wanted to be able to make their own. Nitrogen was the obvious starting point. Every country has plenty of nitrogen in the air. The problem was that, since nitrogen is so unreactive, it is difficult to convert it into nitrogen compounds. The problem was solved in 1908 by a German chemist called Fritz Haber. He managed to get nitrogen to combine with hydrogen to form ammonia:

nitrogen + hydrogen $\rightleftharpoons$ ammonia
$N_2(g) + 3H_2(g) \rightleftharpoons 2NH_3(g)$

This reaction is reversible: it takes place from right to left as well as from left to right. Some of the ammonia formed dissociates into nitrogen and hydrogen. Equilibrium is reached, and a mixture of nitrogen, hydrogen and ammonia is formed. Nitrogen is an unreactive gas, and the position of equilibrium is very far towards the left-hand side.

*The Haber process

Fritz Haber had to try a number of ways to get the equilibrium to move towards the right-hand side and give a bigger yield of ammonia. He took note of **Le Chatelier's Principle**. This states that: *When conditions are changed, a system in a state of equilibrium adjusts itself in such a way as to minimise the effects of the change.* Haber tried changing the pressure and the temperature. He reasoned:

> ## SUMMARY NOTE
>
> Intensive farming is needed to keep the world's population fed. Artificial fertilisers must be used to give big crops. NPK fertilisers contain nitrogen (for protein synthesis), phosphorus (for healthy roots), potassium (to help photosynthesis) and some calcium and magnesium.

What happens when the pressure changes? How can the system minimise the effect of an increase in pressure? Well, the system can minimise the effect of an increase in pressure by decreasing in volume.

How can the system decrease in volume? It can convert nitrogen and hydrogen into ammonia. It follows from the equation that:

> 4 moles of the mixture of nitrogen and hydrogen form 2 moles of ammonia, so
>
> 4 volumes of the mixture form 2 volumes of ammonia (see Section 12.10).

So if the pressure is increased, the mixture will reduce its volume by reacting to form ammonia.

What happens when the temperature changes? How can the system absorb heat? The reaction is exothermic, that is, heat is given out in going from left to right. The reverse reaction, the dissociation of ammonia, is endothermic. The system can absorb heat by the dissociation of ammonia. Running the process at high temperature therefore reduces the yield of ammonia.

What is wrong with running at a very low temperature? If the reactants are at a very low temperature, the system takes a long time to come to equilibrium.

Industry. Modern industrial plants use a high pressure (about 200 atm) and a moderate temperature (about 450 °C). A catalyst (iron or iron(III) oxide) is used to increase the speed of the reaction. (For catalysts, see Section 21.7.)

The yield of ammonia is about 10%. Ammonia is condensed out of the mixture. (It is easily condensed because it has a high boiling point.) The nitrogen and hydrogen which have not reacted are recycled through the plant (see Fig. 15.6).

Fig. 15.6 Flow diagram of the Haber Process

Fig. 15.7 ICI, Billingham

The hydrogen for the Haber process is obtained from natural gas. The method is similar to that shown in Fig. 9.21.

Making fertilisers from ammonia

Ammonia is used to manufacture fertilisers. A mixture of ammonium nitrate, ammonium phosphate and potassium chloride contains all of the three important elements (nitrogen, phosphorus and potassium) mentioned on page 290. Mixtures of these three salts are called NPK fertilisers. Figure 15.8 shows a flow diagram for their manufacture. Potassium chloride is not manufactured; it is mined in the UK.

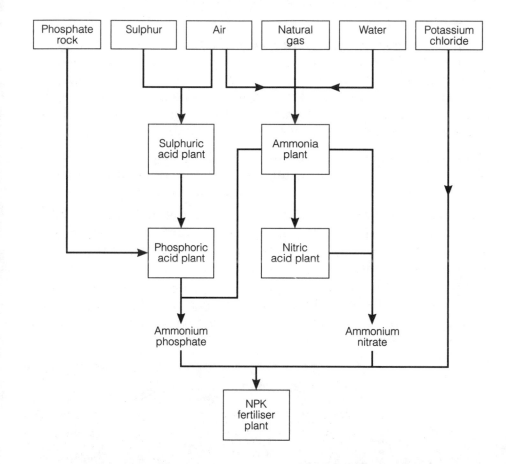

Fig. 15.8 Manufacture of NPK fertilisers (for sulphuric acid, see Section 14.6, for nitric acid, see Section 15.5)

JUST TESTING 88

1 Why does every country need fertilisers? Why is nitrogen one of the elements which fertilisers must contain? What is the advantage of obtaining nitrogen from air, instead of from nitrates?

2 Explain how nitrogen is converted into ammonia. Why do ammonium salts make good fertilisers? What other nitrogen compounds are used as fertilisers?

3 Name three routes by which nitrogen from the air finds its way into the soil. How does the amount of nitrogen in the air stay constant?

4 What do the letters NPK in the popular fertilisers stand for? Why is it important that the fertilisers contain **a** N, **b** P, and **c** K?

*5 Chemists know that the speeds of chemical reactions increase as the temperature rises. Knowing this, why do ammonia manufacturers not run the process at 850 °C instead of 450 °C?

*6 A mixture of gases W and X reacts to form a mixture of two gases Y and Z. The dissociation is reversible, and the system reaches equilibrium:

$$W(g) + X(g) \rightleftharpoons 2Y(g) + Z(g)$$

a Will an increase in pressure increase or decrease the yield of Y and Z?

b If the forward reaction is endothermic, predict what effect a rise in temperature will have on the yield of Y and Z.

SUMMARY NOTE

Sodium nitrate is mined in Chile. It was imported and widely used as a fertiliser in Europe. Now nitrogenous fertilisers are made from ammonia. The Haber Process converts nitrogen and hydrogen into ammonia. Hydrogen is obtained from natural gas, and nitrogen is obtained from air.

15.4 Ammonia

Properties

Ammonia has a distinctive smell — very penetrating and not very pleasant. Wet nappies smell of ammonia. Urine contains a nitrogen compound called urea. When bacteria break down urea, ammonia is formed. In large quantities, ammonia is a poison. Ammonia is a very soluble gas.

Basic reactions of ammonia

Ammonia is a basic gas. It turns damp red litmus blue. When it meets the acidic gas hydrogen chloride, they react to form the salt ammonium chloride, a white solid (Fig. 15.9):

ammonia + hydrogen chloride → ammonium chloride

$$NH_3(g) \quad + HCl(g) \qquad \qquad \rightarrow NH_4Cl(s)$$

Fig. 15.9 Reaction between ammonia and ▷ hydrogen chloride

Clouds of ammonium chloride (a white solid) form when ammonia and hydrogen chloride meet.

This reaction is used as a test for ammonia and also as a test for hydrogen chloride.

Ammonia is a weak base. Its aqueous solution is alkaline. Some cleaning fluids contain ammonia (see Fig. 15.10). Ammonia solution is used as a degreasing agent. Like other alkalis, it **saponifies** grease, converting it into soluble soaps (see Section 7.3).

The alkaline nature of aqueous ammonia is due to the reaction between ammonia and water:

ammonia + water $\rightleftharpoons$ ammonium ions + hydroxide ions

$$NH_3(aq) + H_2O(l) \rightleftharpoons NH_4^+(aq) + OH^-(aq)$$

Ammonia is a weak base. The concentration of hydroxide ions in ammonia solution is low. It is high enough to make ammonia solution act as a typical alkali.

Some typical reactions of aqueous ammonia

1 When ammonia solution is added to a solution containing metal ions, many metals are precipitated as insoluble hydroxides (see Section 7.3). For example,

iron(II) ions + hydroxide ions $\rightarrow$ iron(II) hydroxide

$$Fe^{2+}(aq) + 2OH^-(aq) \rightarrow Fe(OH)_2(s)$$

2 Some metal hydroxides are first precipitated and later dissolved when more ammonia solution is added. Such behaviour is due to the formation of soluble **complex ions**.

Fig. 15.10 Ammonia solution as a cleaning fluid

Fig. 15.11 Some reactions of ammonia

Examples are the tetraamminezinc ion, $(Zn(NH_3)_4)^{2+}$, and the tetraamminecopper(II) ion, $(Cu(NH_3)_4)^{2+}$. The tetraamminecopper(II) ions are deep blue. The formation of this deep blue colour with copper(II) salts is a sensitive test for ammonia.

3 Ammonia solution neutralises acids to give ammonium salts (see Experiments 14.2 and 14.4). For example,

ammonia + sulphuric acid → ammonium sulphate
$$2NH_3(aq) + H_2SO_4(aq) \rightarrow (NH_4)_2SO_4(aq)$$

Figure 15.11 gives a summary of the reactions of ammonia.

Ammonium salts

Ammonium salts are fertilisers (see Section 15.3). Ammonium sulphate and ammonium nitrate are widely used (see Fig. 15.8).

Thermal dissociation

When you heat ammonium chloride (Experiment 14.6), it splits up into ammonia and hydrogen chloride. On cooling, these gases recombine (see Fig. 15.12).

$$\text{ammonium chloride} \underset{\text{cool}}{\overset{\text{heat}}{\rightleftharpoons}} \text{ammonia} + \text{hydrogen chloride}$$

$$NH_4Cl(s) \underset{\text{cool}}{\overset{\text{heat}}{\rightleftharpoons}} NH_3(g) + HCl(g)$$

This behaviour (decomposition on heating followed by recombination on cooling) is called **thermal dissociation**. Many ammonium salts undergo thermal dissociation (see Section 18.4).

Competition between bases

Being a weak base, ammonia is driven out of its salts by strong bases. To test a substance to see if it is an ammonium salt, you can warm it with sodium hydroxide solution. If ammonia is evolved, this proves that the substance is an ammonium salt (see Fig. 15.13 overleaf):

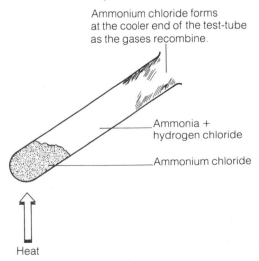

Ammonium chloride forms at the cooler end of the test-tube as the gases recombine.

Ammonia + hydrogen chloride

Ammonium chloride

Heat

Fig. 15.12 Thermal dissociation of ammonium chloride

ammonium chloride	+	sodium hydroxide	→	ammonia	+	sodium chloride	+	water
$NH_4Cl(s)$	+	$NaOH(aq)$	→	$NH_3(g)$	+	$NaCl(aq)$	+	$H_2O(l)$

Damp red litmus paper

Tongs

Sodium hydroxide solution

Substance under test

Warm

JUST TESTING 89

1 Someone tells you that a bottle labelled 'smelling salts' contains ammonium carbonate. What tests would you do in order to find out whether this is true?

2 Describe how you could separate ammonium chloride and sodium chloride. (See Chapter 2 if you need help.)

3 What is formed when ammonia dissolves in water? Give two uses for the solution.

4 Describe how you would make crystals of ammonium sulphate. Why is this compound sold in large quantities?

*5 Describe what happens when ammonia solution reacts with solutions of **a** iron(III) sulphate, **b** iron(II) sulphate, **c** lead(II) nitrate, **d** copper(II) sulphate. Write equations for the reactions that take place in **a**, **b** and **c**.

15.5 Nitric acid

Dynamite

An important use of nitric acid is the manufacture of an oily liquid called nitroglycerine. This liquid explodes when it is ignited by a lighted fuse. After it was first made in 1846 by an Italian chemist, Professor Sobrero, miners and engineers started to use nitroglycerine for blasting away rock. Unfortunately, nitroglycerine can also explode when it receives a sudden blow. This sometimes happened when it was being transported to the site.

Immanuel Nobel began to manufacture nitroglycerine in Sweden in 1863. A year later, an explosion killed his son, Emil, and three other workers in the factory. Nobel's other son, Alfred, continued manufacturing, but he looked for some way to stabilise nitroglycerine so that it would not be exploded by mechanical shock. He experimented with a type of clay called kieselguhr, which was found near the factory. He found that it would absorb three times its own weight of nitroglycerine. The mixture did not explode when it was struck. It could be detonated only by means of a fuse. Alfred Nobel patented it as **dynamite**.

The new, safer explosive was invaluable for mining, making roads and railways, and blasting tunnels. The industrial revolution was taking place, and Nobel made a fortune out of his discovery. Of course, dynamite was used for armaments too. Concern about the use of his invention for warfare led Nobel to become interested in the peace movement. He decided to finance a prize for the person who had done the most effective work to promote peace between nations. When he died, he left £2 million to fund prizes for work towards peace and work in medicine, physics, chemistry and literature. These prizes have been awarded ever since 1901 by the Nobel Foundation in Stockholm.

Industrial manufacture of nitric acid

An industrial chemist called Ostwald invented a way of making nitric acid from ammonia and air and water. A flow diagram of his process is shown in Fig. 15.15.

Fig. 15.15 A flow diagram for the manufacture of nitric acid by the oxidation of ammonia

Fig. 15.14 Dynamite in use: blowing up a cooling tower

The reactions that take place are

Stage 2 ammonia + oxygen → nitrogen monoxide, NO + steam
Stage 3 nitrogen monoxide + oxygen → nitrogen dioxide, NO_2
Stage 4 nitrogen dioxide + oxygen + water → nitric acid, HNO_3

Some properties of concentrated nitric acid are shown in Fig. 15.16.

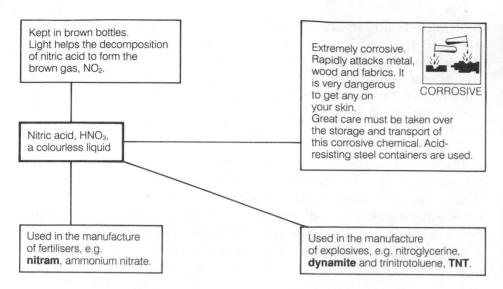

Kept in brown bottles. Light helps the decomposition of nitric acid to form the brown gas, NO_2.

Nitric acid, HNO_3, a colourless liquid

Extremely corrosive. Rapidly attacks metal, wood and fabrics. It is very dangerous to get any on your skin. Great care must be taken over the storage and transport of this corrosive chemical. Acid-resisting steel containers are used.

CORROSIVE

Used in the manufacture of fertilisers, e.g. **nitram**, ammonium nitrate.

Used in the manufacture of explosives, e.g. nitroglycerine, **dynamite** and trinitrotoluene, **TNT**.

Fig. 15.16 Concentrated nitric acid

Reactions of dilute nitric acid

Nitric acid reacts as an acid when dissolved in water.

1 Bases. The reactions of dilute nitric acid with metal oxides, metal hydroxides and metal carbonates are summarised in Fig. 14.16.

2 Metals. Dilute nitric acid reacts with metals to give metal nitrates. Hydrogen is not obtained because dilute nitric acid oxidises it to water, and the gas nitrogen monoxide, NO, is formed. This gas forms the brown gas nitrogen dioxide, NO_2, as soon as it meets the air. Dilute nitric acid is a sufficiently powerful oxidising agent to oxidise copper and lead to their nitrates:

$$\text{copper} + \begin{matrix}\text{nitric acid} \\ \text{(dilute)}\end{matrix} \rightarrow \begin{matrix}\text{copper(II)} \\ \text{nitrate}\end{matrix} + \begin{matrix}\text{nitrogen} \\ \text{monoxide}\end{matrix} + \begin{matrix}\text{nitrogen} \\ \text{dioxide}\end{matrix} + \text{water}$$

*3 Test for a nitrate: the Devarda's alloy test. Nitric acid and nitrates can be reduced to ammonia. The reducing agent is a mixture of sodium hydroxide and Devarda's alloy (aluminium, copper and zinc). Naturally, if ammonium salts are present,

Dilute nitric acid $HNO_3(aq)$ reacts with

METALS, including the less reactive metals, e.g. Cu

ALKALIS, e.g. $NaOH(aq)$ $NH_3(aq)$

BASES, e.g. CaO, ZnO

CARBONATES, e.g. $CaCO_3$

metal nitrate + nitrogen dioxide + water e.g. $Cu(NO_3)_2$ + NO_2 + H_2O

metal nitrate or ammonium nitrate + water e.g. NH_4NO_3 + H_2O

metal nitrate + water e.g. $Zn(NO_3)_2$ + H_2O

metal nitrate + water + carbon dioxide e.g. $Ca(NO_3)_2$ + H_2O + CO_2

NOTE All nitrates are soluble.

TEST for a nitrate: reduced to ammonia by Devarda's alloy and alkali.

Fig. 15.17 Some reactions of nitric acid

Dilute nitric acid has many reactions in common with the other mineral acids. In addition, it is an oxidising agent. It oxidises copper and lead to their nitrates.

Nitrates: For methods of preparation, see Fig. 15.17.

Test: Nitrates give ammonia when they are reduced.

sodium hydroxide will react with them to give ammonia, even in the absence of a nitrate. For this reason, the solution of a suspected nitrate is first boiled with sodium hydroxide solution. When any ammonia present has been driven off, Devarda's alloy is added to the solution. If ammonia is evolved, this proves the presence of a nitrate.

15.6 Nitrates

The preparation of nitrates

The methods for preparing nitrates are summarised in Fig. 15.17. The method of precipitation is *not* used because *all nitrates are soluble*.

JUST TESTING 90

1 Name three substances that will react with dilute nitric acid to give copper(II) nitrate.
  Describe in detail how you would use *one* of these substances to prepare crystals of copper(II) nitrate.

2 What is formed when dilute nitric acid reacts with **a** lead, **b** zinc, **c** calcium carbonate, **d** sodium hydroxide, **e** copper(II) oxide?

3 Describe how you could obtain crystals of sodium nitrate, starting from sodium hydroxide and nitric acid.

4 Write word equations and symbol equations for the formation of nitrates by the reactions between dilute nitric acid and
  a lead(II) oxide
  b sodium hydroxide
  c calcium carbonate.

15.7 Agricultural chemicals

Fertilisers

Three-quarters of Britain is farmland. Thanks to the use of fertilisers, the land is enormously productive (see Section 15.3).

Herbicides

The well-fertilised soil is a good growing ground for weeds as well as for the crops that the farmers sow. At one time, farm workers used to uproot weeds by hand. Now that agricultural workers are better paid, farmers employ fewer people. They cannot afford hand-weeding and use chemical weedkillers, **herbicides**, instead. **Selective** weedkillers will kill one type of plant and leave others, including the crop, untouched. The commonest, e.g. 2,4-D and 2,4,5-T, kill broad-leaved plants but do not harm grasses and cereals with blade-shaped leaves. They kill dandelions but leave grass. They kill thistles and nettles but leave cereals. These herbicides are organic compounds which contain chlorine. Other weedkillers, e.g. paraquat and sodium chlorate(V), are **non-selective**: they kill all plants.

The benefits of chemical weedkillers have been great. It is difficult to see how scientific farming could continue without them. There have also been some disastrous results of using herbicides.

In 1968, the USA was fighting a war in Vietnam. Their enemy, the Vietcong, found shelter in the jungles. US planes dropped a herbicide called **Agent Orange**, which killed all the trees and other vegetation where it landed. It destroyed the trees which sheltered Vietcong fighters and their supply lines and depots. The herbicide contained impure 2,4,5-T. The impurity, **dioxin**, has appalling **teratogenic** effects (effects on unborn babies). Vietnamese mothers gave birth to terribly deformed babies. When US servicemen returned home and started families, some of them were horrified to find that they too had become the parents of seriously defective babies. Agent Orange had affected the fathers' genes. These unforeseen tragedies led to the banning of 2,4,5-T in many countries. It cannot be manufactured without some dioxin appearing as impurity in the product.

Insecticides

If insects were not controlled, they would consume most of the food we grow, and humans would starve. The first chemicals which farmers used to protect their crops from insects were general poisons, e.g. compounds of arsenic, lead and mercury. They kill all animals which swallow them. Farm animals, children and pets can be accidentally poisoned. These poisons are stable compounds: they remain unchanged in water or soil or air for tens of years.

In 1939, the scientist Paul Mueller discovered that a substance called DDT would kill insects and leave other species unharmed. The use of **selective insecticides** took off. DDT is an organic compound which contains chlorine (see Fig. 15.18). It is a petrochemical (see Section 19.9). DDT has saved more lives than any other single substance. By killing insects which eat crops, it preserves crops and fights hunger and starvation. By killing insects which carry disease, it has saved millions of lives and prevented billions of illnesses.

The use of DDT had a brilliant beginning. In 1943, a massive epidemic of typhus broke out in Italy. The disease is carried by lice. By dusting the population with DDT, the epidemic was halted. DDT went on to bring malaria under control in many parts of the world. Malaria is carried by mosquitoes. Typhus and cholera are carried by other insects. By killing the carriers, DDT wiped out the diseases.

In agriculture, DDT was used successfully to control tea parasites in Sri Lanka and cotton pests in the USA. It reduces the damage done by swarms of locusts in the desert regions of North Africa. When locusts consume crops, famine follows and whole populations starve. People predicted that DDT would

By killing locusts, DDT fights famine.

The World Health Organisation says that DDT has saved 5 million lives.

By killing insects, DDT fights disease.

In tropical countries, 550 million people now live free from the threat of malaria.

Fig. 15.18 **A model of a DDT molecule**

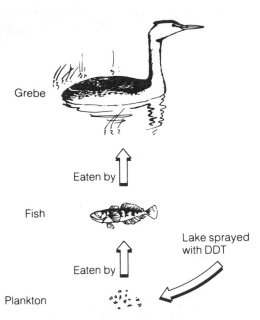

Grebe

↑ Eaten by

Fish

↑ Eaten by

Plankton

Lake sprayed with DDT

Fig. 15.19 The grebes' food chain

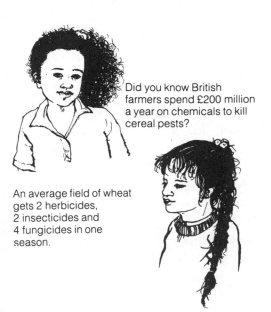

Did you know British farmers spend £200 million a year on chemicals to kill cereal pests?

An average field of wheat gets 2 herbicides, 2 insecticides and 4 fungicides in one season.

Two herons have been found dead this week on a stretch of the River Avon. This brings the total to 16 since March. Disturbingly high amounts of DDT and dieldrin have been found in the carcases of the birds.
(*The Telegraph*, 8 August 1985)

exterminate all insect pests. In 1948, Paul Mueller was awarded the Nobel prize for his discovery.

Sometimes lakes are sprayed with DDT to combat mosquitoes. Clear Lake in California is an example. After the lake was sprayed, the level of DDT in the water was 0.02 p.p.m. (parts per million). This is a very low level, and people were surprised when aquatic birds, such as grebes, died. Scientists found out that the deaths were a result of the food chain that exists in the lake (Fig. 15.19). (You saw another food chain illustrated in Fig. 9.16.) Aquatic animals absorb DDT from the water. DDT is more soluble in fats and oils than it is in water. It dissolves in body tissues, and is not excreted. Fish can build up high concentrations of DDT. As well as taking DDT from the water, they eat smaller animals which have absorbed DDT. Aquatic birds which eat fish can build up still higher levels of DDT.

Ten million tonnes of DDT have been applied to the Earth in the last 25 years. DDT is a stable chemical. It does not react with air and water. The amount of DDT in the world is steadily increasing. It kills insects. In sufficiently large amounts, it kills birds. The human family is at the end of the food chain. We eat fish, and we eat birds. What will DDT do to us? There is no direct evidence that DDT produces cancer in humans. There are, however, statistics to show that cancer victims in the USA have twice as much DDT in their fatty tissues as the rest of the population.

DDT is now banned in the USA and Europe because of the dangerous build-up of DDT in wildlife and in humans. DDT is still used for the toughest jobs, e.g. fighting malaria. For agricultural purposes, we use safer but less effective insecticides, e.g. organic compounds of phosphorus, which are broken down in the course of time to safe compounds. At the same time, scientists are looking for other ways of controlling insects.

Fungicides

Mildew and potato blight are caused by fungi. To prevent these diseases, crops are sprayed with fungicides. Many copper salts are fungicides, e.g. copper(II) sulphate (see Section 14.9).

Molluscicides

Slugs and snails eat crops and spread diseases. Bilharzia is a tropical disease which is spread by snails. Molluscicides are being used to fight the disease (see Section 13.12).

JUST TESTING 91

1 a Why do farmers use chemical insecticides?
 b What advantage does DDT have over the insecticides which were used previously?
 c No-one has ever been poisoned by DDT. Why has its use on farms been banned?
 d For what purpose is DDT still used? Why is it in such demand?

2 Some people think we should give up using chemical insecticides. What would be the result?

3 Birds of prey, such as falcons and eagles, were affected by DDT before the insecticide was banned. These birds do not eat insects. How can they be affected by insecticides?

4 When would copper(II) sulphate have been a welcome fungicide in Ireland? (See Chapter 14 if you need help.)

SUMMARY NOTE

Herbicides and insecticides kill weeds and insects. The use of herbicides ensures that weeds will not rob crops of nutrients. The use of insecticides reduces the fraction of the crops that insects consume. There are dangers in the use of powerful pesticides.

Exercise 15

1 Suggest what A, B, C, D and E might be.
a A is a neutral, rather unreactive gas.
b B is a white solid which gives ammonia when it is warmed with sodium hydroxide. A solution of B gives a white precipitate when barium chloride solution and hydrochloric acid are added.
c A solution of the blue salt C turns a deep blue when ammonia is present.
d The indicator D is turned blue by ammonia.
e The gas E reacts with ammonia to form a white solid.

2 a What class of compounds do plants make from nitrates?
b Why can atmospheric nitrogen not be used as a fertiliser by most plants?
c Name one natural process that produces nitrogen compounds which can enter the soil and be used by plants.
d Explain why natural sources of nitrogen are not sufficient for repeated crop growing on the same land.
e Why are ammonium salts used as fertilisers when plants cannot absorb them?
f Describe how you could make ammonium sulphate crystals.

3 What reactions occur between ammonia and **a** hydrogen chloride gas, **b** lead(II) nitrate solution, **c** copper(II) sulphate solution? In each case, describe the appearance of the product. Write equations for the reactions.

4 Explain how ammonia is manufactured. What steps are taken to increase the yield?

*5 Describe the industrial method of making nitric acid. Explain why it is possible for every country to manufacture nitric acid.

*6 Calculate the percentage by mass of nitrogen in these fertilisers:
a ammonia, **b** ammonium nitrate,
c ammonium sulphate, **d** urea, CON_2H_4.

*7 100 cm³ of 1.00 mol/l ammonia solution just reacted with a measured volume of 1.00 mol/l sulphuric acid. The solution was heated until it was saturated and then allowed to cool. Crystals of ammonium sulphate were formed. The equation for the reaction is

$$2NH_3(aq) + H_2SO_4(aq) \rightarrow (NH_4)_2SO_4(aq)$$

a What volume of 1.00 mol/l sulphuric acid is required to react, according to the equation, with 100 cm³ of 1.00 mol/l ammonia solution?
b Explain what is meant by the expression 'saturated solution'.
c Explain why crystals form when the saturated solution is cooled.
d Calculate the mass of ammonium sulphate formed when 100 cm³ of 1.0 mol/l ammonia solution react with sulphuric acid according to the equation above. (Relative atomic masses: H = 1, N = 14, O = 16, S = 32.)

8 Copy this passage, filling in the missing words.
Nitrogen is obtained by the _____ _____ of liquid air. Hydrogen is obtained from _____ _____ by mixing it with _____ and passing the mixture over a heated _____ catalyst. Nitrogen and hydrogen combine when they are passed at

_____ pressure and _____ temperature over a _____ catalyst. The product is _____.

9 Where are the great reserves of nitrogen in nature?

Which nitrogen reserves are the easiest for us to use?

How does the human race upset the natural distribution of nitrogen?

Are we likely to run out of nitrogen?

What is the problem concerning nitrogen compounds that modern agriculture has created? How can this problem be solved?

10 The concentrations of nitrogen monoxide and nitrogen dioxide in polluted air are not toxic (harmful) to humans. Why, then, are people worried about the presence of these oxides in the air?

11 There is a fertiliser factory at Immingham in South Humberside (see Fig. 15.20). Explain this choice of site for the plant. Consider what the needs of a fertiliser factory are. Show how they are met in this area.

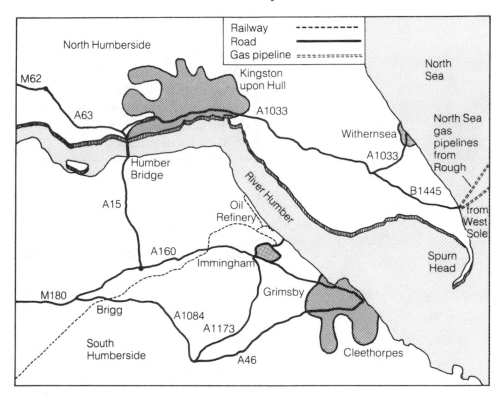

Fig. 15.20 Immingham and surroundings

12 Copy the wordsquare. (You may photocopy the wordsquare, but you may not photocopy other pages.) Ring the answers to the clues. Do not write in this book.

1 Foods of this kind contain nitrogen. (7)
2 A substance which replenishes the soil. (10)
3 Some of these organisms can 'fix' nitrogen. (8)
4 Litmus turns this colour with ammonia. (4)
5 A natural means of returning nitrogen to the soil. (6)
6 A type of fertiliser. (3)
7 An essential element in fertilisers. (9)
8 Plants want these, but we do not want them in our drinking water. (8)

```
F  I  X  B  L  U  E  N  P  K
M  E  P  A  A  E  R  U  N  Y
U  R  R  C  X  A  U  B  I  E
I  E  O  T  C  L  N  D  T  N
S  B  T  E  I  R  A  I  R  A
S  A  E  R  O  L  M  P  A  H
A  H  I  I  A  A  I  B  T  T
T  M  N  A  N  C  N  S  E  E
O  M  U  Y  T  R  E  Y  E  M
P  F  D  O  C  S  T  O  O  R
```

9 You find plenty of nitrogen in this. (3)
10 A nitrogen-containing compound which is used as a fertiliser. (4)
11 Plants use these to take in nutrients. (5)
12 He invented a method of making ammonia. (5)

13 Plants need _____ metals such as copper. (5)
14 To _____ nitrogen is to convert it into compounds. (3)

Career sketch: Biomedical engineer

Chris is a biomedical engineer. His aim is to use engineering principles to solve medical problems. Chris designs and develops heart pacemakers and artificial hearts and kidneys. Other biomedical engineers develop methods for using lasers in surgery. Some of them design devices to measure the flow of blood. Others design equipment for using liquid crystals to measure changes in body temperature. Some members of Chris's company design the incubators which keep tiny premature babies alive.

Biomedical engineers need a degree in mechanical or electrical or chemical engineering. They need to work as members of a team with medical doctors.

Career sketch: Biochemist

Susan has a PhD in biochemistry and works in a hospital laboratory until 3 o'clock before picking up her children from school.

Biochemists study the chemical composition and behaviour of living things. Their work affects medicine, food science and agriculture. They investigate the causes and cures of diseases. They find out which substances we must have in our food to keep healthy. They develop chemical pesticides to kill weeds and insects. Biochemists use a variety of instruments, including centrifuges, electron microscopes and counters which measure radioactivity.

CHAPTER 16

Chemicals from salt

Fig. 16.1 This is how much salt is in your body

Fig. 16.2 The Great Salt Lake

16.1 Sodium chloride

You contain about 0.25 kg (half a pound) of salt. This quantity is enough to fill several salt cellars (Fig. 16.1).

'Salt' is sodium chloride, a compound of the dangerously reactive metal, sodium, and the poisonous gas, chlorine. Salt is an example of a compound which differs greatly from the elements of which it is composed. Although the elements sodium and chlorine are poisonous, sodium chloride is essential for human life. Sodium ions must be present for our nerves to be able to send commands to our muscles. The presence of sodium ions is also essential for the contraction of muscles, including the largest and most important of muscles — the heart. Still another process which requires sodium ions is the digestion of proteins in our food. Sodium chloride regulates the flow of water into and out of our body cells. It controls the way in which food is carried into cells and waste materials are carried out. Without salt, our bodies become paralysed, and we die.

There is a limit to the amount of salt we need. The World Health Organisation recommends no more than 5 grams a day. There is strong evidence linking high salt intake with high blood pressure. High blood pressure often leads both to heart diseases and to strokes.

Through perspiration, the body loses water and salt. This salt must be replaced. Primitive man obtained enough salt from eating meat. When the human race turned to farming instead of hunting, they had to look for salt. A cereal diet does not provide enough salt.

Fortunately, all countries have supplies of salt. Sea water contains sodium chloride (26 g/l). Some countries obtain sodium chloride from sea water (see Section 2.3). Other countries mine salt. The salt deposits are the remains of the inland seas which covered large areas of the globe thousands of years ago. The Great Salt Lake in Utah, USA, was once a vast inland sea. It is saturated with sodium chloride. Its density makes the lake water so buoyant that no swimmer can sink in it (Fig. 16.2). The Dead Sea in Israel is another inland sea, so salty that no fish can live in it.

Salt keeps us alive. Salt keeps our industries alive too. It is the most important of the raw materials which our industries use. Figure 16.3 shows some of the ways we use salt and some of the useful substances which are made from it.

Figure 2.2 shows one way in which salt is mined: solution mining. This is the method used in Northwich, Cheshire. Large underground caverns are created. The ground above them would collapse if it were not supported. The cavities are therefore left full of saturated brine to support the ground above them. (A solution of sodium chloride is called **brine**.)

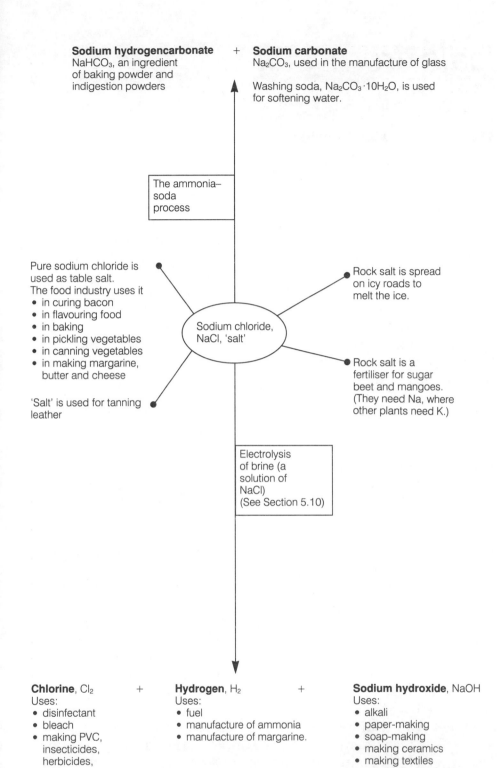

Sodium hydrogencarbonate
NaHCO₃, an ingredient
of baking powder and
indigestion powders

\+   **Sodium carbonate**
Na₂CO₃, used in the manufacture of glass

Washing soda, Na₂CO₃·10H₂O, is used
for softening water.

The ammonia–
soda
process

Pure sodium chloride is
used as table salt.
The food industry uses it
• in curing bacon
• in flavouring food
• in baking
• in pickling vegetables
• in canning vegetables
• in making margarine,
  butter and cheese

'Salt' is used for tanning
leather

Sodium chloride,
NaCl, 'salt'

Rock salt is spread
on icy roads to
melt the ice.

Rock salt is a
fertiliser for sugar
beet and mangoes.
(They need Na, where
other plants need K.)

Electrolysis
of brine (a
solution of
NaCl)
(See Section 5.10)

Chlorine, Cl₂   +
Uses:
• disinfectant
• bleach
• making PVC,
  insecticides,
  herbicides,
  rubber.

Hydrogen, H₂   +
Uses:
• fuel
• manufacture of ammonia
• manufacture of margarine.

Sodium hydroxide, NaOH
Uses:
• alkali
• paper-making
• soap-making
• making ceramics
• making textiles
• extracting aluminium.

Fig. 16.3 Salt (sodium chloride): some of its uses

Fig. 16.4 A salt mine in Cheshire

Figure 16.4 shows a salt mine at Winsford, Cheshire. The operator is using the machine to drill holes in the rock face and insert charges of explosive. When detonated, a single charge can bring down 1 kilotonne of rock. Dumpers take the rock to be crushed.

In hot climates, **solar evaporation** is used. Sea water is evaporated by the sun until salt crystallises (Fig. 2.5).

SUMMARY NOTE

Sodium chloride, common salt, is essential for many of our body processes. Without it, we die. Every country has supplies of salt. It is obtained by solar evaporation, by underground mining and by solution mining. Salt is the basis of many industrial processes.

1 Why does the human body need salt?

2 What would you recommend to a person who does hard physical work and perspires heavily?

3 Roman soldiers were given a **salarium**, that is, money to buy salt. Salt seems to have been more highly valued in hot countries than in cold countries. Can you explain why? What does the word **salary** mean today?

4 Why is no country short of salt deposits? Where is salt mined in this country?

5 What advantages do swimmers in the Great Salt Lake have? What makes swimming in this lake unpleasant? (Hint: What happens easily in a saturated solution?)

6 Why is sodium chloride so different from the elements sodium and chlorine? (Remember Chapter 6.)

7 • When animals are fed diets with a high salt content, their blood pressure rises.
  • When people are fed diets low in salt, their blood pressure drops.
  • The average salt intake in the UK is 8 g/day.
  • In a study of 3000 Scotsmen, aged 45–64, 40% had high blood pressure.
  • In England and Wales in 1980, the number of deaths caused by high blood pressure = 7000, heart disease = 160 500, strokes = 73 500.

From this information, say

a How many deaths in England and Wales in 1980 were thought to be linked to high blood pressure?

b What is the connection between salt and blood pressure?

c What can be done about heart disease?

d What dietary factors other than salt may be involved?

e Imagine that someone asks you to find out whether fat intake or salt intake is more important in controlling blood pressure. You have a supply of laboratory animals and a machine for measuring blood pressure. Plan a set of experiments to answer the question.

16.2 Reactions of hydrochloric acid

1 Hydrogen chloride is a colourless gas. It has an unpleasant, penetrating smell. When it comes into contact with air, it 'fumes', that is, it reacts with water vapour to form a mist.

2 Hydrogen chloride reacts with ammonia to form ammonium chloride (see Section 15.4).

3 Hydrogen chloride is a very soluble gas. When hydrogen chloride dissolves in water, a solution of hydrochloric acid is formed:

hydrogen chloride(g) + water → hydrochloric acid(aq)

The reactions of acids were summarised in Section 7.2. You can study the reactions of hydrochloric acid in Experiment 7.1. They are summarised in Fig. 16.5.

Fig. 16.5 Reactions of hydrochloric acid

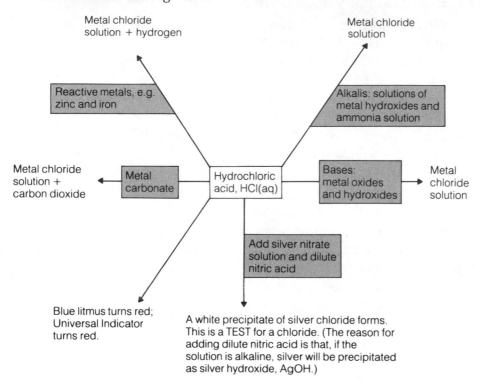

Metal chloride solution + hydrogen

Reactive metals, e.g. zinc and iron

Metal chloride solution

Alkalis: solutions of metal hydroxides and ammonia solution

Metal chloride solution + carbon dioxide

Metal carbonate

Hydrochloric acid, HCl(aq)

Bases: metal oxides and hydroxides

Metal chloride solution

Add silver nitrate solution and dilute nitric acid

Blue litmus turns red; Universal Indicator turns red.

A white precipitate of silver chloride forms. This is a TEST for a chloride. (The reason for adding dilute nitric acid is that, if the solution is alkaline, silver will be precipitated as silver hydroxide, AgOH.)

SUMMARY NOTE

Hydrogen chloride is a fuming gas with a pungent smell. It shows typical acid reactions, reacting with bases and forming an acidic solution in water. A solution of this very soluble gas is made by passing the gas through an inverted funnel into water.

16.3 Preparation of chlorides

All the reactions shown in Fig. 16.5 can be used for the preparation of chlorides (see Experiments 7.5 to 7.8). Some equations for typical reactions are:

magnesium + hydrochloric acid → magnesium chloride + hydrogen

$Mg(s)$ + $2HCl(aq)$ → $MgCl_2(aq)$ + $H_2(g)$

copper(II) oxide + hydrochloric acid → copper(II) chloride + water

$CuO(s)$ + $2HCl(aq)$ → $CuCl_2(aq)$ + $H_2O(l)$

potassium hydroxide + hydrochloric acid → potassium chloride + water

$KOH(aq)$ + $HCl(aq)$ → $KCl(aq)$ + $H_2O(l)$

calcium carbonate + hydrochloric acid → calcium chloride + water + carbon dioxide

$CaCO_3(s)$ + $2HCl(aq)$ → $CaCl_2(aq)$ + $H_2O(l)$ + $CO_2(g)$

silver nitrate + hydrochloric acid → silver chloride + nitric acid

$AgNO_3(aq)$ + $HCl(aq)$ → $AgCl(s)$ + $HNO_3(aq)$

SUMMARY NOTE

Hydrochloric acid reacts with many metals, with bases (metal oxides and hydroxides), with alkalis and with carbonates. These reactions are typical of acids. They result in the formation of chlorides, the salts of hydrochloric acid. The test for a chloride in solution is the formation of a white precipitate with silver nitrate solution and dilute nitric acid.

JUST TESTING 93

1 Nickel chloride, $NiCl_2$, is soluble. What would you need, in addition to hydrochloric acid, to make it? Describe briefly how you would make crystals of this salt.

2 Lead(II) chloride, $PbCl_2$, is insoluble. What would you need, in addition to hydrochloric acid, to make it? Briefly describe how you would make a dry sample of this salt.

3 Describe how you would make a solid specimen of ammonium chloride, starting from ammonia solution and hydrochloric acid.

4 a Name a substance which will react with hydrochloric acid to give hydrogen. Give the word equation for the reaction and a balanced chemical equation.

   b Name a substance which will react with hydrochloric acid to give carbon dioxide. Write a word equation for the reaction and a balanced chemical equation.

5 Say what you would need, in addition to hydrochloric acid, to make a copper(II) chloride, b potassium chloride, c zinc chloride, d silver chloride. In each case, describe what you would do with the starting materials to obtain a solid specimen of the product.
Write word equations for the reactions.
Write balanced chemical equations.

16.4 Chlorine in war

From 1914–1918, Germany was at war with Britain and France. In the spring of 1915, Germany prepared to perform a chemical experiment. Six thousand cylinders of chlorine were dug in over a $3\frac{1}{2}$ mile stretch of battlefield in Flanders. On 22nd April, the wind was blowing away from the German lines towards the British and French trenches. Masked technicians opened the cylinders and set the chlorine free. A green cloud rolled towards the Allied troops. It sank into the trenches, and stung the soldiers' eyes and noses. Minutes later, they were gasping for breath and coughing up blood. The Germans attacked successfully and made a big advance. The Allied casualties were 5000 killed, 6000 captured and 15 000 gassed.

The British were horrified. They had no defence whatsoever against this new menace. Fortunately for them, the German generals were not entirely satisfied with their new weapon. They had treated it as an experiment, and were not prepared to back it up. Its success depended on a favourable wind. For most of the time, winds in Flanders blew from west to east, away from the Allied lines, towards the German lines. Their deadly weapon could well be turned against them.

The choice of chlorine was made by Professor Fritz Haber (see Ammonia, Section 15.4). As well as being poisonous, a suitable gas must be dense; then it will remain for some time at ground level. It must also be easy to make in large quantities and to transport. Chlorine fits the bill. It can be made from rock salt; it is 2.5 times denser than air; it can be stored under pressure in cylinders. A disadvantage is that, having a colour and a smell, chlorine cannot take an enemy by surprise. Haber had planned to store the gas in shells and fire these into the Allied trenches. The shortage of shell cases forced him to settle for relying on the wind to transport the poisonous green cloud.

Chemical weapons have been used since 1915. In the war against Vietnam, the USA used **defoliants** — chemicals which kill trees and plants. These are organic compounds of chlorine. The effects of these chemicals were more lethal than anyone expected (see Section 15.7). There is now an international agreement that no nation will use chemical weapons in war. The USA has signed the treaty banning chemical weapons.

16.5 Chlorine in peace

Chlorine is a non-metallic element. It is one of the halogens, the elements in Group 7 of the Periodic Table. Industrially, chlorine is made by the electrolysis of brine (sodium chloride solution; see Section 5.7). It has not been used to kill human beings since 1915. It is now used to kill bacteria and so to save human lives. It is used to sterilise drinking water (see Section 9.5). Some of the uses of chlorine are shown in Fig. 16.6. Some of the many useful organic compounds of chlorine are mentioned in Sections 15.7 and 18.3.

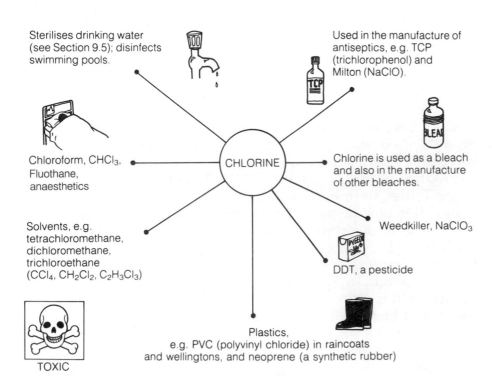

Sterilises drinking water (see Section 9.5); disinfects swimming pools.

Used in the manufacture of antiseptics, e.g. TCP (trichlorophenol) and Milton (NaClO).

Chlorine is used as a bleach and also in the manufacture of other bleaches.

CHLORINE

Chloroform, $CHCl_3$, Fluothane, anaesthetics

Solvents, e.g. tetrachloromethane, dichloromethane, trichloroethane (CCl_4, CH_2Cl_2, $C_2H_3Cl_3$)

Weedkiller, $NaClO_3$

DDT, a pesticide

Plastics, e.g. PVC (polyvinyl chloride) in raincoats and wellingtons, and neoprene (a synthetic rubber)

TOXIC

Fig. 16.6 Some uses of chlorine

16.6 Properties and reactions of chlorine

Table 16.1 Chlorine

1	Appearance	Dense green gas with a horrible, choking smell Very poisonous Moderately soluble in water
2	Damp, blue litmus paper	Turns red and then colourless: chlorine bleaches it. This is a **test for chlorine**.
3	Metals	Chlorine reacts with most metals. Sodium burns in chlorine to form sodium chloride (see Fig. 16.7):

Fig. 16.7 Sodium burns in chlorine

TOXIC

sodium + chlorine → sodium chloride
$$2Na(s) + Cl_2(g) \rightarrow 2NaCl(s)$$

Heated copper reacts with chlorine to form copper(II) chloride:

copper + chlorine → copper(II) chloride
$$Cu(s) + Cl_2(g) \rightarrow CuCl_2(s)$$

Heated iron reacts with chlorine to form iron(III) chloride (see Fig. 16.8):

iron + chlorine → iron(III) chloride
$$2Fe(s) + 3Cl_2(g) \rightarrow 2FeCl_3(s)$$

Fig. 16.8 Iron burns in chlorine

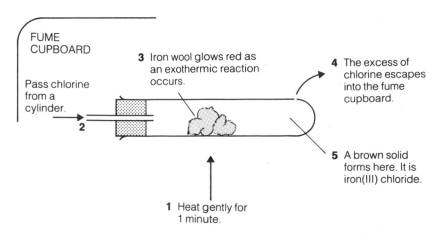

4 Metal ions When a metal has a variable valency, chlorine will oxidise ions of the metal in its lower valency to ions of the metal in its higher valency. Iron(II) chloride is oxidised to iron(III) chloride, and iron(II) sulphate is oxidised to iron(III) sulphate:

$$\text{chlorine} + \text{iron(II) chloride} \rightarrow \text{iron(III) chloride}$$
$$\text{Cl}_2\text{(g)} + 2\text{FeCl}_2\text{(aq)} \rightarrow 2\text{FeCl}_3\text{(aq)}$$

5 Non-metals Hydrogen burns in chlorine to form hydrogen chloride (see Fig. 16.9):

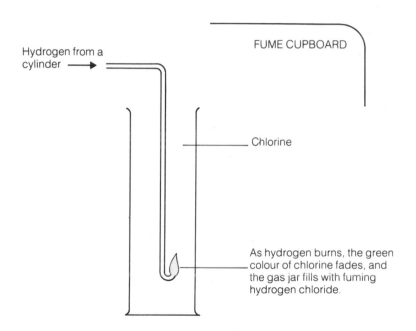

Hydrogen from a cylinder →

FUME CUPBOARD

Chlorine

As hydrogen burns, the green colour of chlorine fades, and the gas jar fills with fuming hydrogen chloride.

Fig. 16.9 Hydrogen burns in chlorine

$$\text{hydrogen} + \text{chlorine} \rightarrow \text{hydrogen chloride}$$
$$\text{H}_2\text{(g)} + \text{Cl}_2\text{(g)} \rightarrow 2\text{HCl(g)}$$

This reaction is used industrially in the manufacture of hydrochloric acid.

6 Chlorine is a bleach Chlorine and 'chlorine water', $\text{Cl}_2\text{(aq)}$, are used to bleach fabrics. If the oxidised form DO of a dye D is colourless, then chlorine can bleach that dye:

$$\frac{\text{chlorine}}{\text{water}} + \text{dye} \rightarrow \frac{\text{oxidised}}{\text{dye}} + \frac{\text{hydrochloric}}{\text{acid}}$$
$$\text{Cl}_2\text{(aq)} + \text{H}_2\text{O(l)} + \text{D} \rightarrow \text{DO} + 2\text{HCl(aq)}$$

7 Other halogens Chlorine will displace bromine from bromides and iodine from iodides (see Experiment 15.1):

$$\text{chlorine} + \text{bromide} \rightarrow \text{chloride} + \text{bromine}$$
$$\text{Cl}_2\text{(aq)} + 2\text{Br}^-\text{(aq)} \rightarrow 2\text{Cl}^-\text{(aq)} + \text{Br}_2\text{(aq)}$$
$$\text{chlorine} + \text{iodide} \rightarrow \text{chloride} + \text{iodine}$$
$$\text{Cl}_2\text{(aq)} + 2\text{I}^-\text{(aq)} \rightarrow 2\text{Cl}^-\text{(aq)} + \text{I}_2\text{(aq)}$$

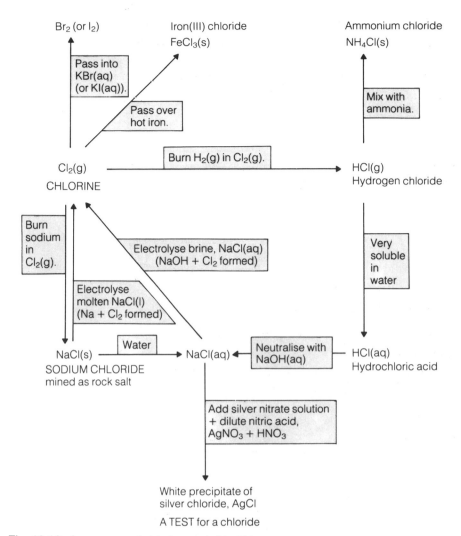

Fig. 16.10 A summary of chlorine and chlorides

*16.7 Oxidation–reduction reactions

The reactions of chlorine are dominated by its readiness to gain electrons and form chloride ions (see Chapter 6).

chlorine molecules + electrons → chloride ions
Cl_2 + $2e^-$ → $2Cl^-$

Chlorine molecules are very reactive; chloride ions are very stable.

The reactions of chlorine illustrate a new aspect of oxidation–reduction reactions. Previously (Section 9.18) an oxidising agent was defined as a substance that gives oxygen to or takes hydrogen from another substance. The reactions of chlorine do not fit in with this definition; yet chlorine is an oxidising agent. Metals burn in chlorine to form chlorides as metals burn in oxygen to form oxides. A new definition of oxidation and reduction is called for. The new definition is: *An oxidising agent is a substance that takes electrons from another substance. A reducing agent is a substance that gives electrons to another substance.*

Example 1   In the reaction between copper and chlorine to form copper(II) chloride, copper atoms give electrons to become copper ions, Cu^{2+}. Chlorine molecules gain electrons to form chloride ions, Cl^-. The reaction can be considered in two parts and a half-equation written for each part.

a $Cu(s) \rightarrow Cu^{2+}(s) + 2e^-$
b $Cl_2(g) + 2e^- \rightarrow 2Cl^-(s)$

Copper loses electrons; it is oxidised. Chlorine gains electrons; it is reduced.
Chlorine is the oxidising agent, and copper is the reducing agent.
Adding the two half-equations, **a** + **b**

$$Cu(s) + Cl_2(g) + 2e^- \rightarrow Cu^{2+}(s) + 2e^- + 2Cl^-(s)$$

The $2e^-$ on the left-hand side (LHS) of the equation and the $2e^-$ on the RHS cancel to give

$$Cu(s) + Cl_2(g) \rightarrow Cu^{2+}(s) + 2Cl^-(s)$$

In this way, the equation for the reaction is obtained by adding two half-equations. The equations for redox reactions are often more complicated than this example, and the method of adding half-equations is a great help.

Example 2   Sodium burns in chlorine to form sodium chloride. The reaction can be considered in two parts and a half-equation written for each part.

a $Na(s) \rightarrow Na^+(s) + e^-$
b $Cl_2(g) + 2e^- \rightarrow 2Cl^-(s)$

Before adding the half-equations, we need to multiply half-equation **a** by 2:

2a $2Na(s) \rightarrow 2Na^+(s) + 2e^-$

Then adding **2a** + **b** gives

$$2Na(s) + Cl_2(g) + 2e^- \rightarrow 2Na^+(s) + 2e^- + 2Cl^-(s)$$

The $2e^-$ on the LHS of the equation cancel out the $2e^-$ on the RHS – this is why we had to multiply half-equation **a** by 2 before adding. The reaction equation becomes:

$$2Na(s) + Cl_2(g) \rightarrow 2Na^+(s) + 2Cl^-(s)$$

Sodium has lost electrons; it has been oxidised. Chlorine has gained electrons; it has been reduced. Chlorine is the oxidising agent, and sodium is the reducing agent.

$$2Na(s) + Cl_2(g) \rightarrow 2Na^+(s) + 2Cl^-(s)$$

oxidation →
reduction →

Reducing   Oxidising
agent   agent

This new definition holds for all oxidation–reduction reactions.

- The substance that is oxidised loses electrons.
- The substance that is reduced gains electrons.
- An oxidising agent accepts electrons.
- A reducing agent gives electrons.

Example 3   When a metal, such as zinc, reacts with an acid, the reaction can be considered in two parts, and a half-equation can be written for each part.

a   zinc atom → zinc ion + electrons

Half-equation **a**

$$Zn(s) \rightarrow Zn^{2+}(aq) + 2e^-$$

b   hydrogen ions + electrons → hydrogen molecule

Half-equation **b**

$$2H^+(aq) + 2e^- \rightarrow H_2(g)$$

The zinc atoms have supplied electrons, and hydrogen ions have accepted electrons.
The zinc atoms have been oxidised, and hydrogen ions have been reduced.
Adding the two half-equations **a** and **b**,

$$Zn(s) + 2H^+(aq) + 2e^- \rightarrow Zn^{2+}(aq) + 2e^- + H_2(g)$$

The electrons on the LHS and the RHS cancel so the equation can be written:

$$Zn(s) + 2H^+(aq) \rightarrow Zn^{2+}(aq) + H_2(g)$$

Why is tap water chlorinated? Is that anything to do with oxidation by chlorine?

Chlorine can kill bacteria because it's such a strong oxidising agent.

Example 4   Some metals form more than one type of ion. When iron(II) compounds are converted into iron(III) compounds, Fe^{2+} ions lose electrons: they are oxidised. The half-equation is

a $Fe^{2+}(aq) \rightarrow Fe^{3+}(aq) + e^-$

The oxidation is brought about by a substance that can accept electrons – an oxidising agent, e.g. chlorine. The half-equation is

b $Cl_2(aq) + 2e^- \rightarrow 2Cl^-(aq)$

Before adding the two half-equations, first multiply half-equation **a** by 2:

2a $2Fe^{2+}(aq) \rightarrow 2Fe^{3+}(aq) + 2e^-$

Now add **2a** + **b**:

$$2Fe^{2+}(aq) + Cl_2(g) + 2e^- \rightarrow 2Fe^{3+}(aq) + 2e^- + 2Cl^-(aq)$$

and cancelling the electrons on the LHS and RHS gives:

$$2Fe^{2+}(aq) + Cl_2(g) \rightarrow 2Fe^{3+}(aq) + 2Cl^-(aq)$$

Example 5 Chlorine displaces bromine from bromides. Since chlorine is a stronger oxidising agent than bromine is, chlorine takes electrons away from bromide ions. Bromide ions are oxidised to bromine molecules, and chlorine molecules are reduced to chloride ions.

$$Cl_2(aq) + 2Br^-(aq) \rightarrow 2Cl^-(aq) + B_2(aq)$$

(reduction: $Cl_2 \rightarrow 2Cl^-$; oxidation: $2Br^- \rightarrow B_2$)

The bromine formed can be detected more easily if a small volume of an organic solvent, e.g. trichloroethane, is added. Bromine dissolves in the organic solvent to form an orange solution.

Similarly, chlorine displaces iodine from iodides, because chlorine is a stronger oxidising agent than iodine. Bromine also displaces iodine from iodides because bromine is a stronger oxidising agent than iodine. The iodine formed can be detected readily by adding a small volume of an organic solvent. The iodine dissolves in the solvent to give a purple solution.

Fluorine is the most powerful oxidising agent of the halogens. It is dangerously reactive and is not used in schools and colleges. In order of oxidising power, the halogens rank:

$$F_2 > Cl_2 > Br_2 > I_2$$

JUST TESTING 94

1 You are familiar with the oxidation:

    copper + oxygen → copper(II) oxide
    $2Cu(s) + O_2(g) \rightarrow 2CuO(s)$

a Define (i) an oxidising agent, and (ii) a reducing agent in terms of the transfer of electrons.

b When Cu is converted into CuO (that is, $Cu^{2+}O^{2-}$), does Cu gain or lose electrons?

c When O_2 is converted into CuO, does O_2 gain or lose electrons?

d Say whether you would classify copper as an oxidising agent or a reducing agent in terms of your definition in **a**, and explain why.

e Say how oxygen fits the definition of an oxidising agent which you gave in **a**.

f Say whether you think this reaction should be called an oxidation reaction, and explain your answer.

16.8 The manufacture of bleach

Chlorine is produced by the electrolysis of sodium chloride solution (brine) (see Section 5.10, including Fig. 5.10). During electrolysis, as chlorine and hydrogen are evolved, the electrolyte changes from sodium chloride into sodium hydroxide. All three

Fig. 16.11 Sodium chlorate(I) as an antiseptic and a bleach

products – chlorine, hydrogen and sodium hydroxide – are valuable. In some plants, the electrodes are rotated to increase the contact between chlorine and sodium hydroxide. Instead of leaving the cell, chlorine reacts in this way:

chlorine + sodium hydroxide $\rightarrow$ sodium chlorate(I) + sodium chloride + water

$$Cl_2(g) + 2NaOH(aq) \rightarrow NaClO(aq) + NaCl(aq) + H_2O(l)$$

Sodium chlorate(I) is separated from the solution that is formed. It is an oxidising agent and a bleach. The chlorine bleaches sold for domestic use are solutions of sodium chlorate(I) or calcium chlorate(I). As an oxidising agent, sodium chlorate(I) kills bacteria, and it is mild enough for use as an antiseptic on the skin. It is sold as Milton®, which is widely used for sterilising babies' bottles.

In other manufacturing plants, the electrolysis of brine with rotating electrodes is carried out at a higher temperature. Then the following reaction takes place:

chlorine + sodium hydroxide $\rightarrow$ sodium chlorate(V) + sodium chloride + water

$$3Cl_2(g) + 6NaOH(aq) \rightarrow NaClO_3(aq) + 5NaCl(aq) + 3H_2O(l)$$

Sodium chlorate(V) is a powerful oxidising agent. It is used as a weedkiller, e.g. Tandol®.

16.9 Tests for oxidising agents and reducing agents

Test for reducing agents

Acidified potassium manganate(VII) is a powerful oxidising agent. It can oxidise – and therefore test for – many reducing agents. A reducing agent will change the colour from the purple of $MnO_4^-(aq)$ ion to the pale pink of $Mn^{2+}(aq)$ ion (see Fig. 16.12).

A piece of filter paper

A spot of acidified potassium manganate(VII) solution

A jar of the gas under test

If the paper turns from purple to a very pale pink, then the gas is a reducing agent.

Fig. 16.12 Testing for a reducing agent

Test for oxidising agents

Many oxidising agents will oxidise the iodide ion, I⁻, to iodine, I_2. Iodine can be detected because it forms a dark blue compound with starch. Potassium iodide solution and starch can therefore be used to test for oxidising agents (see Fig. 16.13).

$$2I^-(aq) \rightarrow I_2(aq) + 2e^-$$
colour-   brown, forms a dark blue
less   compound with starch

A piece of filter paper

A spot of a solution of potassium iodide and starch

A jar of the gas under test

If the colour changes from white to dark blue, then the gas is an oxidising agent.

Fig. 16.13   Testing for an oxidising agent

SUMMARY NOTE

Reducing agents decolorise acidified potassium manganate(VII) solution. Oxidising agents give a dark blue colour with a solution of potassium iodide and starch.

JUST TESTING 95

1 Material which has been bleached by chlorine must be thoroughly rinsed. It is important to remove *two* substances which are present. What are they?

2 Write a word equation for the oxidation of an iodide by chlorine. Write a balanced chemical equation.

3 Write a word equation for the oxidation of an iodide by bromine. Write a balanced chemical equation.

4 You are given two gas jars. One contains hydrogen chloride, and one contains chlorine. What is the difference in the appearance and smell of the two gases? Describe two tests you could do to distinguish between them.

5 There are three bottles on the prep. room shelf. All contain crystalline white solids. Three labels lie on the floor. They read: *Potassium chloride*, *Potassium bromide* and *Potassium iodide*. How would you decide which label to stick on each of the three bottles if all you had to work with was a bottle of chlorine water and an organic solvent?

*6 Three identical half-litre bottles contain solutions of potassium chloride, potassium bromide and potassium iodide. The solutions are all colourless. All have a concentration of 2.0 mol/l. All have lost their labels. Can you think of a way of telling which solution is which without removing the stoppers? (See Section 12.11) for mol/l.)

Bleaches which contain chlorine are powerful oxidising agents. For this reason, you should not use a chlorine bleach together with other chemical cleaning fluids. Detergents which contain ammonia and bleaches which contain hydrogen peroxide will react violently with chlorine. (Remember the story about chlorine in Section 16.4?)

16.10 The halogens

The elements fluorine, chlorine, bromine, iodine and astatine are called the **halogens**. (The name **halogen** is Greek for **salt-former**.) The halogens all combine with metals to form salts, called **halides**, in which the halogen is an anion, X^-. The halogens are all oxidising agents. They all have 7 electrons in their outer shells, and they form Group 7 of the Periodic Table. Their similarity led to their being regarded as a 'family' of elements, and was one of the factors which convinced Mendeleev that he was working along the right lines with the Periodic Table (see Section 4.6).

The first member of the group is fluorine, a poisonous yellow gas. It is so reactive that it is a dangerous element to work with.

Table 16.2 The halogens

Halogen, X_2	Chlorine, Cl_2	Bromine, Br_2	Iodine, I_2
1 State of the element at room temperature	Green gas	Reddish-brown liquid; easily vaporised	Shiny black solid; sublimes when heated
2 Vapour of X_2	Green	Orange-brown	Purple
3 Electron configuration of X	2.8.7	2.8.8.7	2.8.18.8.7
4 Halide ion, X^-	Chloride, Cl^-	Bromide, Br^-	Iodide, I^-
5 Sodium halide, NaX	Sodium chloride, NaCl, a white crystalline solid, soluble in water	Sodium bromide, NaBr, a white crystalline solid, soluble in water	Sodium iodide, NaI, a white crystalline solid, soluble in water
6 Oxidising agents	Cl_2 is $> Br_2 > I_2$	Br_2 is $> I_2$	I_2 is the least powerful.
7 Test for a halide ion in solution, X^-(aq): add $AgNO_3$(aq) + HNO_3(aq)	Precipitate of AgCl, a white solid, soluble in dilute ammonia solution	Precipitate of AgBr, a pale yellow solid, soluble in concentrated ammonia solution	Precipitate of AgI, a yellow solid, insoluble in ammonia solution
8 Hydrogen halide, HX	Hydrogen chloride HCl(g), a colourless gas, fumes in moist air, acidic (with water forms hydrochloric acid, HCl(aq))	Hydrogen bromide HBr(g), a colourless gas, fumes in moist air, acidic (with water forms hydrobromic acid, HBr(aq))	Hydrogen iodide HI(g), a colourless gas, fumes in moist air, acidic (with water forms hydriodic acid, HI(aq))
9 Reaction of X_2 with hydrogen	Hydrogen burns vigorously to form hydrogen chloride, HCl (see Fig. 16.9). Under some conditions, the reaction is explosive.	Hydrogen burns in bromine to form hydrogen bromide, HBr.	When hydrogen and iodine are heated together in a sealed tube, some hydrogen iodide is formed. The reaction does not go to completion.
10 Reaction of X_2 with iron	A vigorous, exothermic reaction gives $FeCl_3$ (see Fig. 16.8).	A less vigorous reaction gives $FeBr_3$ (see Fig. 16.14).	A gentle reaction gives FeI_2 (see Fig. 16.14).

Many of the chemists who did the early experiments on fluorine were injured in explosions. The last member of the group, astatine, is a short-lived radioactive element.

The elements show a gradual change in physical and chemical properties with increasing atomic mass (see Table 16.2).

Iron wool

Liquid bromine (1 cm³)

Heat

The iron wool glows red. Crystals of iron(III) bromide, FeBr₃, form on the surface.

Iron wool

A few crystals of iodine

Heat

The reaction is less vigorous. The crystals which form on the surface are iron(II) iodide, FeI₂.

Fig. 16.14 Bromine and iodine react with heated iron

SUMMARY NOTE

The elements of Group 7 of the Periodic Table are fluorine, chlorine, bromine, iodine and astatine. They are called the **halogens**. The halogens
- are non-metallic
- react readily with metals to form salts
- are oxidising agents
- combine with hydrogen to form acidic hydrogen halides.

There is a gradual change in physical and chemical properties down the group.

JUST TESTING 96

1 'The halogens are a family of elements.' Explain why this statement is often made.

2 Describe two experiments you could do to show that chlorine is more reactive than bromine.
   Which is the most reactive of all the halogens? Why do you not do experiments with this element?

16.11 Fluoride: friend or foe?

Fluorine is a poisonous yellow gas. It attacks glass, and its reactions are often explosive. Yet the British Government passed a law in 1985 to allow water authorities to put sodium fluoride into the drinking water! Research workers noticed that children in some cities had less tooth decay than average. They looked for a cause. They found that there was a high natural concentration of fluorides in the water in these cities. They recommended increasing the concentration of fluorides in other areas. Fluorides are most effective in preventing decay in teeth which are still forming and calcifying, that is, in children up to the age of 8 years. The fluoridation of drinking water must be carefully controlled. Enough sodium fluoride is added to bring the concentration of fluoride ions up to 1 p.p.m. (part per million). Excessive amounts of fluoride ion can damage teeth. Again, young children are more likely to be affected than other people by an excess of fluoride. Some authorities think that fluoridation of drinking water is too risky. They suggest using a toothpaste containing a fluoride instead.

How do fluorides work? The calcium compounds in teeth and bone are calcium carbonate, $CaCO_3$, and calcium hydroxide phosphate, $Ca_5(OH)(PO_4)_3$, 'hydroxyapatite'. Fluoride converts the

Fig. 16.15 Toothpastes with fluoride

320

latter compound into calcium fluoride phosphate, $Ca_5F(PO_4)_3$, 'fluoroapatite'. This is less likely to be attacked by food because it no longer contains the basic hydroxide ion, OH^-.

In large amounts, fluorides are pollutants. There have been cases of pollution arising from the use of fluorides in aluminium smelters (Section 11.12).

JUST TESTING 97

1 What word in the account you have just read means 'laying down calcium'? In which type of person is this process taking place the fastest? What should these people do to protect their teeth?

2 Emma is surprised to hear that fluorides in small quantities are good for teeth because she knows that fluorine is a poisonous gas. What would you say to her to explain the difference between fluorine and fluorides?

16.12 Iodides can be useful too

Scientists at the World Meteorological Organisation are doing a 7-year experiment. They are trying to find out whether they can alter the weather. The tool they are using is silver iodide. This salt has a crystal structure similar to ice. There is evidence that silver iodide will make it rain. Of course, there must be clouds; silver iodide cannot produce rain out of a clear blue sky! The salt has to be dropped into a cloud from a plane or fired into it from the ground. The crystals act as a 'seed' around which water vapour can condense.

You can imagine how the technique could be used to benefit people. It can also be used for evil. A treaty has been signed by members of the United Nations to stop countries from using the weather as a weapon. The USA used cloud seeding in Vietnam to produce floods, but the USA has signed the new treaty.

Scientists are doubtful about the ability of silver iodide to produce more than a 10% to 15% increase in the rainfall.

JUST TESTING 98

1 Cloud seeding is called 'weather modification'. Write a summary of ways in which weather modification could help farmers. In which countries would it help most?

2 Is silver iodide a magic 'rainmaker'? Explain your answer. If it is not magic, how does it work?

3 Are there any dangers connected with the research work? Do you think it should continue?

Exercise 16

1 a Why is chlorine added to the water in swimming pools?

b What colour does chlorine turn damp litmus paper?

c What colour does hydrogen chloride turn damp litmus paper?

d What is formed when hydrogen chloride meets ammonia?

e What is formed when hydrogen burns in chlorine?

2 What do you see and what new substances are formed when chlorine reacts with
a burning sodium, **b** heated copper,
c heated iron?
Write (i) word equations for the reactions,
(ii) balanced symbol equations.

3 With which one of the following pairs of reagents would a displacement reaction take place?

a aqueous bromine and aqueous potassium chloride

b aqueous bromine and aqueous sodium chloride

c aqueous chlorine and aqueous potassium iodide

d aqueous iodine and aqueous potassium bromide.

4 a Why do water boards add chlorine to water supplies?

b Why is the element, chlorine, used, rather than a chloride?

c Why do water boards add fluorides to water supplies?

d Why are fluorides used, rather than the element, fluorine?

5 a Two chlorine atoms join by the formation of a covalent bond to give a molecule of chlorine. By means of a sketch, show what happens to the electrons in the outermost shells of the atoms.

b A chlorine atom combines with a sodium atom by the formation of an electrovalent bond. Sketch what happens to the electrons in the outermost shells of the two atoms. What is formed in the reaction?

c A chlorine atom combines with a hydrogen atom by the formation of a covalent bond. Sketch what happens to the electrons during bond formation. What is formed in the reaction?

6 The first four members of the halogens are
$^{19}_{9}F$ $^{35}_{17}Cl$ $^{80}_{35}Br$ $^{127}_{53}I$

a Write the electron arrangements in an atom of fluorine and an atom of chlorine.

b State one characteristic which is common to the electron arrangements of all the halogen atoms.

c State the number of protons in a chloride ion.

d State the number of neutrons in an iodine atom.

e Which contains more atoms, 1 gram of iodine or 1 gram of chlorine?

7 When dry chlorine is passed over heated iron, a black solid sublimes in the cooler part of the apparatus.

a Name the black solid.

b Explain what is meant by 'sublimes'.

c Write a word equation and a chemical equation for the reaction.

d Will the reaction between fluorine and iron be more or less vigorous than that of chlorine?

8 Hydrogen chloride reacts with water to form a solution which has a pH value less than 7.

a State the type of bonding in hydrogen chloride.

b Explain the reaction that takes place between hydrogen chloride and water.

c Say what is formed when the solution is neutralised by potassium hydroxide solution.

9 Copy this table, and complete it.

Element	Hydrogen	Calcium	Carbon
Formula of the chloride			
State of the chloride at room temperature			

10 Choose your answers to the following questions from these compounds:
$BaSO_4$ $ZnCO_3$ KOH $NaCl$ $AgNO_3$
ZnO $Ca(NO_3)_2$

a Which compound dissolves in water to give a solution which will neutralise hydrochloric acid?

b Which compound gives off a gas when dilute hydrochloric acid is added?

c Solutions of two of the compounds form a white precipitate when they are mixed. Name the compounds.

d Which compound is an insoluble white solid which neutralises hydrochloric acid to form a salt?

11 An aqueous solution of chlorine was added to a colourless solution of a potassium salt. A brown solution formed. When this brown solution was shaken with the organic solvent 'trichlor', the organic liquid turned purple.

  a Name the substance causing the purple colour in the organic liquid.

  b Name the substance causing the brown colour in the aqueous solution.

  c Name the potassium salt.

  d Describe a test you could do to confirm that you are right.

  e Write a word equation for the reaction that took place.

  *__f__ Write an ionic equation for the reaction.

Crossword on Chapter 16

Clues across

  3 See 14 across.
  6 This action of chlorine is useful in cleaning. (9)
  9 across, 7 down A fuming gas which contains chlorine. (8, 8)
  11 across, 8 down . A description of chlorine. (5, 3)
  14 across, 3 across Used for preparing chlorides. (12, 4)
  17 Noble gas used in lights. (4)
  18 An essential element in teeth. (7)
  20 This type of compound always reacts with 14 across, 3 across. (6)

Clues down

  1 The colour of litmus in 14 across, 3 across. (3)
  2 down, 7 down The formation of this is a test for chlorides. (6, 8)
  4 A reddish-coloured metal with a green chloride. (6)
  5 A use for chlorine. (12)
  6 Evaporate on a steam _____. (4)
  7 See 2 down.
  8 See 11 across.
  10 Evaporate a solution in this. (4)
  12 This gas gives a white solid when it reacts with 9 across, 7 down. (7)
  13 The chloride of this metal is 'common salt'. (6)
  15 To liquefy chlorine gas, you must make it much _____ than room temperature. (6)
  16 Common salt is mined in this form. (4)
  19 Symbol for chlorine. (2)

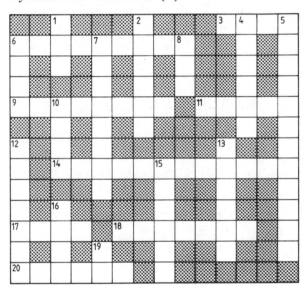

CHAPTER 17 *Analytical chemistry*

Does a sample of drinking water contain nitrates? Which elements are present in this sample of soil? Which pigments are present in this food dye? Does a brand of paint contain lead compounds? Which metals are present in an alloy steel? To find the answers to such questions, we use **analytical chemistry**.

Analysis means separating something into its component parts. The analysis of chemical compounds and mixtures is therefore called **analytical chemistry**. If we need to know which substances are present in a sample, but we do not need to know the quantities of those substances, we use **qualitative analysis**. If we need to know the precise quantities of one or more substances, we use **quantitative analysis**. One method of quantitative analysis is **volumetric analysis**, in which reactions take place in solution. This is described in Section 12.11. Another method is **gravimetric analysis**, in which the masses of reacting substances are found by the use of an accurate balance. This is described in Section 12.8.

In this chapter, we shall be dealing with qualitative analysis. Methods of identifying cations, anions and gases are described below.

17.1 Flame colours

Some metals and their compounds give characteristic colours when heated in a Bunsen flame. The colour can be used to identify the metal ion present in a compound.

17.2 Tests for ions in solution

The following tests can be done on a solution. A soluble solid can be analysed by dissolving it in distilled water and then applying the tests.

Table 17.1 Some flame colours

Metal	Colour of flame
Barium	Apple-green
Calcium	Brick-red
Copper	Green with blue streaks
Lithium	Crimson
Potassium	Lilac
Sodium	Yellow

Table 17.2 Testing for ions in solution

Anion	Test and observation
Carbonate, CO_3^{2-}(aq)	Add dilute hydrochloric acid to the solution (or add it to the solid). Bubbles of carbon dioxide are given off.
Chloride, Cl^-(aq)	Add a few drops of dilute nitric acid followed by a few drops of silver nitrate solution. A white precipitate of silver chloride is formed. The precipitate is soluble in ammonia solution.
Bromide, Br^-(aq)	Add a few drops of dilute nitric acid followed by a few drops of silver nitrate solution. A pale yellow precipitate of silver bromide is formed. The precipitate is slightly soluble in ammonia solution.
Iodide, I^-(aq)	Add a few drops of dilute nitric acid followed by a few drops of silver nitrate solution. A yellow precipitate of silver iodide is formed. It is insoluble in ammonia solution.

Nitrate, NO_3^-(aq)	Make the solution strongly alkaline. Add Devarda's alloy and warm. Ammonia is given off. (If the solution contains ammonium ions, warm with alkali to drive off any ammonia before testing for nitrate ions.)	
Sulphate, SO_4^{2-}(aq)	Add a few drops of barium chloride solution followed by a few drops of dilute hydrochloric acid. A white precipitate of barium sulphate is formed.	
Sulphite, SO_3^{2-}(aq)	Test as for sulphate. A white precipitate of barium sulphite appears, and then reacts with acid to give sulphur dioxide.	

Cation	Add sodium hydroxide solution	Add ammonia solution
Aluminium, Al^{3+}(aq)	Colourless ppt of $Al(OH)_3$(s), which dissolves in excess sodium hydroxide solution.	Colourless ppt of $Al(OH)_3$(s).
Ammonium, NH_4^+(aq)	Warm. Ammonia is given off	—
Copper, Cu^{2+}(aq)	Blue jelly-like ppt of $Cu(OH)_2$(s).	Blue jelly-like ppt which dissolves in excess ammonia solution to form a deep blue solution.
Iron(II), Fe^{2+}(aq)	Green jelly-like ppt of $Fe(OH)_2$(s).	Green jelly-like ppt.
Iron(III), Fe^{3+}(aq)	Rust-brown jelly-like ppt of $Fe(OH)_3$(s).	Rust-brown jelly-like ppt.
Lead(II), Pb^{2+}(aq)	White ppt of $Pb(OH)_2$(s), which dissolves in excess sodium hydroxide solution.	White ppt of $Pb(OH)_2$(s).
Zinc, Zn^{2+}(aq)	White ppt of $Zn(OH)_2$(s), which dissolves in excess sodium hydroxide solution.	White ppt of $Zn(OH)_2$(s), which dissolves in excess ammonia solution.

Note: ppt = precipitate

17.3 Identifying some common gases

If you are testing the smell of a gas, you should do so cautiously (see Fig. 17.1). Tests for common gases are given in Table 17.3. The table shows which gases are poisonous. Use only very small quantities when testing these gases.

Fig. 17.1 How to smell a gas – hold the test-tube away from you and cautiously waft the gas towards you

Table 17.3 Testing gases

Gas	Colour and smell	Test and observation
Ammonia[†]	Colourless Pungent smell	Hold damp red litmus paper or Universal Indicator paper in the gas. The indicator turns blue.
Bromine[†]	Reddish brown Choking smell	Hold damp blue litmus paper in the gas. The litmus turns red and is then bleached.
Carbon dioxide	Colourless Odourless	Bubble the gas through limewater (calcium hydroxide solution). A white solid precipitate appears, turning the solution cloudy.
Chlorine[†]	Poisonous Green gas Choking smell	Test a very small quantity in a fume cupboard. Hold damp blue litmus paper in the gas. The litmus turns red and is quickly bleached. Chlorine turns damp starch–iodide paper blue-black.
Hydrogen	Colourless Odourless when pure	Introduce a lighted splint. Hydrogen burns with a squeaky 'pop'. Keep flames away from hydrogen.
Hydrogen chloride[†]	Colourless Pungent smell	Hold damp blue litmus paper in the gas. The litmus turns red. With ammonia, a white smoke of $NH_4Cl(s)$ forms.
Iodine	Black solid or purple vapour Choking smell	Dissolve in trichloroethane (or other organic solvent) Gives a violet solution.
Nitrogen dioxide[†]	Reddish brown Pungent smell	Hold damp blue litmus paper in the gas. Litmus turns red but is not bleached.
Oxygen	Colourless Odourless	Hold a glowing wooden splint in the gas. The splint bursts into flame.
Sulphur dioxide[†]	Colourless Choking smell	Dip a filter paper in potassium dichromate(VI) solution, and hold it in the gas. The solution turns from orange through green to blue. Potassium manganate(VII) solution turns very pale pink.

[†]These gases are poisonous. Test with care.

Exercise 17

1 A geologist takes samples of barium carbonate and calcium sulphate when she sets out on a field trip. Unfortunately, she mixes up the two samples. Describe two tests she can do to decide which sample is which.

2 A policeman finds a footprint in a flower bed under a window in a burgled house. He suspects Bill Bloggs, who was spotted near the scene of the crime, and who has clay soil on his shoes. The clay soil in the flower bed contains a high percentage of iron(II). How can the police test the clay on Bill's shoes for Fe^{2+}?

3 A solution contains the metal ions $Cu^{2+}(aq)$ and $Zn^{2+}(aq)$. How could you obtain separate precipitates of $Cu(OH)_2$ and $Zn(OH)_2$ from the solution?

4 The chemistry technician discovers three bottles in the prep room. They all contain white solids, and the labels lie on the floor. These read 'Barium oxide', 'Calcium oxide' and 'Magnesium oxide'. Suggest a test the technician could use to tell which label to put on each bottle.

5 A solution contains the sulphates of two metals, A and B. Explain the reactions shown in the flow chart and identify A and B.

Solution of sulphates of A and B

| $NaOH(aq)$

Blue-green precipitate

| $NH_3(aq)$

Blue solution + Green precipitate

CHAPTER 18 *Hydrocarbon fuels*

18.1 Biogas

India and China have millions of **biogas** generators. The biogas which they produce is a fuel used for cooking, heating and lighting. Biogas is the gas produced when organic matter (matter of plant and animal origin) decays in the absence of air. Figure 18.1 shows a biogas generator. The idea is to generate gas by the digestion of animal waste. With about three cattle to every person in India, there is a supply of cattle dung for digestion.

Fig. 18.1 Biogas plant

The gas burns much more efficiently than cakes of cattle dung. As another benefit, the residual sludge is a better fertiliser than raw dung. The output of a biogas digester provides twice as much heat and three times as much useful fertiliser as raw cattle dung. Human waste and some plant waste can also be processed. Both the gas and the residue are clean and odourless.

The biogas digester is simple and robust but, like any other chemical plant, it needs careful operation. Incorrect feed, the wrong temperature or poor mixing can bring production to a halt.

Biogas is about 50% methane. Methane is the gas we burn in Bunsen burners and gas cookers. It is the valuable fuel we call **natural gas** or **North Sea gas**. Methane is the gas which bubbles up through stagnant water. It forms slowly from the anaerobic (without air) decomposition of organic material in the water. It was methane that exploded in the Wyresdale water tunnel in Lancashire in May 1984, killing 11 people. It collects in coal mines, and has been the cause of many pit disasters.

Methane is the gas which forms in the landfill sites where cities store their rubbish (Fig. 18.2). Twenty-five million tonnes of organic waste go into landfills in the UK every year. While some landfill operators are burning methane to get rid of it, others are sinking pipes into the landfill and pumping out methane for sale.

SUMMARY NOTE

Methane is formed when plant and animal matter decays in the absence of air. It is found in coal mines, where it can cause explosions. The methane generated in landfill rubbish sites and in sewage works can be utilised as fuel. Some countries set up biogas generators to make biogas from human, animal and plant waste.

Fig. 18.2 Methane is collected at this landfill in Leicestershire

Fig. 18.3 A commercial biogas plant in Italy

The commercial plant shown in Fig. 18.3 digests a dry pulp of the cereal sweet sorgum. The biogas it produces is used to fuel an electricity generator. The emission of sulphur oxides and nitrogen oxides by the electricity generator is low, and the carbon dioxide emitted is balanced by the carbon dioxide that was absorbed from the atmosphere while the cereal was growing.

JUST TESTING 99

1 What are the advantages of biogas digesters **a** for developing countries, **b** for countries which have advanced technology?

2 Sometimes a flickering flame appears to dance over marshy ground. Country people used to think that the flame was a spirit called 'Will-o'-the-wisp', who lived in marshes. Can you explain what the flame really is?

18.2 Alkanes

Methane is a **hydrocarbon**, a compound of hydrogen and carbon. With formula CH_4, it is the simplest of hydrocarbons. Four covalent bonds join hydrogen atoms to a carbon atom (Fig. 18.4).

Hydrocarbons are **organic compounds**. At one time, the term organic compound meant a compound which was found in plant or animal material, e.g. sugars, fats and proteins. All these compounds contain carbon. Now the term organic compound is used for all carbon compounds, whether they come from plants and animals or were made in a laboratory. Simple compounds like carbon dioxide and carbonates are, however, not usually described as organic compounds. Most organic compounds are covalent. The organic acids form salts which have ionic bonds.

Fig. 18.4 Bonding in methane

Fig. 18.5 (a) Model of methane   (b) Model of ethane   (c) Model of propane

Methane is one of a series of hydrocarbons called the **alkanes** (Fig. 18.5). The next members of the series are ethane (C_2H_6), propane (C_3H_8) and butane (C_4H_{10}). Many hydrocarbons have much larger molecules.

As well as writing the molecular formulas, CH_4, C_2H_6 and C_3H_8, we write **structural formulas**. A structural formula shows the bonds between atoms.

$$
\begin{array}{ccc}
\quad \text{H} & \quad \text{H}\;\;\text{H} & \quad \text{H}\;\;\text{H}\;\;\text{H} \\
\quad | & \quad |\;\;\; | & \quad |\;\;\; |\;\;\; | \\
\text{H—C—H} & \text{H—C—C—H} & \text{H—C—C—C—H} \\
\quad | & \quad |\;\;\; | & \quad |\;\;\; |\;\;\; | \\
\quad \text{H} & \quad \text{H}\;\;\text{H} & \quad \text{H}\;\;\text{H}\;\;\text{H} \\
\text{Methane} & \text{Ethane} & \text{Propane}
\end{array}
$$

The difference between one compound and the next is the group

$$
\begin{array}{c}
\text{H} \\
| \\
\text{—C—} \\
| \\
\text{H}
\end{array}
$$

A set of similar compounds in which one member of the series differs from the next by a CH_2 group is called a **homologous series**. The first members of the alkane series are shown in Table 18.1. The general formula C_nH_{2n+2} can be written for the alkanes. For methane, $n = 1$, giving the formula CH_4; for octane, $n = 8$, giving the formula C_8H_{18}. The alkanes are unreactive towards acids, bases, metals and many other chemicals. Their most important reaction is combustion. The alkanes contain only single bonds between carbon atoms. Such hydrocarbons are called **saturated** hydrocarbons. This is in contrast to the alkenes, which you will study in Section 19.2.

*Isomerism

Sometimes it is possible to write more than one structural formula for a molecular formula. For the molecular formula C_4H_{10}, there are two possible structures:

SUMMARY NOTE

The alkanes are$\overset{Saturated}{\wedge}$hydrocarbons with the general formula C_nH_{2n+2}. They are a homologous series: each member differs from the next by a CH_2 group. Carbon compounds are called organic compounds.

Table 18.1 The alkanes

Methane	CH_4
Ethane	C_2H_6
Propane	C_3H_8
Butane	C_4H_{10}
Pentane	C_5H_{12}
Hexane	C_6H_{14}
Heptane	C_7H_{16}
Octane	C_8H_{18}
and so on	
Alkanes	C_nH_{2n+2}

(a)
$$H-\overset{\displaystyle H}{\underset{\displaystyle H}{\overset{|}{\underset{|}{C}}}}-\overset{\displaystyle H}{\underset{\displaystyle H}{\overset{|}{\underset{|}{C}}}}-\overset{\displaystyle H}{\underset{\displaystyle H}{\overset{|}{\underset{|}{C}}}}-\overset{\displaystyle H}{\underset{\displaystyle H}{\overset{|}{\underset{|}{C}}}}-H \quad \text{and}$$

(b)
$$H-\overset{\displaystyle H}{\underset{\displaystyle H}{\overset{|}{\underset{|}{C}}}}-\overset{\displaystyle H}{\underset{\displaystyle \underset{\displaystyle H-\overset{\displaystyle H}{\underset{\displaystyle H}{\overset{|}{\underset{|}{C}}}}-H}{|}}{\overset{|}{\underset{|}{C}}}}-\overset{\displaystyle H}{\underset{\displaystyle H}{\overset{|}{\underset{|}{C}}}}-H$$

Butane   Methylpropane

The difference is that in (a) there is a straight, unbranched chain of carbon atoms, whereas in (b) there is a branched chain. The formulas belong to different compounds, which differ in boiling point and other physical properties. The compound with formula (a) is called butane; the compound with formula (b) is called methylpropane. These compounds are **isomers**. Isomers are compounds with the same molecular formula and different structural formulas.

JUST TESTING 100

1 Explain what is meant by a **homologous series**.
2 What are alkanes?

18.3 Halogenoalkanes

Alkanes will react with halogens to form halogenoalkanes. For example,

in the presence of sunlight

chlorine + methane → chloromethane + hydrogen chloride
$$Cl_2(g) \quad + CH_4(g) \quad \rightarrow CH_3Cl(g) \qquad + HCl(g)$$

This is a **substitution reaction**. A chlorine atom has been substituted for a hydrogen atom.

Many chloroalkanes are important solvents. Tetrachloromethane, CCl_4, was used for a long time by the dry-cleaning industry. 'Trichlor' (1,1,1-trichloroethane) is now widely used. Fluorohydrocarbons (hydrocarbons which contain fluorine) are very stable, unreactive compounds. They are called **freons** for short. The solvents in aerosol sprays and the liquids which circulate in refrigerators are **freons**.

Trichloromethane, $CHCl_3$, is better known as chloroform, the anaesthetic. Nowadays, there are better anaesthetics available, but chloroform (first used in 1846), ether (first used in 1847) and dinitrogen oxide (laughing gas) were the gases used by the pioneers. The use of anaesthetics brought about a revolution in surgery. Before anaesthesia, a surgeon had to make a quick job of an operation while the patient remained conscious. With the patient anaesthetised, a surgeon was able to explore the best way of dealing with an operation, rather than the quickest. Also, there was less chance of the patient dying of shock.

Chloroform is harmful if given in large quantities. Ether, being very flammable, caused some explosions in operating theatres. Dinitrogen oxide does not produce a very deep anaesthesia. Chemists searched for a better anaesthetic, one which would be safe for the patient, that is, non-toxic and non-flammable. Again, the stability of fluorohydrocarbons made them useful compounds. The fluorohydrocarbon chosen was

```
      F    Br
      |    |
F  —  C  — C  —  Cl
      |    |
      F    H
```

It is a colourless liquid with a pleasant smell. It is non-toxic and non-flammable. It is named Fluothane®. It went into use in 1956 and is the most widely used of anaesthetics.

18.4 Hydrogen

Do you remember how hydrogen is obtained from methane? If not, see Section 9.17.

18.5 Combustion

Hydrocarbons burn to form carbon dioxide and water (see Section 8.10). The reaction is **exothermic**: energy is released.

methane + oxygen → carbon dioxide + water   **Energy is released**

$CH_4(g) + 2O_2(g) \rightarrow CO_2(g) + 2H_2O(l)$

butane (in camping gaz) + oxygen → carbon dioxide + water   **Energy is released**

octane (in petrol) + oxygen → carbon dioxide + water   **Energy is released**

SUMMARY NOTE

The combustion of hydrocarbons is exothermic. The products of complete combustion are carbon dioxide and water. Incomplete combustion releases poisonous carbon monoxide. Halogenoalkanes are useful solvents and anaesthetics.

JUST TESTING 101

Do you remember what you read about combustion in Chapter 8?
Copy this passage, and fill in the blanks.

Hydrocarbons burn to form the harmless combustion products _____ and _____. If there is an insufficient supply of oxygen, however, combustion is _____, and the products _____ (a poisonous gas of formula _____) and _____ (a solid) are also formed. To avoid the formation of the poisonous gas, hydrocarbons must be burned _____.

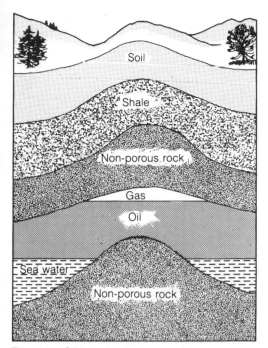

Fig. 18.6 Oil-bearing rock

18.6 Petroleum oil and natural gas

Alkanes are valuable fuels. We obtain them from petroleum oil (usually called simply **oil**; sometimes called **crude oil**) and natural gas. Oil and natural gas are **fossil fuels**: they are the remains of creatures which lived millions of years ago. Dead sea animals and plants sank to the ocean floor to become covered by silt, mud and rocks. Bacteria began to bring about the decay of the soft parts of the creatures' bodies. Decay was slow because there is little oxygen dissolved in the depths of the sea. The covering layer of mud and silt grew thicker over the years, and the pressure on the decaying organic matter increased. The combination of anaerobic bacterial decay, high pressure and heat from the interior of the Earth turned the organic matter into hydrocarbons. This mixture of hydrocarbons is petroleum oil. The sediment on top of the decaying matter became compressed to form rock. Oil is held in between rock grains in porous **oil-bearing rock** (Fig. 18.6). Natural gas is always found in the same deposits as oil.

Many parts of the world have deposits of oil and gas. Sometimes the deposits are buried deep below ground or below the sea. The USA has oil deposits, as have Iran, Nigeria, the USSR and the countries in the Arabian Gulf. The UK has piped ashore oil and gas from beneath the North Sea since 1972 (Fig. 18.7).

Fig. 18.7 Drilling for oil

Fig. 18.8 Pipeline showing laying and landscaping

Oil is transported from oil wells to refineries in pipelines and in oil tankers (Figs. 18.8 and 18.9). Modern tankers are huge, carrying up to 500 000 tonnes of crude oil. When a tanker has an accident at sea, oil is spilt. A huge oil slick floats on the surface of the ocean. It stays there for a long time. Air oxidises it very slowly. Bacteria decompose it very slowly. While the oil floats there, it poisons fish, and glues the feathers of seabirds together so that they cannot fly. When the oil slick washes ashore, it fouls beaches. In 1967 the oil tanker **Torrey Canyon** sank off the coast of the UK. A vast amount of oil escaped into the sea. People tried to disperse the oil by spraying it with huge amounts of detergent. This remedy did not work; it spread the oil over a larger surface, and the detergent killed seabirds and fish. When two tankers collided off San Francisco in 1971, the oil company used bales of straw to mop up the oil. Straw can

Fig. 18.9 An oil tanker

SUMMARY NOTE

Petroleum oil and natural gas were formed from animal and plant remains by slow bacterial decay in the absence of oxygen. They are found in many parts of the world. Drilling for oil and gas needs advanced technology.

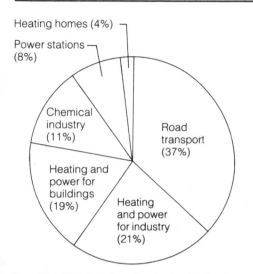

Heating homes (4%)
Power stations (8%)
Chemical industry (11%)
Road transport (37%)
Heating and power for buildings (19%)
Heating and power for industry (21%)

Fig. 18.10 This is how the fuels obtained from oil are used in the UK

SUMMARY NOTE

Crude oil is separated by fractional distillation into useful fuels. The use that is made of each fraction depends on its boiling point range, ignition temperature and other properties. The fuels obtained from crude oil are listed in Table 18.2. In addition, the petrochemicals industry makes useful chemicals from hydrocarbons. Cracking is used to make petrol and kerosene from heavy fuel oils.

soak up many times its own weight of oil. British Petroleum chemists have discovered some chemicals which solidify oil. Sprayed on to a film of oil, they slowly turn it into a rubbery solid. Lumps of the solid can be picked up in fishing nets. This discovery has still to be tried out at sea. In addition to accidents to oil tankers at sea, spillage occurs at oil rigs and at oil terminals where tankers unload. There is also non-accidental discharge of oil by captains who want to save time by washing out their tanks at sea, rather than in port. This pollution is illegal.

There are two ways of getting oil ashore from an oil well in the sea. One way is to lay a pipeline along the sea bed and pump the oil through it. The other method is to use 'shuttle tankers' which pick up the oil from the oil field and transport it to a terminal on land. The choice of method depends on the size of the oil field and the distance between the field and the shore. Natural gas is almost always brought ashore by pipeline.

Crude oil is a black, viscous (syrupy) liquid which does not burn very easily. By fractional distillation (see Section 2.5 and Fig. 2.10) it can be separated into a number of important fuels. The fractions are not pure compounds. They are mixtures of alkanes which boil over a limited temperature range. Alkanes with small molecules boil at lower temperatures than those with large molecules. Alkanes with large molecules are more viscous than alkanes with small molecules. The fractions also differ in the ease with which they burn. When a fuel is heated, some of it vaporises. Eventually, there is enough vapour to be set alight by a flame. When the fuel reaches a temperature called the **ignition temperature**, there is enough vapour for a mixture of the fuel with air to be set alight and *continue to burn steadily*.

The use that is made of each fraction depends on its boiling point range, ignition temperature and viscosity (see Table 18.2). Our need for petrol, naphtha and kerosene is greater than our need for heavy fuel oils. Fortunately, chemists have found a way of converting the high boiling range fractions, of which we have more than enough, into the lower boiling range fractions, petrol and kerosene. The technique used is called **cracking**. Large hydrocarbon molecules are **cracked** (or split) into smaller hydrocarbon molecules. A heated catalyst (aluminium oxide or silicon(IV) oxide) helps the reaction to take place:

Vapour of hydrocarbon with large molecules and high b.p.

→ CRACKING Passed over a heated catalyst →

Mixture of hydrocarbons with smaller molecules and low b.p., and hydrogen

Large molecules → Surface of catalyst → Smaller molecules → Distillation → Fractions

Fig. 18.11 Cracking

Table 18.2 Fractions and their uses

Fraction	Approximate boiling point range in °C	Approximate number of carbon atoms per molecule	Use
Petroleum gases	Below 25	1–4	These gases are liquefied under pressure, and sold in cylinders as 'bottled gas' for use in gas cookers and camping stoves. They burn easily at low temperatures. Sulphur compounds must be removed to make bottled gas clean to use and non-polluting.
Petrol	40–75	4–12	Petrol is liquid at room temperature, but vaporises easily at the temperature of the internal combustion engine.
Naphtha	75–150	7–14	Naphtha is used as a source of a huge number of useful chemicals. The petrochemicals industry manufactures plastics, drugs, medicines and fabrics (see Fig. 18.12).
Kerosene	150–240	9–16	Kerosene, another liquid fuel, needs a higher temperature for combustion. It is used in 'paraffin' stoves. The major use is as aviation fuel.
Diesel oil	220–250	15–25	Diesel fuel is more difficult to vaporise than petrol and kerosene. The special fuel injection system of the diesel engine allows this fuel to burn. It is used in buses, lorries and trains.
Lubricating oil	250–350	20–70	Lubricating oil is a viscous liquid. It does not vaporise sufficiently at the temperatures of vehicle engines to allow it to be used as a fuel. Instead, it is used as a lubricant to reduce wear.
Fuel oil	250–350	Above 10	Fuel oil is a viscous liquid with a high ignition temperature. It is used in ships, industrial machinery, heating plants and power stations. To help it ignite, fuel oil must be sprayed into the combustion chambers as a fine mist of small droplets.
Bitumen	Above 350	Above 70	Bitumen is the residue at the bottom of the distillation column. It has too high an ignition temperature to be used as a fuel. It is used to waterproof roofs and pipes and to tar roads.

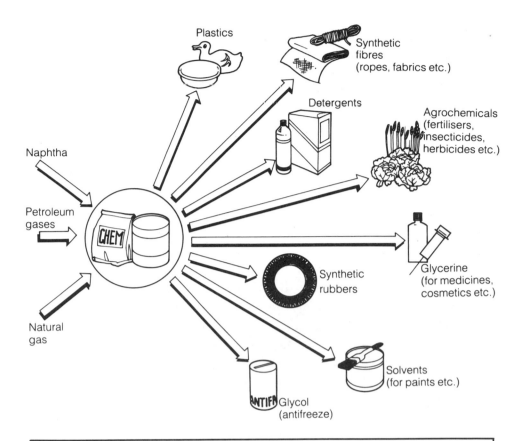

Fig. 18.12 Petrochemicals from naphtha

JUST TESTING 102

1 a Explain what is meant by a **homologous series**.
  b Explain what is meant by the term **isomerism**. Illustrate your answer by referring to pentane, C_5H_{12}.

2 How are halogenoalkanes made from alkanes? What is the name given to this type of reaction?
  What uses are made of halogenoalkanes?

3 How are petrol and kerosene made from high boiling point petroleum oil fractions? What name is given to this type of reaction? What are the economic reasons for carrying out this reaction?

18.7 Coal

Millions of years ago, the Earth was covered with trees and other plants. When the plants died, they started to decay. In the swampy conditions of that era, they formed peat. In time, layers of mud and sand covered the peat. The peat layer was compressed over millions of years by the deposits above it. Eventually, it turned into coal. The mud became shale and the sand became sandstone. Fuels that have been formed from the remains of living things are called **fossil fuels**. The energy of fossil fuels is derived from the energy of the sun. Coal is a fossil fuel derived from plants, and sunlight is needed for plants to grow. Oil and natural gas are fossil fuels derived from animals, and animals obtain their energy by eating plants or by eating animals which have eaten plants.

Many countries have coal deposits. The largest coal mining countries are the USSR, the USA, China, Poland and the UK, though the UK has greatly reduced the number of mines during the 1990s. Coal is a complicated mixture of carbon, hydrocarbons and other compounds. When it burns, the main products are carbon dioxide and water:

carbon (in coal) + oxygen → carbon dioxide

hydrocarbons (in coal) + oxygen → carbon dioxide + water

Uses of coal

Three-quarters of the coal used in the UK is burned in power stations. The heat given out in burning raises steam. This steam drives turbines which generate electricity.

Coal can be **destructively distilled**. In this process, air is absent so that the coal does not burn. Four main fractions are obtained:

COAL
- Coal gas → Used for industrial heating, is mainly carbon monoxide + hydrogen
- Ammonia → Used to make fertilisers, e.g. ammonium sulphate
- Coal tar → Used to make creosote, pitch, paints and other products
- Coke → Used in iron and steel making; used as a 'smokeless fuel' for heating

The importance of coal, oil and natural gas is discussed in Section 20.1.

SUMMARY NOTE

Coal is a fossil fuel derived from plant remains. It is burned in power stations. The distillation of coal gives useful products.

JUST TESTING 103

1 Study Fig. 18.13.
   Why does the coal graph drop after 1960?
   Why does the oil imports graph rise in 1960 and then fall after 1970?
   Why is the oil production graph so recent an addition to the picture?
   How long do you think the oil production graph will go on rising?

Fig. 18.13 Coal and oil in Britain, 1860–1980

Exercise 18

1 Explain what is meant by the terms **a** *organic* compound, **b** hydrocarbon, **c** alkane.

2 Where are alkanes found in nature? How were they formed? How are alkanes obtained from natural deposits? What is the chief use that we make of alkanes?

3 What important properties do halogenoalkanes possess?

4 The molecular formula for propane is C_3H_8.
   a Write the structural formula for propane.
   b What information does the structural formula give that the molecular formula does not tell you?
   c Write the molecular and structural formulas of two compounds which belong to the same **homologous series** as propane.
   d Explain what is meant by the term **homologous series**.

5 Coal and diamond are both minerals. Diamond is pure carbon; coal contains a high percentage of carbon. Both substances are valuable, but diamond is more expensive than coal. Can you explain why?
What value does coal have which diamond does not share?
Which of the two substances could we more easily do without? Explain your answer.
How does diamond help in the search for fuels?

6 **a** Briefly describe how plant and animal material can be fermented to produce fuel gas.
   b What problems can you see in adapting the process to produce fuel gas for domestic use?
   c Can you think of any situations in which such a gas generator might be valuable both from an economic point of view and from an environmental point of view?

7 What is **crude oil**? Where is it found? What has to be done to crude oil before it is useful? What useful substances are obtained from crude oil?

Career sketch: Chemical engineer

Seamus needs a knowledge of chemistry, physics, and mechanical and electrical engineering in his job as a chemical engineer. He works as one of a team. They first design a pilot plant to test out a new chemical process. Then they convert the pilot plant into a full scale manufacturing plant. They work out ways of removing chemical contaminants from the waste materials which the process produces. They also look for ways to make the waste materials of their industry useful to another industry.

Since chemical engineering is so complex, chemical engineers often specialise in a particular process, such as polymerisation or pollution control.

CHAPTER 19   *Alkenes, alcohols and acids*

19.1 Plastic sand: what next?

Many Third World countries are plagued by drought. In long periods without rain, plants die and the soil becomes eroded. A British chemist called Allan Cooke has invented a plastic grain that could help these arid countries. He believes that his invention, Agrosoke®, will enable deserts to be turned into arable land. Agrosoke is a **polymer**. You will find out what a polymer is later in this chapter. Allan Cooke discovered something special about this polymer: it can absorb 40 times its own mass of water. It has the chemical name poly(propenamide). Cooke believes that a mixture of the polymer with sand should help plants to grow in arid regions. The idea is that the polymer soaks up water and then releases it gradually to the roots of plants. Field trials have been made on

- sunflower plants in Egypt, grown for the edible oil from the seeds
- acacia trees in the Sudan, grown for the gum arabic they produce
- eucalyptus trees in India, grown for shade
- seed germination in India.

In all these cases, plants grown with polymer have survived while control specimens have died (Fig. 19.1).

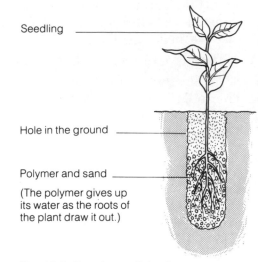

Seedling

Hole in the ground

Polymer and sand

(The polymer gives up its water as the roots of the plant draw it out.)

Fig. 19.1 Growing well thanks to a polymer

Fig. 19.2 A model of ethene

19.2 Alkenes

Ethene is a hydrocarbon of formula C_2H_4 (see Fig. 19.2). It is formed when alkanes are cracked (see Section 18.6). The bonding in ethene is shown in Fig. 19.3. The carbon atoms share two pairs of electrons: there is a double bond between them (see Section 6.3). Hydrocarbons, such as ethene, which contain double bonds between carbon atoms are described as **unsaturated hydrocarbons.** They will react with hydrogen to form saturated hydrocarbons:

ethene + hydrogen → ethane

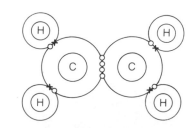

Fig. 19.3 The bonding in ethene

Reactions of this kind are called **addition reactions** (see Fig. 19.4).

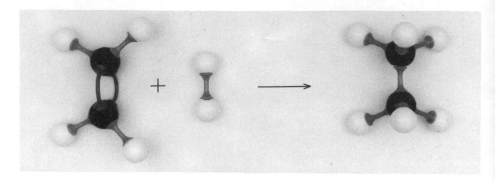

Fig. 19.4 The addition reaction between ethene and hydrogen

340

Table 19.1 The alkenes

Ethene	C_2H_4
Propene	C_3H_6
Butene	C_4H_8
Pentene	C_5H_{10}
Alkenes	C_nH_{2n}

SUMMARY NOTE

Alkenes are a homologous series of unsaturated hydrocarbons. They possess a double bond between carbon atoms. The general formula is C_nH_{2n}.

Ethene is the first member of a homologous series called the alkenes. Propene (see Fig. 19.5) is the next member. Table 19.1 lists some members of the series. The general formula of alkenes is C_nH_{2n}.

Fig. 19.5 A model of propene

19.3 Reactions of alkenes

Combustion

Alkenes burn in the same way as alkanes:

$$\text{ethene } + \text{ oxygen } \rightarrow \text{ carbon dioxide } + \text{ water}$$

$$C_2H_4(g) + 3O_2(g) \rightarrow 2CO_2(g) + 2H_2O(l)$$

Alkenes are not used as fuels because they are an important source of other compounds. Their unsaturated nature makes them chemically reactive. The petrochemicals industry uses alkenes as starting materials in the manufacture of plastics, solvents and other chemicals.

Addition reactions

The double bond enables alkenes to take part in **addition reactions**. Bromine adds to alkenes. A solution of bromine in an organic solvent or in water is brown. If an alkene is bubbled through a solution of bromine, the solution loses its colour (see Experiment 17.1). Bromine has added to the alkene to form a colourless compound. The reaction can be shown as

ethene + bromine   1,2-dibromoethane

The product has single bonds: it is a saturated compound. With two carbon atoms in the molecule, it is named after ethane. With two bromine atoms in the molecule, it is a dibromo-compound,

1,2-dibromoethane. The numbers 1,2- tell you that one bromine atom is bonded to one carbon atom and the second bromine atom is bonded to the second carbon atom. The decolourisation of a bromine solution is used to distinguish between an alkene and an alkane. Chlorine adds to alkenes in a similar way.

Hydration

A molecule of water also will add across the double bond. Combination with water is called **hydration**:

$$
\begin{array}{ccc}
\text{H} & & \text{H} \\
| & & | \\
\text{H—C} \quad \text{H} & & \text{H—C—H} \\
\| \; + \; | & \rightarrow & | \\
\text{H—C} \quad \text{O—H} & & \text{H—C—O—H} \\
| & & | \\
\text{H} & & \text{H}
\end{array}
$$

The product is ethanol, C_2H_5OH. This is the compound we commonly call **alcohol**. It is an important industrial solvent. Ethanol is made by passing ethene and steam over a heated catalyst at high pressure. Only about 10% of the ethene is converted, and the unreacted gases are recycled.

$$
\text{ethene + steam} \xrightarrow[\text{(phosphoric acid), under pressure}]{\text{Pass over a heated catalyst}} \text{ethanol}
$$
Recycle unreacted gases over the catalyst

Hydrogenation

The reaction between alkenes and hydrogen is used in the production of margarine. Animal fats, such as butter, are solid. Vegetable oils, such as olive oil and sunflower seed oil, are liquid. Insufficient butter is produced to satisfy our demand for solid fats, but more vegetable oil is produced than we need for cooking. Manufacturers therefore convert liquid oils into solid fats. They make use of the fact that solid fats are saturated, while liquid oils are unsaturated. Hydrogenation (the addition of hydrogen) will convert an unsaturated compound into a saturated compound. The vapour of a liquid oil is passed with hydrogen over a nickel catalyst:

$$
\begin{array}{c}
\text{vegetable oil} \\
\text{(unsaturated)}
\end{array}
+ \text{hydrogen} \xrightarrow[\text{heated nickel catalyst}]{\text{Pass over}}
\begin{array}{c}
\text{solid fat} \\
\text{(saturated)}
\end{array}
$$

The solid fat produced is sold as margarine. If some of the double bonds are left intact by partial hydrogenation, soft margarine is obtained.

SUMMARY NOTE

Alkenes burn to form carbon dioxide and water. The double bond makes alkenes reactive. They take part in addition reactions with bromine and chlorine, with water (in the presence of a catalyst) and with hydrogen. This reaction is used to turn vegetable oils into saturated fats.

Polymerisation

This reaction is called **polymerisation**. Many molecules of the **monomer**, ethene, join together (**polymerise**) to form the **polymer**, poly(ethene). In poly(ethene), 30 000–40 000 molecules of the monomer form one molecule of polymer. The conditions needed for polymerisation are high pressure, a moderate temperature and a catalyst:

You have seen poly(ethene) many times, although you may know it better by its trade name of **polythene**. It is the material used for making plastic bags, kitchenware (buckets, bowls etc.), laboratory tubing and toys. It is flexible and difficult to break.

19.4 Polymers

Polymers such as poly(ethene) and other polyalkenes are plastics. Plastics are materials which soften on heating and harden on cooling. Objects can be moulded easily from plastics. There are two subsets of plastics.

Thermosoftening and thermosetting plastics

Thermosoftening plastics can be softened by heating, cooled and resoftened many times:

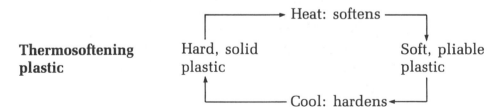

a thermosetting plastic can be softened by heat only once.

The reason for the difference in behaviour is a difference in structure. **Thermosoftening plastics** consist of long polymer chains. The forces of attraction between the chains are weak. Manufacturers find thermosoftening plastics convenient to work with. They can buy tonnes of thermosoftening plastic in the form of granules, melt the material and mould it into the shape of the object they want to make. Plastics of this sort can be moulded several times during the manufacture of an article. Another advantage is colour. A pigment can be added to the molten plastic and thoroughly mixed. Then the moulded objects will be coloured all through. This is a big advantage over a coat of paint which can be chipped.

Thermosetting plastics have a different structure. When a thermosetting plastic is softened and moulded, the chains react with one another. Cross-links are formed, and a huge three-dimensional structure is built up. This is why thermosetting plastics can be formed only once (Fig. 19.6). Thermosetting plastics are polymerised and moulded at the same time. A batch process must be used. This is less efficient and more costly than a continuous process.

The chief thermosetting polymer families are not poly(alkenes). They are epoxy resins (used as glues), polyester resins (used in glass-reinforced plastics), polyurethanes (used in varnishes), melamine (used in kitchen surfaces and on bench tops) and bakelite (used in electrical fittings). Both types of plastics have their advantages. The materials used for electrical fittings and counter tops must be able to withstand high temperatures without softening. For these purposes, 'thermosets' are used.

Sometimes gases are mixed with plastics during shaping to make low density plastic foams. Such foams are used in car seats, for thermal insulation of buildings, for insulation against sound and for packaging. Plastics can also be strengthened by the addition of other materials. Glass-fibre-reinforced plastic is strong enough to be used for the manufacture of boat hulls and car bodies (see Fig. 19.7).

Fig. 19.6 (a) Thermosoftening plastic;
(b) thermosetting plastic

Fig. 19.7 GRP (glass-reinforced plastic) boat

SUMMARY NOTE

Plastics are either **thermosoftening**: can be softened by heat many times, or **thermosetting**: can be softened by heat only once before setting permanently.

Poly(alkenes)

Table 19.2 Some poly(alkenes) and their uses

Poly(ethene); trade name polythene

Monomer	Polymer	Uses:
$\begin{array}{cc} H & H \\ \vert & \vert \\ C = C \\ \vert & \vert \\ H & H \end{array}$	$\left(\begin{array}{cc} H & H \\ \vert & \vert \\ C - C \\ \vert & \vert \\ H & H \end{array}\right)_n$	Polythene is used to make plastic bags. High density polythene is used to make kitchenware, laboratory tubing and toys.

Poly(chloroethene); trade name PVC

Monomer	Polymer	Uses:
$\begin{array}{cc} Cl & H \\ \vert & \vert \\ C = C \\ \vert & \vert \\ H & H \end{array}$	$\left(\begin{array}{cc} Cl & H \\ \vert & \vert \\ C - C \\ \vert & \vert \\ H & H \end{array}\right)_n$	PVC is used to make plastic bottles, wellingtons and raincoats, floor tiles, insulation for electrical wiring, gutters and drainpipes.

Poly(propene)

Monomer	Polymer	Uses:
$\begin{array}{cc} H & CH_3 \\ \vert & \vert \\ C = C \\ \vert & \vert \\ H & H \end{array}$	$\left(\begin{array}{cc} H & CH_3 \\ \vert & \vert \\ C - C \\ \vert & \vert \\ H & H \end{array}\right)_n$	Poly(propene) is resistant to attack by chemicals and does not soften in boiling water. It can be used to make hospital equipment which must be sterilised. Poly(propene) is drawn into fibres and used to make ropes and fishing nets.

Poly(tetrafluoroethene); trade names PTFE and teflon

Monomer	Polymer	Uses:
$\begin{array}{cc} F & F \\ \vert & \vert \\ C = C \\ \vert & \vert \\ F & F \end{array}$	$\left(\begin{array}{cc} F & F \\ \vert & \vert \\ C - C \\ \vert & \vert \\ F & F \end{array}\right)_n$	PTFE is a hard, waxy plastic which is not attacked by most chemicals. Few substances can stick to its surface. It is used to coat non-stick pans and skis.

Perspex

Monomer	Uses:
$\begin{array}{cc} H & CO_2CH_3 \\ \vert & \vert \\ C = C \\ \vert & \vert \\ H & CH_3 \end{array}$	Perspex is an important plastic because it is transparent and can be used instead of glass. It is more easily moulded than glass and less easily shattered.

Polystyrene

Monomer	Uses:
$\begin{array}{cc} H & H \\ \vert & \vert \\ C = C \\ \vert & \vert \\ H & C_6H_5 \end{array}$	Polystyrene is a hard, brittle plastic used for making food containers (e.g. yoghurt cartons) and construction kits. Polystyrene foam is made by blowing air into the softened plastic. It is used for making ceiling tiles and packaging fragile goods, e.g. cameras.

Oil: a fuel and a source of petrochemicals

The number of plastics and the uses found for them are constantly growing. The raw materials used in their manufacture come from oil. The Earth's resources of oil will not last for ever. It seems wasteful to burn oil as fuel when we need it to make plastics and other petrochemicals.

SUMMARY NOTE

Plastics are petrochemicals. The more oil we use as fuel, the less oil we shall have in the future to give us petrochemicals.

Some drawbacks

Summerland Amusement Park in the Isle of Man used to have an enormous amusement hall covered with plastic panels. In 1973, some boys playing with matches set the whole structure on fire. Within ten minutes, more than 50 people had died. Many were not burned to death. Most of the casualties were overcome by poisonous gases that had been produced when the plastic burned. The tragedy made manufacturers of building materials stop and investigate their products. They needed to check whether, if plastics should happen to burn, they would produce harmful substances.

Many buildings are insulated with plastic foam or furnished with plastic materials. Plastics have lower ignition temperatures than materials like wood, metal, brick and glass. Fires can spread very rapidly when plastics burn.

You must at some time have drunk coffee and soft drinks out of disposable cups. These are made of polyurethane or polystyrene. Like other plastics, these polymers are **non-biodegradable**. They cannot be decomposed by natural biological processes. All the plastic cups, spoons and food containers which people use and throw away have to be burned or dumped in ever-increasing rubbish tips. Chemists are now trying to make new plastics which will be easier to dispose of.

SUMMARY NOTE

Polymerisation is an important reaction of alkenes. Many molecules of monomer join to form a huge molecule of polymer. Many poly(alkenes) are plastics with important uses. Poly(ethene), poly(chloroethene), poly(propene), poly(tetrafluoroethene), perspex and polystyrene are plastics with a huge number of uses.

There are some disadvantages in the use of plastics:
● they are non-biodegradable
● they ignite easily
● some of them have toxic combustion products.

Biodegradable plastics

Biodegradable plastics are plastics which can be broken down by micro-organisms. They are of two kinds: **biopolymers**, which are made by living organisms, and **synthetic plastics**. Synthetic biodegradable plastics include photodegradable plastics and plastics that dissolve in water.

Biopolymers. A biopolymer called PHB produced by certain bacteria is manufactured by ICI in the UK. The material is attacked by micro-organisms in the soil, in river water and in the human body, and broken down within 9 months. However, PHB is very expensive and is used only for special applications, e.g. surgical stitches which slowly dissolve inside the body.

Photodegradable plastics. A photodegradable polymer has been manufactured by a Canadian firm. It is incorporated in polystyrene cups. When the cups are exposed to sunlight for 60 days, they break down into dust particles.

Synthetic biodegradable plastics. An Italian company has produced a biodegradable polymer from poly(ethene) and starch. The long poly(ethene) molecules and long starch molecules interweave to form a material which is strong enough for shopping bags. When the material is buried, micro-organisms begin to feed on the starch, converting it into carbon dioxide and water, and in time the polymers dissolve in water. The cost of carrier bags made from this material is at present about twice that of a conventional plastic bag.

Dissolving plastics. Plastics that dissolve in water can be designed to be soluble in cold water, in warm water or only in hot water. Poly(ethenol), $(—CH_2—CHOH—)_n$ is an example.

Recycling plastics

The recycling of plastics is still at the experimental stage. Recycling would not only reduce the problem of disposing of plastic waste, it would also save raw materials.

When plastics are heated in the absence of air, they do not burn: they are **pyrolysed** (split up by heat). The products can be separated by fractional distillation and then used in the manufacture of other materials, including plastics.

A problem is that plastics of different kinds need to be separated before pyrolysis.

SUMMARY NOTE

Non-biodegradable plastics cause litter problems and problems of disposal. Biodegradable plastics are of two kinds:
1 biopolymers (made by living organisms)
2 synthetic plastics, including photodegradable plastics, synthetic biodegradable plastics and plastics that dissolve in water.
Research workers are investigating methods of recycling plastics.

JUST TESTING 104

1 What advantage has a plastic doll over a china doll?

2 Toy farmyard animals and soldiers used to be made out of lead. Why do you think lead was the metal chosen for the purpose? What advantages do plastic toys have over lead toys?

3 Which plastic would be used to make a motorbike windscreen? What advantages does it have over glass?

*4 Agrosoke® (see Section 19.1) is poly(propenamide). Propenamide is

$$H—C—CONH_2$$
$$\|$$
$$H—C—H$$

Draw the formula of poly(propenamide).

Poly(ethenol) can absorb hundreds of times its own mass of water. The monomer is $CH_2{=}CHOH$. Draw the formula of the polymer.

5 a What does the word **plastic** mean?
  b There are two big classes of plastics, which behave differently when heated. Name the two classes. Describe the difference in behaviour. Say how this difference is related to the molecular nature of the plastics.

6 a Many plastic bags are made of poly(ethene). Explain how poly(ethene) is obtained from petroleum. In your view, is this a good use of petroleum? Explain your answer.

b What methods are used for disposing of plastic waste? How would the use of biodegradable plastics help with disposal?

7 Polystyrene foam containers are used for serving food in take-away restaurants.

a What is the advantage of these containers?

b For how long is such a polystyrene foam package in use?

c What happens to the polystyrene it contains?

d What happens to the gas it contains?

8 Suggest **a** applications for a dissolving plastic, and **b** items for which a dissolving plastic would not be suitable.

9 Suggest **a** applications for a photodegradable plastic, and **b** items for which a photodegradable plastic would not be suitable.

*19.5 Review of materials

You have studied materials of many types. We shall now draw these materials together, to compare the properties of different solid materials, and to see how these properties make different materials useful for different purposes.

1 Metals

The nature of the metallic bond and the crystalline structure of metals were described in Section 11.2. The uses of metals and alloys were covered in Section 11.7. Metals

- are generally hard, tough and shiny
- change shape without breaking (are ductile and malleable)
- are mostly strong in tension (stretching) and compression (loading)
- are good thermal and electrical conductors
- are in many cases corroded by water and acids.

These properties result from the nature of the metallic bond (see Section 11.2). The bonds are non-directed in space. Metals are strong in tension and in compression because the bonds between the atoms are strong. Metals are giant structures in which some electrons are free to move. These mobile electrons allow metals to conduct heat and electricity. Metals can change shape without breaking because the metallic bond allows layers of atoms to slide over one another when the metal is under stress. Metals are crystalline. They contain dislocations (see Section 11.3) which will move under stress and allow the metal to change shape. Glass can withstand larger loads than metals without changing shape.

2 Ceramics

Ceramics (see Section 13.13) are crystalline compounds of metallic and non-metallic elements. Ceramics

- are very hard and brittle
- are strong in compression but weak in tension
- are electrical insulators
- have very high melting points
- are chemically unreactive.

In most ceramics, the bonds are covalent and directed in space. The structure of a ceramic is therefore more rigid and less flexible than that of a metal. This structure makes ceramics harder than metals, and also more brittle. Ceramics have lower densities and higher melting points than metals.

3 Glasses

Glasses are similar to ceramics. Glasses
- have lower melting points than ceramics
- are generally transparent.

Plate glass is transparent because it is non-crystalline, so light can pass through without meeting any reflecting surfaces. It is brittle because of the rigid bonds.

Glass should be a strong material because the bonds between atoms are strong and there are no dislocations. It is able to withstand mechanical loading without breaking. However, glass shatters easily. The brittleness of glass is due to surface defects or scratches. Glass breaks easily if a scratch is first made on its surface. Cracks find it harder to grow in metals because of the movement of dislocations.

Glass fibres can be bent without cracking because they are free of surface scratches.

4 Plastics

Plastics (see Section 19.4)
- are usually strong in relation to their mass
- are mainly (but not all) soft, flexible and not very elastic
- soften easily when heated and melt or burn
- are thermal and electrical insulators.

Plastics consist of a tangled mass of very long polymer molecules. The structure is described as **amorphous** (shapeless)

Fig. 19.8 The arrangement of chains in high-density poly(ethene)

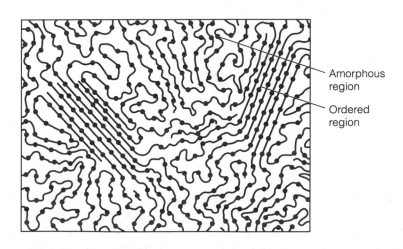

Amorphous region

Ordered region

Fig. 19.9 A polymer with ordered and amorphous regions

because the polymer chains take up a random arrangement. The bonds between chains are weak in thermosoftening plastics and strong in thermosetting plastics.

In some polymers there are regions where the chains are packed together in a regular way (see Fig. 19.8). In high-density poly(ethene), the chains pack closely together to give a material which is stronger than low-density poly(ethene) and is not as easily deformed by heat. Many polymers are a mixture of ordered regions and amorphous regions (see Fig. 19.9).

If you break a plastic ruler, made of poly(methyl methacrylate), about 90% of the fracturing is due to individual polymer chains being pulled out of the material, rather than the breaking of covalent bonds. In other polymers, the molecular chains are more densely packed and more entangled, and the plastics are more difficult to break. It is possible to alter the shapes of some plastics by straightening out the polymer chains. Examples are rubber, polyesters, polyamides and polycarbonates.

5 Synthetic fibres

Fibres are made by drawing (stretching) plastics. Molten plastic is forced through a fine hole. As the fibre cools and solidifies, it is stretched to align its molecules along the length of the fibre. This is why fibres have great tensile strength along the length of the fibre.

6 Concrete and most types of rock

Concrete and most types of rock are
- strong in compression (loading)
- weak in tension (stretching).

Reinforced concrete is described below.

7 Composite materials

Some materials are not homogeneous. They include composite materials, e.g. reinforced concrete, and cellular materials, e.g. cork. In a composite material, the properties of the different components combine to give a material that is more useful for a particular purpose than the individual components.

Reinforced concrete.   Reinforced concrete is the material you see around you in large structures, such as high-rise buildings, bridges and oil platforms. Concrete (see Section 13.1) is weak in tension, strong in compression and brittle. When it is reinforced with steel wires or bars, which are strong in tension, the combination is a tough, relatively cheap material.

The reason why unreinforced concrete has low tensile strength is that it contains microscopic pores. One method of reducing the porosity and increasing the tensile strength is to drive air out of the cement powder before mixing it with water. This can be done by vibrating the powder. Another method is to add to the cement–water mixture a material, such as sulphur or a water-soluble polymer, which will fill the spaces between the cement particles. Other filler materials include glass fibre, silicon carbide and aluminium oxide particles and fibres.

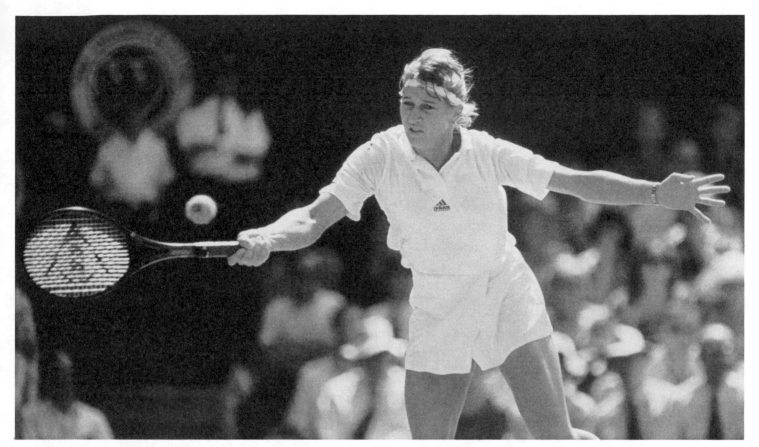

Fig. 19.10 Carbon-fibre-reinforced epoxy resin in use

Fibre-reinforced plastics.   Epoxy resin and polyester resin are composite materials consisting of fibres and thermosetting plastics. They are chosen for uses that require a stronger material than thermoplastics. However, thermoplastics have the advantage of being easy to mould, and this encouraged chemists to develop fibre-reinforced thermoplastics. These can be used for some applications which were traditionally filled by metals. Examples of fibre-reinforced plastics are:

- glass-fibre-reinforced-polyester: the polyester is flexible but weak. The glass fibres are extremely strong, but relatively brittle. The combination of the two materials produces a tough, strong material. The composite has many applications, including small boats, skis and motor vehicle bodies (see Fig. 19.7).
- carbon-fibre-reinforced epoxy resin: this is used in tennis racquets and in aircraft. It is stronger and lower in density than conventional materials, e.g. aluminium alloys.

The fibres in fibre-reinforced plastics may be glass, carbon, silicon carbide, poly(ethene), kevlar or other substances. The tensile strength of carbon fibres is not high but they are stiff and therefore included in materials used for the frames of aircraft. Fibres of kevlar, $(—C_6H_4CONH—)_n$, are five times as strong as steel, low in density and flexible. They are used to strengthen car tyres.

Composite materials are expensive. However, lightweight vehicles use less fuel, and the decreased fuel consumption could increase the use of composites in vehicle bodies.

8 Cellular materials

The properties of cellular materials depend on their cellular structure. Examples are
- cork, which is used as an insulator against heat and sound and as floats
- wood
- aluminium honeycomb structures (see Fig. 19.11)
- paper honeycomb structures, used for packaging and internal doors.

Cellular structure of aluminium

Thin strong layers of metal or composite

Fig. 19.11 A honeycomb structure in an aircraft wing

JUST TESTING 105

1 Explain why it is possible to bend a sheet of poly(ethene) tubing more easily than **a** a sheet of metal, and **b** a sheet of glass.

2 Explain why a piece of metal is dented by a hammer blow but a piece of glass shatters.

3 What advantage does glass-fibre-reinforced polyster have for building boats **a** over wood, and **b** over metal?

4 Give **a** an advantage, and **b** a disadvantage of GRP compared with steel for use in vehicle bodies.

5 For each material below, choose the uses to which it can be put. Each material may have more than one use.

Materials	*Uses*
1. Alloy	A Squash racquet
2. Ceramic	B Ovenware
3. Glass-fibre-reinforced polyester	C Electrical plug
4. Thermosoftening plastic	D Vehicle body
5. Thermosetting plastic	E Packaging
6. Synthetic fibre	F Bridge
7. Reinforced concrete	G Rifle
8. Carbon-fibre-reinforced epoxy resin	H Carrier bag
9. Paper honeycomb	I Clothing

19.6 Alcohols

Ethanol and party-goers

Angela thoroughly enjoyed the party (Fig. 19.12). She felt relaxed and happy and had a great time. Next morning, however, she woke up with a splitting headache and a feeling of sickness. The substance responsible for these effects on her body was **ethanol**, the liquid we usually call **alcohol** (Fig. 19.13).

Ethanol is a drug. It depresses the central nervous system. That does not mean that it makes people feel depressed. In small quantities, it makes people relaxed by suppressing feelings of fear and tension. Ethanol dissolves completely in water. When ethanol is swallowed, it is absorbed through the stomach and intestines. It can take up to 6 hours for the ethanol in a single drink to be absorbed when the stomach is full, but only about 1 hour when the stomach is empty. This is why people feel the effects of a drink faster on an empty stomach than on a full one. When ethanol is in the bloodstream, it moves rapidly into the tissues until the concentration of ethanol in the tissues equals that in the blood. The concentration of ethanol in the breath or in urine can be used to indicate the level of ethanol in the blood. As the concentration of ethanol in the blood increases, speech becomes slurred, vision becomes blurred and reaction times increase. This is why it is so dangerous to drive 'under the influence' of alcohol. Drinking large amounts of ethanol regularly causes damage to the liver, kidneys, arteries and brain. Many people do not **use** alcohol properly, that is, in moderation: they **abuse** alcohol. Such people become addicted to alcohol, and their health suffers.

Fig. 19.12 Angela enjoying the party

Fig. 19.13 A model of ethanol

Ethanol and the alcohols

Ethanol is a member of a homologous series of compounds called **alcohols**. Alcohols possess the group

$$-\overset{|}{\underset{|}{C}}-O-H$$

and have the general formula $C_nH_{2n+1}OH$. Some formulas are given in Table 19.3. The formulas are written as CH_3OH etc. rather than CH_4O to show the —OH group and to make it clear that they are alcohols. The members of the series have similar physical properties and chemical reactions. Ethanol is the only alcohol that can be safely drunk. Methanol, CH_3OH, is very toxic. Drinking only small amounts of methanol can lead to blindness and death. The structural formulas of some alcohols are shown below.

Table 19.3 The alcohols

Methanol	CH_3OH
Ethanol	C_2H_5OH
Propanol	C_3H_7OH
Alcohols	$C_nH_{2n+1}OH$

SUMMARY NOTE

Alcohols are a homologous series of formula $C_nH_{2n+1}OH$. Ethanol is the alcohol which people drink. When the concentration of ethanol in the blood rises above a low safe level, it damages the body's co-ordination. Regular abuse of alcohol ruins your health.

Formulas of alcohols

Methanol

$$H-\overset{\overset{\displaystyle H}{|}}{\underset{\underset{\displaystyle H}{|}}{C}}-O-H$$

Ethanol

$$H-\overset{\overset{\displaystyle H}{|}}{\underset{\underset{\displaystyle H}{|}}{C}}-\overset{\overset{\displaystyle H}{|}}{\underset{\underset{\displaystyle H}{|}}{C}}-O-H$$

Propanol

$$H-\overset{\overset{\displaystyle H}{|}}{\underset{\underset{\displaystyle H}{|}}{C}}-\overset{\overset{\displaystyle H}{|}}{\underset{\underset{\displaystyle H}{|}}{C}}-\overset{\overset{\displaystyle H}{|}}{\underset{\underset{\displaystyle H}{|}}{C}}-O-H$$

Ethanol has been made for centuries by the fermentation of sugars and starches. These substances are **carbohydrates**. They are compounds of carbon, hydrogen and oxygen which have 2 atoms of hydrogen for every atom of oxygen, e.g. the sugar glucose, $C_6H_{12}O_6$, and starch, $(C_6H_{10}O_5)_n$. Glucose can be converted into ethanol by an enzyme called zymase, which is found in yeast. An enzyme is a catalyst which is found in a plant or animal. Yeast is a living plant. If you make ethanol in Experiment 17.3, you will see that carbon dioxide is evolved. The reaction is called **fermentation**:

$$\text{glucose} \xrightarrow{\text{enzyme in yeast}} \text{ethanol} \quad + \text{ carbon dioxide}$$
$$C_6H_{12}O_6(aq) \longrightarrow 2C_2H_5OH(aq) + 2CO_2(g)$$

Fruit juices contain sugars. When yeast is added, the juice ferments to give ethanol. When the ethanol content reaches 14%, it kills the yeast. A more concentrated solution of ethanol (96% ethanol) can be obtained by distillation.

Fermentation is also involved in bread-making. However, in baking, the important product of fermentation is carbon dioxide rather than ethanol. Bread dough is made commercially by mixing flour, water, yeast, salt, sugar and fat. The yeast starts to act on the sugar in the dough. The dough is divided into portions and kept in a warm container until the carbon dioxide produced has made it 'rise'. Then a conveyor belt takes the risen dough through a hot oven, from which it emerges as baked loaves.

Ethanol can be made from starchy foods, such as potatoes, rice, malt, barley, hops and others. Starch is hydrolysed by an enzyme in malt (germinated barley) to a mixture of sugars. Then yeast is added to ferment the sugars:

$$\text{starch} \quad + \text{ water} \xrightarrow{\text{enzyme in malt}} \text{sugar}$$
$$(C_6H_{10}O_5)_n(aq) + nH_2O(l) \longrightarrow nC_6H_{12}O_6(aq)$$

Ethanol is sold in four main forms:
- absolute alcohol: 96% ethanol, 4% water
- industrial alcohol or methylated spirit: 85% ethanol, 10% water, 5% methanol (this is added to make the liquid unfit for drinking)
- spirits: whisky, brandy, rum, gin, which contain about 35% ethanol
- fermented liquors: beer, wine, cider, etc. These contain flavourings, colouring matter and fragrant oils. Beers and ciders contain 3%–7% ethanol; wines contain 12%–14%.

Ethanol for industrial use is not made by fermentation. It is made by the catalytic hydration of ethene (see Section 19.3). When ethanol is dehydrated, it gives ethene. Figure 19.14 shows a method of passing the vapour of ethanol over a dehydrating agent to give ethene.

Women who drink heavily in pregnancy have babies with 'fetal alcohol syndrome'. The babies are very small at birth and have facial deformities such as a flattened nose, misshapen ears and a long lower jaw. Many have heart murmurs, hearing defects and defective hip joints. The babies do not grow out of these birth defects; they get worse. No-one knows how much alcohol, if any, a pregnant woman can safely drink.

SUMMARY NOTE

Ethanol is made from sugars by fermentation, a reaction which is catalysed by an enzyme in yeast. Starches can be hydrolysed to sugars and then fermented to give ethanol.

Aluminium oxide
(acts as a dehydrating agent)

Ethene

Ceramic wool
soaked in
ethanol

Heat

Valve prevents
'sucking back'.

Fig. 19.14 Making ethene by the dehydration of ethanol

The hydration of ethene can be run as a continuous process, with ethene fed in and ethanol led off. Fermentation can be run only as a batch process – a certain quantity of sugar is left to ferment to form ethanol, and is then replaced by another quantity of sugar. Table 19.4 shows a comparison of the two methods.

Table 19.4 A comparison of the methods of manufacturing ethanol

Method	Raw materials	Speed	Quality of product	Type of process
Fermentation	Sugars (a renewable resource)	Slow	Impure ethanol	Batch process
Catalytic hydration	Ethene (from oil, a finite resource)	Faster, but energy must be supplied as heat and pressure	Pure ethanol	Continuous process

Ethanol is an important solvent. It is a volatile liquid, with b.p. 78 °C. It is used in cosmetics and toiletries, in thinners for lacquers and in printing inks. Being volatile, the solvent evaporates and leaves the solute behind. Other alcohols, e.g. methanol, propanol and butanol, are also used as solvents for shellacs, lacquers, paints and industrial detergents. Alcohols have a big advantage as solvents in that they are miscible with both water and a number of organic liquids.

Ethanol is oxidised by air if the right micro-organisms are present. The reason why wine goes sour if it is open to the air is that the ethanol in it is oxidised to ethanoic acid. Vinegar is 3% ethanoic acid.

$$\text{ethanol} + \text{oxygen} \xrightarrow{\text{certain micro-organisms}} \text{ethanoic acid} + \text{water}$$

$$C_2H_5OH(aq) + O_2(g) \longrightarrow CH_3CO_2H(aq) + H_2O(l)$$

A faster method of oxidising ethanol is to use acidified potassium dichromate(VI), $K_2Cr_2O_7$. This powerful oxidising agent is orange. Dichromate(VI) ions, $Cr_2O_7^{2-}$, are reduced by ethanol and other reducing agents to chromium(III) ions, which are blue. As the reaction proceeds, the colour changes from orange through green to blue. This colour change was the basis of the first 'breathalyser' test. A motorist suspected of having too much ethanol in his or her blood had to breathe out through a tube containing some orange potassium dichromate(VI) crystals. If they turned green, he or she was 'over the limit' (Fig. 19.15).

SUMMARY NOTE

Ethanol for industrial use is made from ethene by catalytic hydration. It is an important solvent. Ethanol is oxidised to ethanoic acid.

Fig. 19.15   The Alcolyser – a self-test kit for motorists to use before driving if they think they may be 'over the limit'

Fig. 19.16   Some reactions of ethanol

1 Ethanol is made from petroleum in three stages. Say what they are and how they are carried out.

2 **a** Explain what is meant by **fermentation**.
  b What commercially important substances are made by this method?

3 **a** Why does wine turn sour on standing?
  b What is the difference between drinking ethanol and drinking methanol?

Gasohol

During World War II, many German vehicles ran on ethanol which had been made from potatoes. Petrol engines are designed to operate at a temperature at which petrol will vaporise. Any substitute fuel must vaporise at the operating temperature and it must dissolve in petrol. Ethanol can be used in a petrol engine because it boils at the same temperature as heptane, it does not freeze and it dissolves in alkanes. The combustion of ethanol produces 70% as much heat per litre as petrol combustion. Ethanol burns well in vehicle engines, and the atmospheric pollution produced is small. A petrol engine will take 10% ethanol in the petrol without any adjustments to the carburettor (which controls the ratio of air to fuel in the cylinders).

Ethanol has made a come-back in the car. The costs of petroleum and gas and the energy spent in cracking oil fractions have increased. Countries which have to import oil want to find alternatives. The fermentation method of making ethanol needs sunlight to grow crops. Countries with land available for growing crops to supply sugar or starch for fermentation and sunlight to ripen the crops are interested in using ethanol as a fuel.

Brazil produces ethanol for use as a vehicle fuel. Brazil has very

Fig. 19.17 Alcohol being stored in Brazil

357

little oil, but plenty of land and sunshine. Most of the petrol there now contains 10% ethanol, which has been made by the fermentation of cane sugar. Of the land area, 0.5% is devoted to growing sugar cane for fermentation. By the year 2000, Brazil hopes to provide for 75% of its motor fuel needs by using 2% of its land for growing crops for fermentation (Fig. 19.17).

SUMMARY NOTE

Ethanol is a clean fuel: it burns to form carbon dioxide and water. It can be used as a fuel in petrol engines. Brazil has no oil and has plenty of arable land to grow crops which can be fermented. Brazil is using ethanol mixed with petrol in vehicle engines. Other countries are following suit.

JUST TESTING 107

1 What is the source of energy in the cracking process?

2 What is the source of energy in fermentation?

3 Europe has a surplus of grain. Cereals can be turned into ethanol. This can replace tetraethyl lead as an octane-booster in lead-free petrol. You know that people in Asia and Africa are short of food. Should the surplus grain that Europe produces be used to fuel cars?

What's 'gasohol'? Do you drink it or burn it?

Better put it in the tank! It's the unleaded petrol with 10% ethanol that American 'gas' stations sell. The ethanol in it is made from corn.

19.7 Ethanoic acid

Ethanoic acid has the structural formula

$$
\begin{array}{ccc}
 & H & O \\
 & | & \diagup\!\!\diagup \\
H - & C - C & \\
 & | & \diagdown \\
 & H & O - H
\end{array}
$$

Ethanoic acid is a member of a homologous series called **carboxylic acids**.

Other members of the series are

methanoic acid, HCO_2H
propanoic acid, $C_2H_5CO_2H$

Carboxylic acids have the general formula $C_nH_{2n+1}CO_2H$.
The carboxylic acids have the group $—CO_2H$, which is called the **carboxyl group**. This is the functional group of the carboxylic acids. The carboxyl group ionises in solution to give hydrogen ions:

carboxylic acid + water $\rightleftharpoons$ hydrogen ions + carboxylate ions
$RCO_2H(aq) \rightleftharpoons H^+(aq) + RCO_2^-(aq)$

R is an alkyl group, e.g. CH_3, C_2H_5. Since they are only partially ionised, carboxylic acids are weak acids.
Some of the reactions of ethanoic acid are shown in Fig. 19.19.

Fig. 19.18 A model of ethanoic acid

Fig. 19.19 Reactions of ethanoic acid

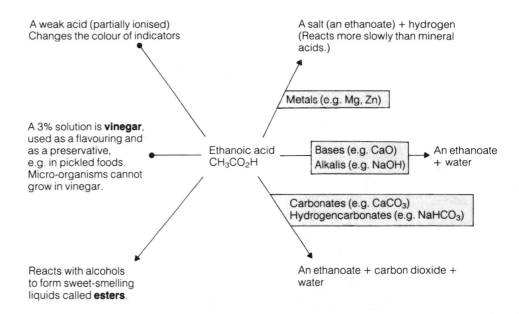

*19.8 Esters

Alcohols react with organic acids to form sweet-smelling liquids called **esters**. For example,

$$\text{ethanol + ethanoic acid} \xrightarrow{\text{conc. sulphuric acid}} \text{ethyl ethanoate + water}$$
$$\text{C}_2\text{H}_5\text{OH(l) + CH}_3\text{CO}_2\text{H(l)} \rightarrow \text{CH}_3\text{CO}_2\text{C}_2\text{H}_5\text{(l) + H}_2\text{O(l)}$$

Concentrated sulphuric acid is added to catalyse this **esterification** reaction, and to combine with the water that is formed. The structural formula for ethyl ethanoate is:

The formula is usually written as $\text{CH}_3\text{CO}_2\text{C}_2\text{H}_5$.

Esters with small molecules are liquids with fruity smells. They occur naturally in fruits. They are used as food additives to give flavour and aroma to processed foods. Esters are used as solvents. Many glues contain esters as solvents. Some people enjoy the effects of inhaling esters so much that they become 'glue sniffers'. It is really the solvent, which may be a hydrocarbon or an ester, that they are sniffing. This dangerous pastime is called **solvent abuse**. Solvent abuse produces the same symptoms as ethanol abuse. In addition, sniffers who are 'high' on solvents may believe that they will come to no harm if they jump out of windows or walk through traffic. Most of the deaths which occur through solvent abuse are caused by such disoriented behaviour or by sniffers passing out and suffocating on their own vomit.

SUMMARY NOTE

Ethanoic acid is a carboxylic acid. It is a weak acid. It has the same reactions as mineral acids, but reacts more slowly. Carboxylic acids react with alcohols to form **esters**. These compounds are used as food additives and as solvents.

359

Animal fats and vegetable oils are esters. They are liquids or solids, depending on the size and shape of their molecules. They are esters of glycerol, an alcohol which has three hydroxyl groups:

CH₂OH
|
CHOH
|
CH₂OH

Each of the —OH groups can esterify with a molecule of a carboxylic acid. Acids called **fatty acids** combine with glycerol to form fats. Fatty acids include hexadecanoic acid, $C_{15}H_{31}CO_2H$, octadecanoic acid, $C_{17}H_{35}CO_2H$, and others. (Hexadecane means 16, and octadecane means 18. If you count the number of carbon atoms, you will see how they get their names.)

Soap is made by boiling fats and oils with a concentrated solution of sodium hydroxide. The reaction can be represented:

fat or oil + sodium hydroxide → glycerol + soap

where GA_3 represents the fat or oil, $G(OH)_3$ represents glycerol and NaA represents the sodium salt of the fatty acid. The sodium salt of a fatty acid, e.g. sodium hexadecanoate or sodium octadecanoate, is a soap. This important reaction is called **saponification**.

SUMMARY NOTE

Esterification is the reaction between carboxylic acids and alcohols to form esters. These compounds are used as food additives and as solvents. Solvent abuse is a dangerous habit. Fats and oils are esters of glycerol and fatty acids. They can be used for soap-making.

JUST TESTING 108

1 Name three substances which will react with ethanoic acid. Name the products of the reactions.

*2 Explain why ethanoic acid is less reactive than hydrocholoric acid. (See Section 7.5 if you need help.)

3 Explain the terms **a** esterification, and **b** solvent abuse.

4 Explain how soaps emulsify oil and water (see Section 9.11).

19.9 The chemical industry

Many of the chemicals we use are **petrochemicals**, derived from petroleum oil. The petrochemical industry is not the whole of the chemical industry. The industry can be divided roughly into ten sections.

1 Heavy chemical industry: oils, fuels etc. (see Chapter 18).
2 Agriculture: fertilisers, pesticides etc. (see Chapter 15).
3 Plastics: poly(ethene), poly(styrene), PVC etc. (see Chapter 19).
4 Dyes (see Chapter 19).
5 Fibres: nylon, rayon, Courtelle etc. (see Chapter 14).
6 Paints, varnishes etc. (see Chapter 14).
7 Pharmaceuticals: medicines, drugs, cosmetics (see Section 19.10).
8 Metals: iron, aluminium, alloys etc. (see Chapter 11).
9 Explosives: dynamite, TNT etc. (see Chapter 15).
10 Chemicals from salt: sodium hydroxide, chlorine, hydrogen, hydrochloric acid (see Chapter 16).

Figure 19.20 shows some of the petrochemicals which are obtained by the route

petroleum oil → naphtha → ethene → petrochemical

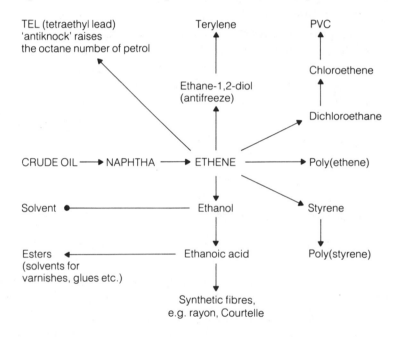

NOTE Propene reacts similarly. It is a source of rubber, detergents, paints and glues.

Fig. 19.20 Petrochemicals

19.10 Organic compounds in medicine

Many organic compounds are used in **chemotherapy**, the treatment of illness by chemical means. Chemotherapy makes our lives safer, longer and more free from pain. Some of the chemicals which relieve pain and cure diseases are mentioned in this section. There are many more.

Pain-killers

For the relief of moderate pain, aspirin is the all-time favourite. Aspirin is manufactured on a large scale. We in the UK each swallow an average of 200 aspirins a year. Many other drugs contain aspirin. When you swallow aspirin, there is slight bleeding of the stomach wall. In most people, this is not serious. In some people, severe loss of blood occurs. You should always swallow plenty of water with aspirin to reduce irritation of the stomach wall.

Codeine is a stronger pain-killer, used in headache tablets and in cough medicines. Morphine is used to relieve intense pain, and many a soldier wounded in battle has been glad of its almost magical quality. Morphine is *addictive*. People who use it become unable to do without it. Morphine can only be used under a doctor's supervision.

Heroin is even more potent and more addictive than morphine. The ease with which people become addicted to heroin explains why the medical profession has rejected it as a pain-killer. It also explains why it is so popular among drug pushers, who want to keep their customers eager to buy again and again.

The ideal pain-killer would be one which relieves even intense pain without causing addiction. A massive effort is being made by the pharmaceutical industry to find such a compound. New compounds are made and tested. In the search, a new compound 10 000 times more powerful and quick-acting than morphine has been made; this is the M-99 compound manufactured by Reckitt and Colman. They call it the 'rhino-dropper' and sell it to vets to use for anaesthetising large animals. The vet fires a pellet of M-99 into the animal; the animal drops unconscious. The new compound is, however, addictive, and the search for a new pain-killer continues.

Sedatives and tranquillisers

Barbiturates are drugs which have important medical uses, e.g. the treatment of high blood pressure and mental illness. They are also used as sedatives (sleeping tablets). They are habit-forming. Many people have accidentally killed themselves by taking an overdose of barbiturates.

Tranquillisers are substances which relieve tension and anxiety without producing sleep. They are sold in vast quantities by the drug industry. About one person in twenty takes tranquillisers every day. Medical researchers are beginning to look into the long-term effects of taking tranquillisers in this way.

During the 1950s, a tranquilliser called **thalidomide** was put on the market before it had been thoroughly tested. Terribly deformed babies were born to women who had taken the drug. The thalidomide scandal led to the passing of a new law. Since that time, drug companies have had to carry out a huge battery of tests on new drugs before they are sold.

Nicotine is a compound which occurs naturally in the tobacco plant. It is a poisonous oily liquid with an unpleasant smell, a burning taste and an alkaline reaction. Horrible though it sounds, people become addicted to it! Nicotine increases the pulse rate and the blood pressure. It depresses breathing. It makes the stomach wall contract, causing nausea, vomiting and diarrhoea. People become able to tolerate nicotine when they take small quantities regularly. This is why, although people feel sick or vomit when they start to smoke, after a while these symptoms do not occur. People like smoking because it produces a calming effect. Smoking may result in worsening eyesight, headaches, irregular heartbeat and cancer. Nicotine is the habit-forming compound in tobacco smoke. There are more than 1000 compounds in tobacco smoke. The tar that condenses in the lungs of smokers is a mixture of carcinogenic (cancer-producing) hydrocarbons.

Stimulants

Stimulants are produced naturally in the body. **Adrenaline** is a substance which the body produces when it needs to prepare for strenuous activity: for 'fight or flight'. It stimulates the heart to beat faster, makes a person keyed up and ready for action. Some people take **amphetamines** (pep pills) because they have similar effects on the body. With repeated use, people can become addicted. People who *abuse* (misuse) amphetamines are excitable and talkative, with trembling hands, enlarged pupils and heavy perspiration.

Antiseptics

A century ago, a surgeon called James Lister could not understand why so many patients who lived through operations died later in the wards. Something seemed to be going wrong *after* the operation. He realised that their wounds were becoming infected. He sprayed the operating theatre and the wards with a mist of phenol and water. The results were spectacular. The death rate was drastically reduced. Phenol is an **antiseptic**. It prevented micro-organisms from infecting the surgical wounds. Phenol is not a pleasant antiseptic to use. Its vapour is toxic, and solid phenol will burn the skin. Research chemists have discovered other compounds which work as well as phenol and are safer to use. TCP® and Dettol® are antiseptics which contain trichlorophenol.

Antibiotics

Antibiotics are used to fight diseases carried by bacteria. At the beginning of this century, thousands of people died every year from infectious diseases such as tuberculosis and pneumonia. The discovery of the **sulphonamide** drugs in 1935 completely changed the picture. They brought about marvellous recoveries from diseases which would otherwise have been fatal. Gerhardt Domagh was given the Nobel prize in 1939 for his discovery of the power of sulphonamide drugs. The first patient on whom he tested the drug was his daughter. She was dying of an infection called 'child-bed fever', which used to affect many women just after the birth of a baby. The drug worked! It is largely because of the discovery of powerful antibiotics that having a baby is so much safer than it was at the beginning of this century.

Penicillin was discovered in 1928 by Sir Alexander Fleming, who was working in a London hospital. During World War I, Fleming had seen many wounded soldiers dying in field hospitals. Many men died not from the severity of their wounds but from infection that set in later. Contamination from dirty clothing and mud caused gangrene, and the men died a slow, painful death. None of the existing antiseptics did much good. After the war, Fleming went back to his work as a **bacteriologist**. His ambition was to discover a substance which would kill bacteria. One day, a mould called **Penicillium** appeared on a dish of bacteria which he was culturing. It killed the bacteria. His efforts to treat infected patients with it were unsuccessful. When **penicillin**, an extract of the mould, was injected into a patient, substances in the blood made the **bacteriocide** inactive.

In 1940, two chemists called Howard Florey and Ernst Chain took up the work on penicillin. World War II had started, and the need for a powerful bacteriocide was urgent. Working in Oxford, Florey and Chain were able to purify Fleming's penicillin and make a stable extract. They tested penicillin on mice and then on human patients. In 1941, mass-production of penicillin started in the USA. The following year, penicillin was used on battle casualties with spectacular results. Fleming was knighted, and in 1945, he shared the Nobel prize for medicine with Florey and Chain.

Penicillin has been widely used since 1942 to treat infections of various parts of the body. Penicillin is broken down by acids, e.g. stomach acid. This disadvantage is not shared by **tetracycline**. Tetracycline is a 'broad spectrum' antibiotic, used against a large number of bacteria. Between them sulphonamides, penicillin, tetracycline and other antibiotics changed the pattern of medicine. Infectious diseases are no longer the killers they were.

JUST TESTING 109

1 What benefits does the manufacture of aspirins give us? Why should you take water with aspirins?

2 Do you think people should take tranquillisers regularly? Is there anything else people can do to relieve tension?

3 If you were employed as a pharmaceutical chemist by a drug company, and you discovered a new pain-killer, would you be in a hurry to see your discovery on the shelves of a 'chemist's shop'? Would you pressure your group-leader to speed up trials of your new drug?

4 Someone you know feels so tired that she is thinking of taking pep pills before going into an examination. What would you say to her?

5 A friend tells you that you should smoke for relaxation. Describe to him the effects of nicotine on the body. Tell him what other harmful substances are present in cigarette smoke. Suggest to him another way of relaxing.

6 What difference has the discovery of antiseptics made to surgery?
   What difference has the discovery of anaesthetics made to surgery? (See Section 18.3 if you need help.)

7 How long did it take for Florey and Chain to go from tests on animals to tests on humans? It would take them much longer in the 1980s than it did in the 1940s. What has happened to slow down the trials of new drugs on patients?

8 Morphine is a very effective pain reliever. Why do doctors not allow most patients to use it continuously? For what types of patients is morphine prescribed?

Exercise 19

1 What is a polymer? Give the structural formula of a named example. Say what use is made of the polymer you name.

2 PTFE is a polymer of

Draw the structure of the polymer. Give **a** the name of the monomer, **b** a use for the polymer.

3 List ten objects which are made from plastics. Say what material would have been used to make each object before the age of plastics. Explain what advantage plastics have over the other material.

4 Explain what is meant by 'cracking'. Why is it an important process?

5 What is the difference between thermosetting plastics and thermosoftening plastics? For which purposes are thermosetting plastics the better choice? Why are thermosoftening plastics preferred for other jobs?

6 PVC is a widely used plastic. Its proper name is poly(chloroethene). Draw the structural formula. What dangerous substances are formed if PVC burns?

7 a What class of chemical compound do soaps belong to?
b Explain how soaps work.
c What advantage do detergents have over soaps?
(See Section 9.11 if you need to revise.)

8 Alkenes can be made by passing the vapour of an alcohol over heated aluminium oxide.
a Sketch an apparatus in which you could carry out this reaction. Show how you would collect the alkene.

b Describe how you would test the alkene to show that it is **unsaturated**. Explain what the word **unsaturated** means.
c Write a word equation and a symbol equation for the reaction of a named alcohol.

9 a Name three plastics, and give examples of the uses to which these plastics are put.
b Point out why plastics are used for these purposes.
c Give two reasons why plastic furniture is more dangerous than wood furniture in a fire.

10 'Ethanoic acid is a weak acid which can be made by the oxidation of ethanol.'
a Write the structural formulas for ethanoic acid and ethanol.
b Explain what is meant by **oxidation**.
c Explain what is meant by **weak acid**.
d Describe two experiments you could do to show that ethanoic acid is a weaker acid than hydrochloric acid.

11 The plastic containers we use and throw away are non-biodegradable. The mass of discarded plastic in our tips and landfills is steadily increasing. Do you think we should
a burn discarded plastic in incinerators and use the heat generated or
b pay for research to develop biodegradable plastics or
c make it compulsory for the present almost indestructible plastics to be recycled? Explain the reasons for your answer.

12 In 1938, Dr Roy Plunkett was working for the Dupont chemical company. He needed a large quantity of tetrafluoroethene for his research. As no manufacturer made it, Plunkett built a small plant to make his own. He stored tetrafluoroethene in gas cylinders. In his experiments, he passed the gas from a storage cylinder into a reaction chamber. One day, the flow of gas stopped only minutes after the cylinder had been opened. The weight of the cylinder showed that there were still many grams of gas inside it. The valve was open: a piece of wire could be passed through it. The gas must still be in the cylinder, but it would not come out. In desperation, Plunkett seized a hacksaw and cut the cylinder in two. Inside was a large quantity of a white powder. He did not know what it was, but he was soon busy doing experiments to find out.

a Write the formula for tetrafluoroethene.

b Name the white powder that formed in the cylinder.

c Write its formula.

d Say what use we make of this substance.

e Do you think Dr Plunkett was just lucky to make this discovery? What else besides luck came into it?

13 Ethanol is made by using yeast to ferment a sugar solution.

a What is the name given to the catalysts in yeast?

b Why is the rate of fermentation not increased by raising the temperature above 25 °C?

c When ethanol is to be used as a fuel, the solution that is obtained by fermentation is filtered and fractionally distilled. What is the reason for (i) filtration and (ii) fractional distillation?

d Why is Brazil using ethanol made in this way to fuel motor vehicles? Why does the UK not do the same?

e What is the advantage to the environment of burning ethanol instead of petrol?

14 On the one hand, in the UK,

● The tax on alcoholic drinks brings in £4000 million a year.

● The manufacture, distribution and sales of alcoholic drinks provides employment for $\frac{3}{4}$ million people.

● Exports (mainly whisky) bring in £1000 million a year.

But, on the other hand, in the UK,

● Alcoholism costs industry £1600 million a year.

● One-third of the drivers killed in car accidents are drunk.

● One-quarter of pedestrians killed in road accidents are killed by drunken drivers.

● In many cases of murder, the murderer is drunk.

a Can you add some more points for and against alcohol consumption? You may like to turn this question into a group discussion.

b When does the *use* of alcohol turn into *abuse*?

CHAPTER 20　Energy

20.1 The energy crisis

You will have heard about the **world energy crisis**. It features constantly in newspaper headlines and television programmes. The problem is that we are consuming energy faster and faster. One day, unless we can find new sources of energy, we shall come to the end of the Earth's supplies of energy. The Earth's reserves of coal and oil and natural gas are limited. Coal, oil and natural gas are fossil fuels. They were made millions of years ago. Once we have used up the Earth's deposits, the supplies will not be renewed. Reserves of oil and natural gas are likely to run out in 20 to 30 years. Our present way of life is geared largely to oil and gas. Our agriculture depends on them: the petrochemicals industry provides farmers with pesticides to protect their crops from insects and weeds. The industries which manufacture most of our possessions depend on the oil industry. Our means of transport use oil: without oil, our cars, trains, boats and planes would be useless. Without the petrochemicals industry, we should have few modern drugs and medicines. Without oil and gas, our whole economy would collapse, leaving us shivering and starving in a primitive world. Unless scientists find alternatives to oil and gas, our future will be one of low technology.

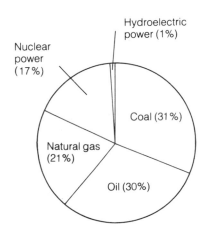

Fig. 20.1　Sources of energy in the UK

20.2 Some solutions

Nuclear power

The simplest solution is to obtain all the world's power needs from nuclear reactors. This solution is not free of difficulties. The dangers of accidents in nuclear reactors and the problems of storing long-lived radioactive material are discussed in Section 4.10.

Coal

Another solution is to make more use of coal. Already there are methods of making liquid fuels from coal:

The fuel produced can be used to power diesel engines. German planes flew on it in 1945. South Africa has enormous plants for making transport fuel from coal, which make the country independent of oil imports. Coal 'liquefaction' plants are not healthy places to work because prolonged contact with many hydrocarbons can cause skin cancer.

　　Making gaseous fuels from coal is less risky and less expensive than making liquid fuels from coal. The production of gaseous fuels involves heating coal and then allowing the residue to react with steam. A mixture of gaseous fuels is formed:

coal $\xrightarrow[\text{2 React with steam}]{\text{1 Heat}}$ fuel gas (carbon monoxide + hydrogen + methane)

The UK has coal deposits that will last for 200–250 years. Coal mining on an increased scale, however, will blight our countryside. Open-cast mining devastates the landscape. Underground mining creates spoil heaps. A spoil heap is a great mountain of soil and rock that have been dug out of the mine. A spoil heap collapsed on the Welsh village of Aberfan in 1970, killing dozens of people. This has made people fearful of living under the shadow of a spoil heap.

Table 20.1 A comparison of coal, oil and gas

	Coal	Oil	Natural gas
Origin	Fossil fuel	Fossil fuel	Fossil fuel
UK reserves	200–250 years	20–30 years	20 years
World reserves	200–250 years	30–40 years	20 years
Effect on the environment	Open-cast mining devastates the landscape. Spoil heaps are ugly and dangerous. Mining is still a dangerous job.	The sea is polluted by accidental spills from tankers and by ships illegally washing out their tanks at sea.	
Combustion	Air is polluted by sulphur dioxide, carbon monoxide, oxides of nitrogen, hydrocarbons, soot.	Air is polluted by sulphur dioxide, carbon monoxide, oxides of nitrogen, hydrocarbons, soot.	Natural gas is a clean fuel.

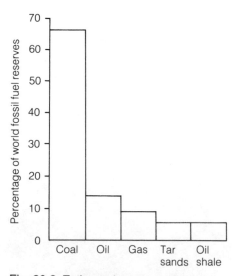

Fig. 20.2 Estimated reserves of fossil fuels in the world

Tar sands and oil shales

Some countries, e.g. Canada, have deposits of hydrocarbon tar mixed with sand. At present, the cost of obtaining a fuel from these deposits is too high to make the working of the deposits pay.

Oil shales are deposits of oil in porous shale rocks. Extracting the oil is too costly to be worthwhile at present.

Renewable energy sources

The idea of utilising **renewable energy sources** appeals to a lot of people. The sun, the wind and the tides are renewable energy sources. They derive their energy from the sun. As we use them, the sun renews them.

Solar energy. Solar energy is the name given to energy derived from sunlight. Sunlight is converted into electricity by the crystals in **photoelectric cells** (see Section 1.5). A solar power station is a vast area covered with rows of photoelectric cells. The cost of building a solar plant is high. The world's largest solar power plant is in southern California. California has plenty of sunshine and plenty of spare land to cover with solar panels. A big advantage of solar electric power plants is the complete absence of pollution.

Fig. 20.3 Solar panels on a house in Edinburgh

Windpower. Recently, the attention of scientists and engineers has turned to windmills and the attraction of their 'free' fuel. They have invented many new designs of wind machines (Fig. 20.4).

Waterpower. Hydro-electric power is obtained by damming a river at a high level and letting it flow under gravity to drive turbines lower down. The force of the tides can be used to drive turbines and generate electricity.

Geothermal energy. The rock layers thousands of metres below the surface of the Earth are hot. In some places, the hot rocks are only hundreds of metres down. Water can be pumped down over the hot rock and up to the surface. Water heated in this way is used to heat buildings in Paris. Steam generated in this way drives electric power generators in Italy.

Biomass. Material of biological origin can be converted into

Fig. 20.4 Wind machine

fuels. The use of methane from digesters of animal manure, toilet effluent and household waste has been described (see Section 16.1). Methane can be converted into methanol. This is a liquid fuel which can be used in the internal combustion engine. Some countries grow crops to be converted into fuel. Sugar cane and grain can be fermented to give ethanol (see Section 19.6). Biological material is called **biomass**.

20.3 Exothermic reactions

We need energy for many purposes. We obtain energy from the combustion of hydrocarbons, from the combustion of foods and from other chemical reactions. The chemical reactions and nuclear reactions which give out energy are **exothermic reactions** (ex = out; therm = heat). You have met many of them already, and only a summary is given in this chapter.

Combustion

Coal is a mixture of carbon and hydrocarbons. When it burns,

$$\text{carbon (in coal)} + \text{oxygen} \rightarrow \text{carbon dioxide} \qquad \textbf{Heat is given out}$$

$$\text{hydrocarbons (in coal)} + \text{oxygen} \rightarrow \text{carbon dioxide} + \text{water} \qquad \textbf{Heat is given out}$$

Natural gas is largely methane, CH_4. When it burns,

$$\text{methane} + \text{oxygen} \rightarrow \text{carbon dioxide} + \text{water} \qquad \textbf{Heat is given out}$$

$$CH_4(g) + 2O_2(g) \rightarrow CO_2(g) + 2H_2O(l)$$

To warm our homes and buildings, we use the combustion of methane and other hydrocarbons. To power our vehicles, we use the combustion of hydrocarbon fuels such as octane, C_8H_{18}.

Fig. 20.5 This car gets its energy from combustion

When octane burns,

octane + oxygen → carbon dioxide + water **Heat is released**

- An oxidation reaction in which heat is given out is a **combustion**.
- Combustion accompanied by a flame is **burning**.
- A substance which is oxidised with the release of energy is a **fuel**.

Respiration

We use a different kind of fuel to supply our bodies with energy. The 'energy foods' are sugars and starches. Sugars and starches are **carbohydrates**. These compounds contain carbon and hydrogen and oxygen in the ratio of 2H to 1O (as in H_2O). Glucose, $C_6H_{12}O_6$, is a sugar. It is oxidised to carbon dioxide and water with the release of energy:

glucose   + oxygen → carbon dioxide + water   **Energy is given out**

$$C_6H_{12}O_6(aq) + 6O_2(g) \rightarrow 6CO_2(g) + 6H_2O(l)$$

This reaction takes place inside our body tissues. Oxygen in the air we breathe oxidises sugars in our foods to provide us with energy. This reaction is called **respiration**. Respiration is an exothermic reaction.

A starch molecule consists of a string of $C_6H_{10}O_5$ units.

In the stomach, starch is hydrolysed (split up by water) to form sugars. Once formed, sugars are oxidised to give energy.

Neutralisation

When an acid neutralises an alkali (Experiment 18.2), heat is evolved. Neutralisation is an exothermic reaction.

hydrogen ion + hydroxide ion → water   **Heat is given out**

$$H^+(aq) \quad + OH^-(aq) \quad \rightarrow H_2O(l)$$

Hydration

When concentrated sulphuric acid reacts with water, heat is given out (see Section 14.7):

concentrated sulphuric acid + water → dilute sulphuric acid   **Heat is given out**

When anhydrous copper(II) sulphate combines with water, it forms a **hydrate**. This is the name for a salt combined with water of crystallisation.

copper(II) sulphate + water → copper(II) sulphate-5-water   **Heat is given out**

$$CuSO_4(s) + 5H_2O(l) \rightarrow CuSO_4 \cdot 5H_2O(s)$$

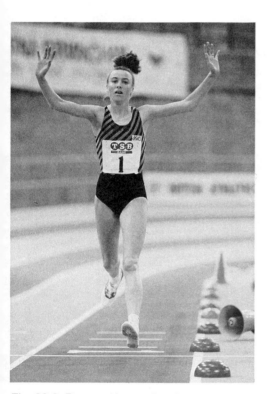

Fig. 20.6 Powered by combustion

SUMMARY NOTE

In **exothermic reactions**, energy is released. Examples are
- the combustion of hydrocarbons
- the combustion of sugars and starches in respiration
- neutralisation
- hydration
- chemical cells
- nuclear reactions.

Chemical cells

In chemical cells (see Section 5.11), chemical energy is transformed into electrical energy. Examples are the Daniell cell, dry cells, the lead–acid accumulator and fuel cells.

Nuclear reactions

You can read about nuclear reactions in Section 4.8.

20.4 Endothermic reactions

Some reactions take in energy; they are **endothermic reactions**.

Photosynthesis

Plants are able to convert the simple compounds carbon dioxide and water into sugars. They do this by converting the energy of sunlight into the energy of the chemical bonds in the sugar molecules. The reaction is called **photosynthesis**. It is an endothermic reaction. It takes place in the leaves of green plants, where the green pigment chlorophyll catalyses the reaction:

carbon dioxide + water   → glucose   + oxygen
(from the air)   (from the soil)   (sugar)

$$6CO_2(g) \quad + \quad 6H_2O(l) \quad \rightarrow C_6H_{12}O_6(aq) + 6O_2(g)$$

Energy is taken in

Dissolving

Many salts dissolve in water exothermically; some dissolve endothermically. Ammonium chloride and potassium nitrate dissolve endothermically (see Experiment 18.1 and Section 20.5).

Thermal decomposition

Many substances decompose when they are heated. Examples are

zinc carbonate → zinc oxide + carbon dioxide   **Heat is taken in**

$$ZnCO_3(s) \quad \rightarrow ZnO(s) \quad + CO_2(g)$$

copper(II) hydroxide → copper(II) oxide + water   **Heat is taken in**

$$Cu(OH)_2(s) \quad \rightarrow CuO(s) \quad\quad + H_2O(l)$$

copper(II) sulphate -5-water → copper(II) sulphate + water   **Heat is taken in**

$$CuSO_4 \cdot 5H_2O(s) \quad \rightarrow CuSO_4(s) \quad + 5H_2O(l)$$

Compare this last reaction with **hydration**.

—Dehydration is endothermic→

copper(II) sulphate -5-water ⇌ anhydrous copper(II) sulphate + water

←Hydration is exothermic—

Thermal dissociation

Many compounds decompose when they are heated. If the products recombine on cooling, then the reaction is described as **thermal dissociation**. In the thermal dissociation of ammonium chloride,

—The salt dissociates when heated→

ammonium chloride ⇌ ammonia + hydrogen chloride

$$NH_4Cl(s) \qquad \rightleftharpoons NH_3(g) \quad + HCl(g)$$

←The products recombine when cooled—

The reaction is **reversible**. It goes from left to right or from right to left, depending on the temperature. From left to right, it is endothermic; from right to left, it is exothermic.

You should revise the thermal dissociation of calcium carbonate (Section 13.3).

*20.5 Heat of reaction

Why is energy (heat energy and other forms of energy) given out or taken in during a chemical reaction? Chemicals possess energy of two kinds. One is **kinetic energy** — energy of motion. The atom or ions or molecules of a substance are constantly moving (see Section 1.4). To do this, they must possess kinetic energy. The second kind of energy is the **energy of chemical bonds**. The atoms or ions or molecules in a substance are held together by chemical bonds (see Chapter 6). Energy must be supplied if these chemical bonds are to be broken. There are no chemical bonds that fly apart by magic: energy must always be supplied to break bonds. When bonds are created, energy is given out.

The reactants and the products will have roughly the same kinetic energy at the same temperature. They will have different bond energies because the bonds in the substances are different. The energy content of the products is different from the energy content of the reactants (see Figs. 20.7 and 20.8).

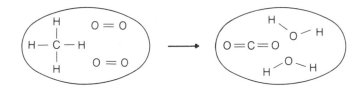

These bonds are broken.
Energy must be taken in.

These new bonds are made.
Energy is given out.

The energy taken in is less than the energy given out:
this reaction is exothermic.

Fig. 20.7 Bonds broken and made when methane burns

The symbol H is used for the energy content of a substance. The symbol ΔH is used for the heat taken in or given out during a reaction. ΔH is called the **heat of reaction**. Figure 20.9 is an **energy diagram**. It shows the energy content of the reactants and

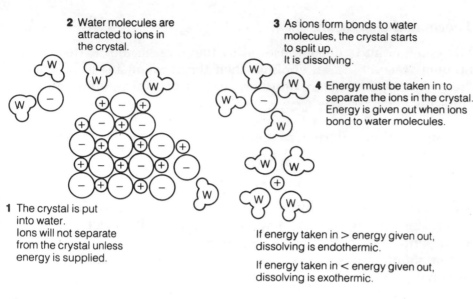

2 Water molecules are attracted to ions in the crystal.

1 The crystal is put into water. Ions will not separate from the crystal unless energy is supplied.

3 As ions form bonds to water molecules, the crystal starts to split up. It is dissolving.

4 Energy must be taken in to separate the ions in the crystal. Energy is given out when ions bond to water molecules.

If energy taken in > energy given out, dissolving is endothermic.

If energy taken in < energy given out, dissolving is exothermic.

Fig. 20.8 Bonds broken and made when a crystal dissolves

Fig. 20.9 An energy diagram for an exothermic reaction

the products. The products of the reaction shown in Fig. 20.9 contain less energy than the reactants. When the reactants change into the products, they have to get rid of their extra energy. They give out heat to the surroundings: this is an exothermic reaction.

The difference ΔH between the energy of the products and the energy of the reactants is called the **heat of reaction**. By definition,

Heat of reaction ΔH = Energy of products − Energy of reactants

You can see that, because the products of the reaction shown in Fig. 20.9 have less energy than the reactants, ΔH is negative.

For an exothermic reaction, ΔH is negative.

Figure 20.10 is a second energy diagram. In this reaction, when the reactants change into the products, they have to ascend to a higher energy. To do this, they must take energy from the surroundings: they cool the surroundings. This is an endothermic reaction. Since by definition,

Heat of reaction ΔH = Energy of products − Energy of reactants

in this reaction, ΔH is a positive quantity.

For an endothermic reaction, ΔH is positive.

JUST TESTING 110

1 Draw an energy diagram for the combination of hydrogen ions and hydroxide ions to form water. Re-read if you have forgotten whether it is exothermic or endothermic. Mark the heat of reaction on your diagram. State whether it is positive or negative.

2 Draw an energy diagram for the combustion of petrol to form carbon dioxide and water. Mark ΔH on your diagram, and state whether it is positive or negative.

3 Is the dissolving of ammonium chloride exothermic or endothermic? Illustrate your answer by an energy diagram.

Fig. 20.10 An energy diagram for an endothermic reaction

*20.6 Getting over the barrier

The combustion of hydrocarbon fuels is exothermic. There is no doubt about this: the energy given out drives our vehicles and warms our homes. When you mix petrol with air at room temperature, however, it does not immediately burst into flames. You have to warm it up before combustion takes place. The energy given out in combustion is greater than the energy you have to put in to start the reaction. The products are at a lower energy level than the reactants but there is a barrier to be surmounted before the reactants can roll down the energy hill to form the products (see Fig. 20.11).

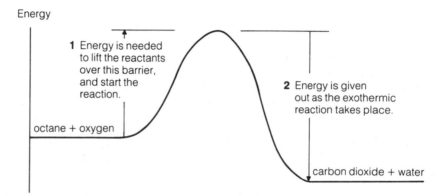

Fig. 20.11 The energy barrier

JUST TESTING 111

1 Describe the reaction that takes place when you heat a mixture of iron and sulphur (see Chapter 3). What do you see to tell you that this reaction is exothermic?
   - Why do you have to heat to start the reaction?
   - Write an equation for the reaction.
   - Draw an energy diagram for the reaction.

2 Describe the reaction that takes place when you heat magnesium ribbon in air. What do you see to tell you that the reaction is exothermic? What forms of energy are released?
   - Why do you have to heat to start the reaction?
   - Draw an energy diagram.

*3 'There is an energy barrier to be climbed before substances can react.'
   Explain this statement.
   Is this barrier a nuisance? If energy barriers were suddenly abolished, what would happen to **a** petrol and **b** magnesium ribbon?

*20.7 Calculations on heat of reaction

In stating the value of the heat change that occurs during a chemical reaction or a physical change, we give the value for 1 mole of substance. Heat is measured in joules (J) and kilojoules (kJ)

(1000 J = 1 kJ). Heats of reaction are expressed in kilojoules **per mole** (kJ/mol).

Molar heat of neutralisation is the heat taken in when 1 mole of hydrogen ions is neutralised:

hydrogen ions + hydroxide ions → water   **Heat is given out**

$$H^+(aq) \qquad + OH^-(aq) \qquad \rightarrow H_2O(l) \quad \Delta H = -57 \text{ kJ/mol}$$

Molar heat of combustion is the heat taken in when 1 mole of a substance is completely burnt in oxygen:

methane + oxygen → carbon dioxide + water   **Heat is given out**

$$CH_4(g) \quad + 2O_2(g) \ \rightarrow CO_2(g) \ + 2H_2O(l) \quad \Delta H = -890 \text{ kJ/mol}$$

Molar heat of formation is the heat taken in when 1 mole of reactant is formed from its elements. In the formation of carbon dioxide:

$$C(s) + O_2(g) \rightarrow CO_2(g) \qquad\qquad \Delta H = -394 \text{ kJ/mol}$$

Heat of reaction is the heat taken in when a reaction occurs between the number of moles of reactants shown in the equation. For the reaction:

$$2N_2(g) + 2H_2O(g) + 5O_2(g) \rightarrow 4HNO_3(l) \qquad \Delta H = -220 \text{ kJ/mol}$$

The value of ΔH could be given per mole of nitrogen or per mole of nitric acid, but in fact it is given per mole of the equation as written, that is, for the reaction between 2 moles of nitrogen and 2 moles of water and 5 moles of oxygen.

Example 1   Camping gaz is butane, C_4H_{10}. The molar heat of combustion of butane is -2880 kJ/mol. Calculate the heat given out when 1 kg of camping gaz burns completely.

Method
Molar mass of butane, $C_4H_{10} = (4 \times 12) + (10 \times 1) = 58$ g/mol
1 mol of butane, that is, 58 g of butane, give out 2880 kJ
therefore 1000 g of butane give out
    $2880 \times 1000/58$ kJ $= 49\,700$ kJ

1 kg of camping gaz (butane) gives 49 700 kJ.

Example 2   50.0 cm³ of 1.00 mol/l sodium hydroxide solution are neutralised by an acid. The heat given out is 2.85 kJ. Calculate the molar heat of neutralisation.

Method
Amount (in moles) of sodium hydroxide
        = Volume (l) × Concentration (mol/l)
        $= 50.0 \times 10^{-3} \times 1.00$ mol
        $= 5.0 \times 10^{-2}$ mol

Heat evolved in the neutralisation of 5.0×10^{-2} mol $= 2.85$ kJ

Molar heat of combustion = heat taken in when 1 mole of substance is burned completely.

Molar heat of neutralisation = heat taken in when 1 mole of hydrogen ions are neutralised.

Heat evolved in the neutralisation of 1.00 mol
$$= 2.85 \times 1.0/(5.0 \times 10^{-2}) \text{ kJ}$$
$$= 57 \text{ kJ}$$

The molar heat of neutralisation is -57 kJ/mol.

JUST TESTING 112

1 The molar heat of combustion of glucose ($C_6H_{12}O_6$) is -2800 kJ/mol. What mass of glucose must be combusted to release 400 kJ of energy?

2 The combustion of 0.80 g of methanol releases 17.9 kJ of energy. Calculate the molar heat of combustion of methanol, CH_3OH.

3 One-third of a litre of sodium hydroxide solution of concentration 0.1 mol/l was neutralised by dilute nitric acid. The heat given out was 1.90 kJ. Calculate the molar heat of neutralisation.

4 Solutions of sodium hydroxide (1.00 mol/l) and hydrochloric acid (1.00 mol/l) are mixed, and the temperature rise is measured. The volume of each solution is 50 cm³, and the heat evolved is calculated as 2.85 kJ.
   a Calculate the heat of neutralisation.
   b Say whether the value for nitric acid would be greater, less or the same for the same experiment.

*20.8 Using bond energy values

Chemists have measured how much energy it takes to break different chemical bonds. To break 1 mole of C—H bonds requires 412 kJ, and we therefore say that the bond energy of the C—H bond is 412 kJ/mol. Table 20.2 lists the bond energies of some bonds. To break a chemical bond, energy must be supplied, so all the bond energies are positive.

We can use bond energy values to calculate a value for the heat of reaction.

Table 20.2 Some bond energy values

Bond	Bond energy in kJ /mol
H—H	436
O=O	496
C—C	348
C=C	612
C≡C	837
C—H	412
C—O	360
C=O	743
H—O	463
Br—Br	193
C—Br	276

Example Use bond energies to calculate ΔH for the reaction:

$$CH_4(g) + 2O_2(g) \rightarrow CO_2(g) + 2H_2O(l)$$

Method
First show the bonds that are broken and the bonds that are made:

$$\begin{array}{c} H \\ | \\ H—C—H + 2\,O{=}O \rightarrow O{=}C{=}O + 2H—O—H \\ | \\ H \end{array}$$

Next list the bonds that are broken and the bonds that are made and their bond energies.

Bonds broken are

4(C—H) bonds; energy = 4×412 = 1648 kJ/mol
2(O=O bonds; energy = 2×496 = 992 kJ/mol
Total energy required = +2640 kJ/mol

Bonds made are

2(C=O) bonds; energy = -2×743 = −1486 kJ/mol
2(H—O) bonds; energy = -4×463 = −1852 kJ/mol
Total energy given out = −3338 kJ/mol

$$\text{Heat of reaction} = \text{Energy required to break old bonds} + \text{Energy given out when new bonds are made}$$
$$= +2640 - 3338 = -698 \text{ kJ/mol}$$

JUST TESTING 113

Find the heats of reaction for the following reactions. Use the bond energies in Table 20.2.

1

H—C=C—H + H_2 → H—C—C—H (with H, H above and H, H below both carbons)

(*Hint:* Add the energies of the bonds that are broken (positive) and the energies of the bonds created (negative).)

2 $2H_2(g) + O_2(g) \rightarrow 2H_2O(l)$

3

$H_3C—C—CH_3(g) + H_2(g) \rightarrow H_3C—C—CH_3(g)$ (ketone with O double bond becoming alcohol with O—H and H)

4 $H_2C=CHCH_3(g) + Br_2(g) \rightarrow H_2BrCCHBrCH_3$
(*Hint:* Draw structural formulas to show all the bonds.)

5

$CH_3CH_2OH(g) + O_2(g) \rightarrow CH_3C=O + H_2O(g)$ (with H above the C)

20.9 The nuclear debate

You may have heard of **the nuclear debate**. The burning question is nuclear power stations. One side of the debate is worried by the dangers of radioactive materials. The other side claims that we need nuclear power because coal and oil supplies will start to run out by the end of this century. A nuclear debate is in session at Newtown High School.

Jill   I'm dead against nuclear reactors. After that terrible accident in Russia, I think we ought to scrap nuclear power stations.
Neil   You mean the Chernobyl disaster in 1986? That was

dreadful, when that nuclear reactor exploded and burned for days with no-one knowing whether they could put it out. It was two weeks before they brought it under control. At one time it got so hot they thought it might burn its way down into the Earth.

Beth You mean like that Jane Fonda film, The China Syndrome, where they thought the reactor might burn through the Earth to China?

Jill How did they put the fire out?

Neil Firemen put out the fire in the building which housed the reactor. Most of them died later because they got such a huge dose of radioactivity. The core of the reactor was white-hot graphite at 5000 °C. No-one could get near it. Helicopters dropped sand, lead and boron on the burning reactor to cool it.

Beth Besides the twenty people killed, there were hundreds taken to hospital with radiation sickness.

Mark People who got a smaller dose of radiation could get leukaemia or cancer in a year's time or in ten year's time.

Chris It wasn't only people in the plant who were affected. The explosion spread radioactive gases and particles over miles and miles of the Ukraine.

Jill The Ukraine is the farming area where most of the grain in Russia is grown, isn't it? I don't think they'll want to eat grain that has been contaminated with radioactivity.

Beth Does anyone know which radioactive isotopes are formed when uranium-235 splits?

Mark Strontium-90, iodine-131 and caesium-137.

Neil Strontium-90 is very dangerous. You see, strontium compounds behave like calcium compounds. They would be laid down in your bones and teeth.

Jill Iodine builds up in the thyroid gland in your throat. That makes iodine-131 a dangerous isotope too. Caesium compounds get into your body in the same way as sodium and potassium compounds do.

Chris Did you know that there was once a nuclear accident in Britain? Those radioisotopes escaped from Sellafield nuclear power station.

Mark You mean when the reactor caught fire in 1964. They called it Windscale nuclear power station then. The reactor overheated, and a load of graphite rods caught fire. They had to flood the reactor with water to put out the fire.

Neil The Lake District was showered with radioactivity. People were worried that cows would produce radioactive milk. When they tested the milk, they found there was only a very low level of iodine-131 in it. They dumped all the milk for a few weeks to be on the safe side.

Jill Iodine-131 has a half-life of one week. They were lucky it wasn't a long-lived radioisotope.

Chris Did the Russian accident happen in the same way?

Beth The Russians haven't explained what happened at Chernobyl. I expect it was similar to the accident at Three Mile Island in the USA in 1979. No-one was injured that time, but it was a big scare.

Mark That crisis started when the pumps which feed in cold water to cool the reactor stopped.

Chris It was mad not having a back-up system.

Mark There was one, but the emergency pumps couldn't come on because someone had shut off their water supply. Human error, they call it. Dozens of warning signals lit up. After a few minutes, they found out what was wrong and opened the valve.

Jill Was that the end of the panic?

Mark No. There was mechanical failure as well as human error. When the reactor started to heat up, a safety valve opened to release steam. It should have closed again, but it didn't. It let water and steam escape. Losing water sent up the temperature of the reactor. The hot metal reacted with steam to form hydrogen.

Neil Wow! I know hydrogen. It's an explosive. They must have been scared of a hydrogen explosion. I bet there was a hydrogen explosion at Chernobyl. Could there have been a nuclear explosion as well?

Chris No, that can't happen. The construction of a nuclear reactor is completely different from an atomic bomb. The danger is that the core might get hot enough to melt the metal and concrete shielding. Then *all* the radioactivity would escape. Also a steam explosion or a hydrogen explosion would let radioactive material escape.

Jill Well, what did happen at Three Mile Island?

Mark After two hours, the operators finally discovered that the steam valve was open. After they closed it, the temperature fell. It took them a week to get the temperature down. The plant is still closed because of the radioactive contamination.

Neil I still think that if a nuclear power station is operated properly, it's safe. You don't hear many people worrying about whether coal mining is safe, do you?

Beth Even when they are working properly, nuclear reactors produce plutonium. That's dangerous stuff, isn't it? I know it's the isotope they use to make atom bombs. I think terrorists could steal it and use it to make an atomic bomb. Then they could threaten to blow up a whole city if they didn't get what they wanted.

Chris The group of terrorists would have to include a pretty good physicist, a chemist and an engineer at least. They would need the right equipment. Making an atomic bomb is a really difficult and dangerous job.

Jill Perhaps you're right. I suppose terrorists can find easier ways of threatening people than making an atomic bomb.

Neil The biggest problem with nuclear reactors is the spent fuel that is taken out of them. One of the fission products it contains is plutonium-239. It is tremendously radioactive. It gives off heat as well. It needs to be cooled and stored in a safe place for a long time.

Jill A very long time. Strontium-90 and caesium-137 have half-lives of about 90 years. They need to be stored for 400 years. Plutonium-239 has a half-life of 24 000 years. It needs to be stored for a quarter of a million years before most of its activity has gone.

Beth West Germany stores radioactive waste in old salt mines. Britain pipes very low level radioactive waste into the sea and stores the rest until a proper storage place can be found for it. The USA packs radioactive waste in steel canisters and dumps them at sea.

Chris The French have worked out a method of turning liquid radioactive waste into glass. They pack the radioactive glass in steel drums. Then they bury the drums beneath concrete. This should store the waste safely until it isn't radioactive any longer.

Jill I hope you're right. Remember, that means a quarter of a million years for plutonium-239.

Chris What no-one has said yet is that we need nuclear power. Coal and oil won't last for ever. Well, not for more than 20 to 30 years, they say. Then what? I don't want the sort of life people used to have without electricity.

Beth Already we get 18 per cent of our electricity from nuclear power.

Neil The Americans get 17 per cent and the French 65 per cent.

Jill At least nuclear power stations are clean. They don't put the pollution in the air that coal and oil power stations do. You don't get sulphur dioxide and nitrogen oxides and soot from nuclear power stations.

Mark I think it's a terrible waste to burn oil when the petrochemical industry can make all those useful things from it.

Beth You mean plastics and paints and so on?

Chris I think there's a future for renewable energy sources. You know, wind and waves and solar power. People are building some modern windmills with great designs. Wind is free, and windmills don't make pollution.

Beth There are so many things to weigh up. I can't make up my mind about the best way to get energy.

Some questions for you to discuss

(The energy crisis and the nuclear debate are complicated topics. You may well like to form groups to discuss these questions. There are no short answers.)

1 Why is radioactive waste stored for a long time?
2 Why is it often stored underground? Why are old salt mines chosen?
3 Why is it often stored behind thick walls of concrete? What is the advantage of vitrifying (making into glass) radioactive waste?
4 What is the danger of dumping it in steel cans at sea?
5 Someone suggested launching radioactive waste into space. Can you see anything wrong with this idea?
6 Why are people worried about earthquakes disturbing underground stores?
7 Why do strontium compounds behave as calcium compounds do?
  Why do caesium compounds behave as sodium compounds do?

8 Why are nuclear power stations so useful to us? What advantages do they have over coal-burning electric power stations?

9 Explain the advantages of making use of renewable energy sources.
Describe some methods of utilising renewable energy sources which were not mentioned by the students.
What difficulty is there in using solar power?

10 What is wrong with burning petrol and other hydrocarbon fuels?
(There are at least two answers to this question.)

11 The accident at Chernobyl sent a radioactive cloud drifting towards Poland. The Russians did not warn the Poles of the danger that was approaching. Had the Poles known, they could have taken some precautions against radiation.

   a What do you think should be the agreed code of behaviour for nuclear powers if an accident happens?

   b If Poland had known that a cloud of radioactivity was approaching, what precautions could that country have taken?

In conclusion

I cannot offer you a solution to the problem. Beth, Jill, Chris, Neil and Mark have not covered all the points in the nuclear debate. You will see people discussing it on television. You will read about it in the papers. You would be wise not to make up your minds yet. Find out more about the problem. Keep thinking about it. Keep on discussing it.

Exercise 20

1 a Explain the difference between **exothermic** and **endothermic** reactions.

   b Give an example of an exothermic reaction of vital importance in everyday life. Explain why it is so important to you.

   c Give an example of an endothermic reaction of vital importance. Explain why it is so important to you.

2 a Why do people say there is an **energy crisis**?

   b Do you think the energy crisis is going to affect your life?

   c What are **renewable** energy sources? What advantages do they have over coal and oil?

   d If someone asked you which renewable energy source Britain should invest in, what would you say? Explain your choice.

3 What advantages do nuclear power stations have over coal-fired and oil-fired electricity power stations?

4 a Name one radioactive element which is mined for use in nuclear power stations.

   b Name one radioactive element which is made in nuclear power stations.

   c Describe one of the risks involved in running a nuclear power station. Say what is done to avoid an accident.

   d Why do people worry more about the possibility of an accident in a nuclear power station than about accidents in coal mines?

5 The half-life of plutonium is 24 000 years.
  a What is meant by the term 'half-life'?
  b What problem is created by this long half-life of plutonium?
  c What attempts have been made to solve the problem?

6 a Name two sources of energy which do not depend on radioactive isotopes or fossil fuels.
  b Explain the advantages of utilising these sources of energy.
  c Outline the difficulties which have to be overcome before we can make good use of them.

7 What is **biomass**? Name two kinds of biomass from which fuels are obtained. Explain why some countries are exploiting this source of fuels more than the UK. In what way could the UK make more use of biomass as a source of fuel?

*8 a What is hydrocarbon?
  b One of the hydrocarbons in petrol is octane, C_8H_{18}. Write a word equation for the complete combustion of octane. Write a symbol equation.
  c The molar heat of combustion of octane is -5520 kJ/mol. Calculate the heat that is released by the complete combustion of 57 g of octane.
  d Why is the quantity of energy obtained when 57 g of octane burn in a car engine less than the calculated quantity?

9 'The reaction

anhydrous cobalt chloride + water → cobalt chloride-6-water

is exothermic.'
By means of a diagram, show an experiment by which you could find out whether this statement is true.

CHAPTER 21 *The speeds of chemical reactions*

21.1 Why reaction speeds are important

Making cheese takes time. When milk is allowed to age, bacteria in the milk feed on a sugar called **lactose**, which is present in milk. They turn it into **lactic acid**. Acids make some of the proteins in milk clot. When this happens, the sugar lactose and butterfat are trapped in the clotted milk, making a soft **curd** with a pleasant taste. The liquid part of the curdled milk is called **whey**.

As more proteins clot, curd turns gradually into cheese. Curd takes some days to age naturally. The process can be speeded up by adding a substance called **rennin**. Rennin is a **catalyst**. This is the name for a substance which makes a reaction take place faster, even though it is not itself used up in the reaction. Rennin **catalyses** the clotting of proteins. It is a great help to cheese-makers, who want to minimise the time for which they have to store ageing milk and maximise their production of cheese. Fortunately, rennin is in good supply. It is obtained from the gastric juices in calves' stomachs. A catalyst which is obtained from an animal or a plant is called an **enzyme**. You will learn more about catalysts and enzymes in Section 21.7.

Cheese manufacturers are interested in speeding up the chemical reactions which produce cheese. The more tonnes of cheese they can produce in a month, the more profit they will make. Other people are interested in slowing down chemical reactions. Car manufacturers want to slow down the rusting of iron. Butter manufacturers want to slow down the rate at which butter turns rancid. Conservationists want to slow down the rate at which acid rain attacks stone. Everyone prefers to store their milk in a refrigerator to slow down the rate at which milk turns sour.

In a chemical reaction, the starting materials are called the **reactants**, and the finishing materials are called the **products**. It takes time for the reactants to react to form the products of the reaction. If the reactants take only a short time to change into the products, that reaction is a **fast reaction**. The **speed** or **rate** of that reaction is high. If a reaction takes a long time before it is completely finished (before the reactants have changed into the products), it is a **slow reaction**. The speed or rate of that reaction is low.

Many people are interested in knowing how to alter the speeds of chemical reactions. A number of factors can be changed. These are investigated in Experiments 19.1–19.6. They are

- the size of the particles of a solid reactant
- the concentrations of reactants in solution
- the temperature
- the presence of light
- the addition of a catalyst.

Little Miss Muffet
sat on a tuffet,
eating the products of
a slow chemical reaction.

SUMMARY NOTE

A fast chemical reaction is one in which the reactants change rapidly into the products. Such a reaction has a high **speed** or **rate**. A reaction with a low **speed** or **rate** takes a long time to change the reactants into the products.

A catalyst is a substance which can alter the rate of a chemical reaction without being used up in the reaction.

21.2 How does the size of solid particles affect the speed at which they react?

Remember the reaction you used for the preparation of carbon dioxide (see Section 12.5). One of the reactants, calcium carbonate (marble) is a solid:

calcium carbonate + hydrochloric acid → carbon dioxide + calcium chloride + water

$$CaCO_3(s) + 2HCl(aq) → CO_2(g) + CaCl_2(aq) + H_2O(l)$$

You can use this reaction to find out whether large lumps of a solid react at the same speed as small lumps of the same solid. In Experiment 19.1, you compared the rate of this reaction for small marble chips and for large marble chips. In Fig. 21.1, you can see a different method for finding the rate of the reaction. The carbon dioxide formed, being a gas, escapes from the flask. As it escapes, the mass of the flask and contents decreases.

3 Cotton wool prevents spray from escaping.

2 Hydrochloric acid (50 cm³ of bench acid)

1 Calcium carbonate (20 g of large chips)

4 Top-loading balance

Note the mass of the flask + acid + marble chips. Add the chips to the acid, and start a stopwatch. After 10 seconds, note the mass. After 30 seconds, note the mass. Continue for 5–10 minutes: note the mass every 30 seconds.

Fig. 21.1 Apparatus for following the loss in mass when a gas is evolved

The mass of the flask and contents is noted at various times after the start of the reaction. The mass can be plotted against time. Figure 21.2 shows typical results. These results show that the smaller the size of the particles of calcium carbonate, the faster the reaction takes place (see Fig. 21.3). There is a larger surface area in 20 g of small chips than in 20 g of large chips.

SUMMARY NOTE

This section is about reactions in which one reactant is a solid. Such reactions take place faster when the solid is divided into small pieces. The reason is that a certain mass of small particles has a larger surface area than the same mass of large particles.

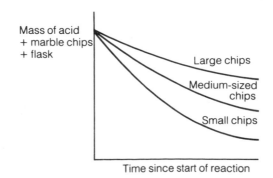

Mass of acid + marble chips + flask

Large chips

Medium-sized chips

Small chips

Time since start of reaction

Fig. 21.2 Results obtained with different sizes of marble chips

The acid attacks the surface of the marble. It can therefore react faster with small particles than with large particles.

JUST TESTING 114

1 When potatoes are cooked, a chemical reaction occurs. Potatoes contain both starch and water. When the temperature is high enough, granules of starch react with water to form a gel. Two things decide how fast potatoes cook. One is the temperature of the oven. The other is the speed at which heat is transferred from the surface of the potato to its centre. What can you do to increase this speed?

2 There is a danger in coal mines that coal dust may catch fire and start an explosion. Explain why coal dust is more dangerous than coal.

3 Why does soluble aspirin act faster on a headache than aspirin tablets?

4 Your uncle is suffering from 'acid indigestion'. In the medicine cabinet are some *Fixit* indigestion tablets and some *Mendit* indigestion powder. He asks you which will work faster. Both these remedies are alkalis. Explain how you could test them in the laboratory with a bench acid before giving an opinion.

I'd rather peel 5 pounds of big potatoes than 5 pounds of littl'uns.

21.3 Concentration and speed of reaction

Many chemical reactions take place in solution. In Experiment 19.2, the reaction studied is

sodium thiosulphate + hydrochloric acid →

sulphur + sodium chloride + sulphur dioxide + water

$$Na_2S_2O_3(aq) + 2HCl(aq) \rightarrow S(s) + 2NaCl(aq) + SO_2(g) + H_2O(l)$$

It's the ratio of surface area to mass that makes the difference!

Fig. 21.3 Large and small particles

Sulphur appears in the form of very small particles of solid. The particles remain in suspension. Figure 21.4 shows how you can study the speed at which sulphur is formed.

1 Acid and sodium thiosulphate solution are reacting to form sulphur.

2 You are timing how long it takes to form enough sulphur to block your view of the cross.

3 You do this with different concentrations of sodium thiosulphate.

Fig. 21.4 Experiment on reaction speed and concentration

(a) The measurement

Fig. 21.4

4 The results show that the cross disappears soonest when the solution is most concentrated.

(b) The results

5 When 1/(time for cross to disappear) is plotted against concentration, a straight line is obtained. This shows that for this reaction,

1/time ∝ concentration

(c) A different way of plotting the results

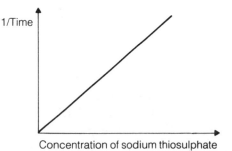

SUMMARY NOTE

This section has covered reactions in which at least one of the reactants is in solution. For the reactions studied, the rate of the reaction is proportional to the concentration of the reactant (or reactants). (That is, the speed doubles when the concentration is doubled.)

The speed of the reaction is **inversely proportional** to the time taken for the reaction to finish:

Speed of reaction ∝ 1/time

Since, in **5**,

1/time ∝ concentration,
speed of reaction ∝ concentration.

In this experiment, only one concentration was altered. You may have extended Experiment 19.3 by keeping the concentration of sodium thiosulphate constant and altering the concentration of acid. You will have found that the speed of the reaction is *proportional to* the concentration of the acid. If the acid concentration is doubled, the speed doubles. This is because the ions are closer together in a concentrated solution. The closer together they are, the more often the ions collide. The more often they collide, the more chance they have of reacting.

Fig. 21.5 Collisions are frequent in crowds

JUST TESTING 115

1 Acid rain attacks stone buildings. Why does this reaction take place faster in some parts of the country than others?

2 Imagine you want to investigate the marble chips–acid reaction. You want to find out how changing the concentration of acid will affect the speed of the reaction. Explain how you could adapt the experiment shown in Fig. 21.1 for this purpose.

21.4 Pressure and speed of reaction

When gases react, the speed of the reaction can be increased by increasing the pressure. The result is to push the gas molecules closer together. This means that they collide more often and react faster.

21.5 Temperature and speed of reaction

The reaction between sodium thiosulphate and acid can also be used to study the effect of temperature on the speed of a chemical reaction (see Experiment 19.4). There is a steep increase in the speed of the reaction as the temperature is increased (see Fig. 21.6). This reaction goes approximately twice as fast at 30 °C as it does at 20 °C. It doubles in speed again between 30 °C and 40 °C and so on.

You raise the temperature of a solution by putting heat energy into it. At the higher temperature, the ions have more energy. They move through the solution faster. They collide more often and more vigorously. They have to collide before they can react. Once they have collided, there is a chance that they will react (Fig. 21.7).

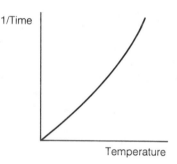

Fig. 21.6 The effect of temperature on the speed of reaction

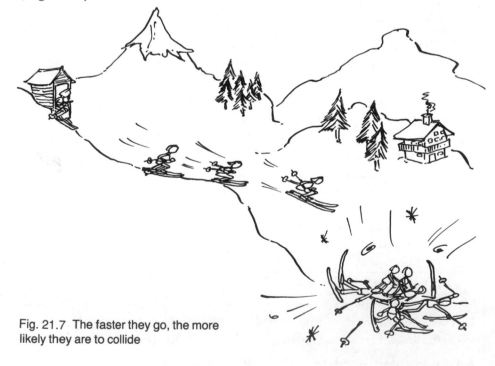

Fig. 21.7 The faster they go, the more likely they are to collide

21.6 Light affects the speeds of some reactions

Heat is not the only form of energy that can speed up reactions. Some chemical reactions take place faster in the presence of light. The formation of silver from silver salts takes place when a photographic film is exposed to light (see Section 7.9). Photosynthesis, the reaction by which green plants synthesise sugars, takes place in sunlight (see Section 13.6).

1 **Food storage**: The changes which occur when foods decay are chemical reactions. Like other chemical reactions, these changes take place quickly or slowly, depending on the temperature. Study this list of Australian cities and their average temperatures:

City	Average temperature in °C
Melbourne	15
Sydney	17
Brisbane	19
Cairns	25
Darwin	28

a In which of these cities will food keep longest?
b In which of these cities will food go off fastest?
c Look at the results you obtained from Experiment 19.4 on the reaction of sodium thiosulphate at different temperatures. What effect does a 10 °C rise in temperature have on the rate of this reaction?
Suppose that a change in temperature has a similar effect on the rates of the reactions which take place when food decays. Then, how much more difficult is it to keep food fresh in Cairns than in Melbourne?
How do Sydney and Darwin compare when it comes to keeping food fresh?

2 Someone asks you to do experiments to find out what effect temperature has on the rate of a chemical reaction. Choose a reaction. Say how you could find out how fast the reaction was going. Say what measurements you would make. Sketch the apparatus you would use.

Oxygen collects in the syringe. The volume can be read.

Readings of volume and time since the start of the reaction can be tabulated.

Hydrogen peroxide solution

Catalyst

Fig. 21.8 Apparatus for measuring volume of gas evolved

21.7 Catalysis

Experiment 19.5 makes a good introduction to catalysis. The reaction studied is

hydrogen peroxide → oxygen + water
$$2H_2O_2(aq) \rightarrow O_2(g) + 2H_2O(l)$$

This is the reaction you used to prepare oxygen (see Section 8.8). Figure 21.8 shows how the oxygen evolved can be collected and measured in a gas syringe. The evolution of oxygen is very slow at room temperature. There are substances which will speed up the reaction. Manganese(IV) oxide is one of them. When manganese(IV) oxide is added to hydrogen peroxide, the evolution of oxygen takes place much more rapidly (see Fig. 21.9). Manganese(IV) oxide is not used up in the reaction. At the

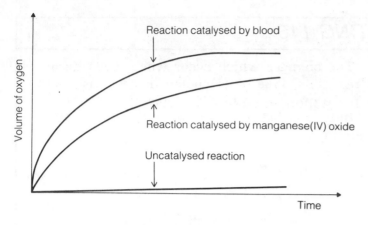

Fig. 21.9 Catalysis of the decomposition of hydrogen peroxide

end of the reaction, the manganese(IV) oxide is as good as new. It can be filtered off and used again. A substance which increases the speed of a chemical reaction without being used up in the reaction is called a **catalyst**. Manganese(IV) oxide will not catalyse all reactions. It catalyses a small number of reactions.

The chemical reactions that take place in animals and plants need catalysts. There are very powerful catalysts, called **enzymes**, in living things. Blood and potato contain enzymes. (You saw their effect in Experiment 19.6.) One of them is called **peroxidase**. It catalyses the decomposition of hydrogen peroxide.

Catalysts will only catalyse certain reactions. Platinum catalyses a number of oxidation reactions. Nickel catalyses hydrogenation reactions (see Table 21.1).

Table 21.1 Some catalysts

Catalyst	Reaction which is catalysed
Platinum	Ammonia + air → nitrogen monoxide Used in the oxidation of ammonia to give nitric acid
Vanadium(V) oxide	Sulphur dioxide + oxygen → sulphur trioxide Part of the contact process for making sulphuric acid
Nickel	Alkene + hydrogen → alkane Used in the hydrogenation of unsaturated oils to form fats
Iron	Nitrogen + hydrogen → ammonia The Haber process

Catalysts are very important in industry. Plastics are made under high pressure. Industrial plastics plants must be well built of strong materials to withstand pressure. A plastics manufacturer tries to find a catalyst which will enable the reaction to give a good yield of plastics at a lower pressure. Then the plant will not have to withstand high pressures. A less costly method of construction can be used. Industrial chemists are always doing research on new catalysts.

Some reactions need high temperatures in order to give good yields of product. This involves the manufacturer in high fuel

costs. If an industrial chemist can find a powerful catalyst, the
reaction will take place at a lower temperature. This will cut
down running costs.

All the processes which take place in our bodies need
enzymes. The digestion of food takes place in stages. Each stage
needs the presence of a different enzyme. The conduction of
nerve impulses along our nerves also needs enzymes.

There are substances which slow down reactions. They have a
negative catalytic effect. They are called **inhibitors**. Nerve gases
are inhibitors. They slow down the chemical reactions which
take place when messages pass along nerve fibres. This leads to
paralysis and then to death. Curare is an inhibitor of the same
kind. It prevents the enzyme which enables the nerves to
conduct messages to the muscles from doing its job. South
American Indians used to tip their arrows with curare. What do
you think happened to an animal or an enemy who was hit by
one of these arrows?

JUST TESTING 117

1 Copy this graph into your workbook. Add a line to show
the shape of the graph you would obtain for a catalysed
reaction.

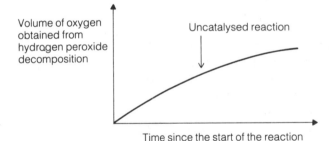

Does the rate of reaction increase or decrease as the time
that has passed since the start of the reaction increases?
Why?

Exercise 21

1 Zinc reacts with sulphuric acid to give
hydrogen. Mention three ways in which you
could speed up the reaction.

2 In a set of experiments, magnesium was
allowed to react with hydrochloric acid.
Each time, 0.5 g of magnesium was used.
The volume of hydrochloric acid was
different each time. The volume of hydrogen
formed was measured each time. The results
are shown in the table.

Volume of hydrochloric acid in cm³	Volume of hydrogen in cm³
5	100
15	300
25	500
35	500
45	500

a Plot, on graph paper, the volume of hydrogen produced against the volume of acid used.

b From the graph, find (i) what volume of hydrochloric acid will produce 400 cm³ of gas, (ii) what volume of gas is produced if 50 cm³ of hydrochloric acid are used, (iii) what volume of hydrochloric acid is just sufficient to react with 0.5 g of magnesium.

3 A few small marble chips were dropped into a large volume of hydrochloric acid. The gas evolved was collected and measured. The results obtained are shown in the table.

Time in minutes	Volume of gas in cm³
0.5	14
1.0	23
2.0	35
3.0	41
4.0	44
5.0	44

a What gas was formed during the reaction?

b On graph paper, plot the volume of gas against the time taken for it to be formed.

c From the graph, say what time was taken to collect (i) 20 cm³, (ii) 30 cm³ of gas.

d Suggest three ways in which you could make the reaction take place more slowly.

4 A solution of hydrogen peroxide decomposes slowly to give oxygen. Someone tells you that nickel oxide will catalyse the reaction. What do they mean by **catalyse**? How could you find out whether your information is correct? Draw the apparatus you would use, and say what you would do.

5 What has keeping food in a refrigerator to do with chemical reactions?

6 What catalysts are there inside your body? What do they do?

*__7__ A question about deep freeze:
What is the **storage life** of a food? Trained food tasters are employed to find out how long it takes for the food to show the first signs of spoilage. The storage life of the food is judged to be six times this length of time. After its storage life has passed, the food

will no longer be of high quality, but it will still be eatable.

Different foods have different storage lives. The storage life of any food depends on the temperature at which it is kept. Graph A shows how the storage life of frozen chickens depends on the temperature at which they are kept. Graph B shows the same for frozen chips and peas.

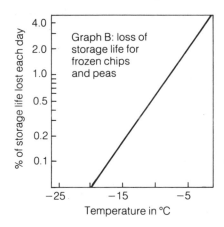

a How much faster does frozen chicken deteriorate (go off) at −5 °C than at −15 °C?

b How much faster do frozen chips and peas deteriorate at −5 °C than at −15 °C?

c Why do the foods keep better at the lower temperature?

d Compare chicken kept at −10 °C and peas kept at −10 °C.
(i) What is the rate at which chicken deteriorates?
(ii) What is the rate at which peas deteriorate?
Can you think of an explanation of the difference?

8 You are provided with
● marble chips in three sizes (small, medium and large)

- dilute hydrochloric acid
- a conical flask with a side-arm, rubber tubing and bung
- a measuring cylinder and a trough.

Design an experiment to find out which react fastest: small, medium or large chips. The experiment should be different from those in this book.

9 You are provided with
- magnesium ribbon
- dilute sulphuric acid
- a thermometer.

Describe how you would find out the effect of temperature on the rate of the reaction between magnesium and dilute sulphuric acid. Say what measurements you would make and what you would do with your results.

Crossword on Chapter 21

Clues across

2, 5 down This is what a catalyst does to a chemical reaction. (5, 2)

7 A catalyst for the decomposition of hydrogen peroxide. (6)

8 The size of these affects the speed of their reactions. (9)

9 The oxide of this metal catalyses the decomposition of hydrogen peroxide. (9)

10 As this increases, the rate of reaction increases. (11)

12, 18 across Needed for measuring reaction rates. (4, 5)

15 This is a negative catalyst. (9)

17 This is formed in the decomposition of hydrogen peroxide. (6)

18 See 12 across.

Clues down

1 This is what you often want chemicals to do. (5)

3 These react faster than lumps. (7)

4 A chemical word for 'split up'. (9)

5 See 2 across.

6 Same clue as 10 across. (13)

11 How to make 3 down from lumps. (5)

12 Symbol for antimony. (2)

13 Invert 'to'. (2)

14 Symbol for polonium. (2)

16 Symbol for platinum. (2)

Career sketch: Pharmacist

Sarah is a pharmacist. She works in a 'chemist's' shop dispensing medicines prescribed by doctors. Sarah must understand the medicines she is dispensing. Her work is demanding as she must never make a mistake. She also supplies many medicines which people can buy without a prescription. Customers often ask her advice about what to take for their ailments. Sarah took A-levels, including chemistry and then went to university for a three-year course in pharmacy.

Some pharmacists work in hospitals, dispensing medicines and giving advice to doctors on the drugs available.

Career sketch: Hairdressing

Stuart is an apprentice hairdresser. He left school after GCSE to start work in a salon. He goes for one day a week to take a City and Guilds course at the College of Further Education. Chemistry is one of the subjects he studies. He must learn about the structure of hair and the effects of the chemicals in perming solutions, bleaches and colour rinses.

Career sketch: Synthetic organic chemist

Julie is one of a team of five organic chemists in a company which manufactures weed-killers. If the research department of the firm wants a certain compound, Julie and her group synthesise it (make it) for them. Julie may have to carry out a synthesis involving many stages. Her work is varied because she is always being asked for new compounds. She is looking forward to moving into the research department where she will be able to continue her work on synthesis and also test new compounds as herbicides.

Julie left school after A-levels and is taking Higher National Certificate by day release.

Career sketch: Technical writer

Bryn is a technical writer. His skill is to put scientific and technical information into everyday language which people can readily understand. To make sure his work is accurate, Bryn must spend a long time finding out about the area he is covering, say, lasers or liquid crystals. His writing must be clear and easy to follow. He must write good English and express complicated ideas in simple language. Bryn writes articles for a scientific magazine. Most technical writers work for industrial companies and Government departments.

Bryn has a degree in chemistry.

Career sketch: Teacher

Javed is a chemistry teacher. When asked about his job, Javed says that it is difficult to explain the satisfaction he gets from helping girls and boys to grow in knowledge, understanding and competence. He enjoys the company of young people and the extra-curricular activities. Javed plays the flute in the school orchestra and coaches the junior football team. One of the good features of the job is being part of a friendly team of sixteen science teachers and three laboratory technicians. There is always someone ready to share, both in difficulties and in successes.

Outside school hours, Javed is discussing with a local chemical firm how to create a link between the school and industry. He is organising school visits to the firm and also planning some new practical work, based on the work of the firm, for use in school.

Javed spent four years at university, gaining a BSc in Chemistry and a Postgraduate Certificate in Education.

22.1 What's in our food?

Carbohydrates

Carbohydrates are the energy-giving foods in the diet. They include **sugars**, which we obtain from fruits and many manufactured foods, e.g. cakes, biscuits and jams. They also include **starches**, which we obtain from cereals, e.g. wheat and rice, from pulses, e.g. peas and beans, and from root crops, e.g. potatoes and yams. **Cellulose** is a carbohydrate. Although it is not digested by mammals, cellulose has an important function. It provides **dietary fibre** or **roughage**, which adds bulk to food and prevents constipation.

Fats and oils

Fats and oils are used by the body to form cell membranes and other structures. They are also a source of energy. We obtain fats and oils from animal sources, e.g. meat, milk, cheese, butter and margarine, and from plant sources, e.g. nuts and seeds, such as sunflower seeds.

Proteins

Proteins are foods that we need to build new tissues and to repair damaged tissues. We obtain protein from animal sources, e.g. lean meat, fish, milk, cheese and eggs, and from plant sources, e.g. nuts, cereals and pulses (peas and beans).

Mineral salts

We need small quantities of **mineral salts** in our diet. Some people eat diets that lack iron salts. These are essential for the manufacture of red blood cells, and a shortage of iron salts causes anaemia. Red meat, eggs, spinach and other vegetables are sources of iron salts. Calcium salts are essential for the formation of bones and teeth. Cheese and milk are sources of calcium salts.

Vitamins

The body requires small quantities of **vitamins**. Vitamins are not used as a source of energy. Their function is to work with enzymes to catalyse cell reactions. Some diets lack the following vitamins:
- Vitamin B12: present in meat and in dairy products. A shortage causes anaemia.
- Vitamin C: present in fresh fruits and vegetables. A shortage lowers resistance to infection.
- Vitamin D: present in foods that contain fats and oils. A severe shortage causes rickets (soft bones).

Fig. 22.1 (a) Model of a glucose molecule (b) The formula in shorthand form

Water

Water is an essential part of the diet. About 70% of most body tissues consists of water. The water lost by sweating, breathing and urinating must be replaced. We need to drink about 1.5 litres a day, in addition to the water contained in solid food.

Food additives

Food additives are substances that are not naturally present in food. The food processing industry adds certain substances to food. The purpose of these food additives is to preserve the food, or to alter its colour, flavour or texture (see Section 22.5).

22.2 Carbohydrates

Simple sugars

Sugar and starch, the cell walls of plants and the exoskeletons of insects are all carbohydrates. A **carbohydrate** is a compound of carbon, hydrogen and oxygen only. The number of hydrogen atoms in the molecule is twice the number of oxygen atoms, giving carbohydrates the general formula $C_mH_{2n}O_n$, where m and n are integers. One of the simplest carbohydrates is the sugar **glucose**, $C_6H_{12}O_6$. A molecule of glucose contains a ring of six atoms – five carbon atoms and one oxygen atom, see Fig. 22.1a. A shorthand way of writing the formula is shown in Fig. 22.1b. The sugar **fructose**, $C_6H_{12}O_6$, is an isomer (see Section 18.2) of glucose, having molecules that contain six carbon atoms. Sugars whose molecules contain one ring structure are called **monosaccharides** (mono = one). Some monosaccharides are **hexoses**, which contain six carbon atoms, e.g. glucose and fructose. Others are **pentoses**, which contain five carbon atoms, e.g. ribose, $C_5H_{10}O_5$.

The sugar you see in sugar bowls is **sucrose**, $C_{12}H_{22}O_{11}$. It is a **disaccharide**: its molecules contain two ring structures. It is made up of glucose and fructose:

glucose + fructose → sucrose + water
$$C_6H_{12}O_6(aq) + C_6H_{12}O_6(aq) \rightarrow C_{12}H_{22}O_{11}(aq) + H_2O(l)$$

For the reaction of sucrose with concentrated sulphuric acid, see Section 14.7.

Maltose, $C_{12}H_{22}O_{11}$, is a disaccharide formed from glucose:

glucose + glucose → maltose + water
$$2C_6H_{12}O_6(aq) \rightarrow C_{12}H_{22}O_{11}(aq) + H_2O(l)$$

The formula of maltose can be shown as in Fig. 22.2.

Fig. 22.2 The formula for maltose

397

The vital function of carbohydrates in all living organisms is to provide energy. When carbohydrates are oxidised, carbon dioxide and water are formed, and energy is released.

glucose + oxygen → carbon dioxide + water
$$C_6H_{12}O_6(aq) + 6O_2(aq) → 6CO_2(g) + 6H_2O(l)$$
Energy is given out

If you burn glucose in the laboratory, you will observe that the release of energy is very rapid. Inside the cells of a plant or animal, however, oxidation is controlled in such a way that energy is supplied to the organism gradually. The process is called **cellular respiration**. Living organisms can also respire fats, oils and proteins.

Starch, glycogen, cellulose and chitin

Plant cells store the food substance **starch**. Animal cells store the food substance **glycogen**. Both these substances are

(a)

(b)

One glucose unit

Fig. 22.3 (a) Part of a starch molecule
(b) Structure of a starch molecule

polysaccharides, that is, carbohydrates whose molecules consist of a large number (several hundred) of sugar rings (see Fig. 22.3a). Polysaccharides differ in the length and structure of their chains (see Fig. 22.3b).

Starch and glycogen are only slightly soluble in water. They can remain in the cells of an organism without dissolving and therefore make good food stores. When an organism needs energy, its cells convert starch and glycogen into glucose, which is soluble, and then oxidise the glucose.

Cellulose and **chitin** are insoluble polysaccharides. The walls of plant cells consist of a tough framework of cellulose fibres. Chitin forms the exoskeleton that encloses the body of an insect.

JUST TESTING 118

1 Match up each item in Column 1 with an item in Column 2.

Column 1	Column 2
1 Glucose	A Food store in plants
2 Sucrose	B Cell walls of plants
3 Starch	C Exoskeleton of insects
4 Glycogen	D Food store in animals
5 Chitin	E Table sugar
6 Cellulose	F Monosaccharide

2 Cyclists in the Tour de France ate pasta with their evening meals. Why did they believe this would give them energy?

SUMMARY NOTE

Carbohydrates are compounds of carbon, hydrogen and oxygen only.
Monosaccharides are sugars. They include hexoses, which have six carbon atoms in the molecule, e.g. glucose and fructose, and pentoses, which have five carbon atoms, e.g. ribose.
Disaccharides have two sugar rings in the molecule, e.g. sucrose and maltose.
Polysaccharides have molecules with a large number of sugar rings. They include starch (a food store in plants) and glycogen (a food store in animals), cellulose (in plant cell walls) and chitin (in insect exoskeletons).

3 Glucose, sucrose, starch and cellulose are carbohydrates.
   a Which of them are very soluble in water?
   b Which elements occur in all four?
   c What is the ratio (number of H atoms)/(number of O atoms) in (i) glucose, $C_6H_{12}O_6$, and (ii) sucrose, $C_{12}H_{22}O_{11}$?
   d How does your answer to c explain the name 'carbohydrate'?
4 How can sucrose be converted into sugar charcoal? (See Section 14.7.)

22.3 Fats and oils

Fats and oils are together called **lipids**. They are compounds of carbon, hydrogen and oxygen only. Fats and oils are insoluble in water. At room temperature, most fats are solid and most oils are liquid. They have several important functions in living organisms.

Source of energy.   Fats and oils are important food stores in living organisms. The oxidation of lipids gives carbon dioxide and water with the release of energy. Lipids provide about twice as much energy per gram as do carbohydrates.

Food.   Some vitamins which are essential to health, e.g. vitamins A, D and E, are insoluble in water and soluble in lipids. The diet must include foods containing lipids to provide these vitamins.

Thermal insulation.   Mammals have a layer of fat under the skin. This acts as a thermal insulator.

Protection.   A layer of fat protects delicate organs, e.g. kidneys, from injury.

Cell membranes.   Lipids are part of the structure of cell membranes.

Saturated and unsaturated fats and oils

Have you seen brands of margarine and cooking oil described as 'high in polyunsaturates' and wondered what it means? Many people believe that it is unhealthy to have too much fat in their diet, particularly **saturated fats**. Let us look at what the term 'saturated' means here.

Fats and oils contain esters of glycerol with fatty acids (see Section 19.8). Fatty acids are carboxylic acids with long alkyl groups (see Section 19.7). The fatty acid may be saturated or unsaturated. A **saturated** fatty acid has no carbon–carbon double bonds. The compound is described as **unsaturated** if there is one

Fig. 22.4   (a) Model of a molecule of glycerol
(b) Model of a molecule of a fatty acid (hexadecanoic acid)

(c) The formula of glycerol

(d) The formula of hexadecanoic acid

399

carbon–carbon double bond in the molecule. If there is more than one carbon–carbon double bond, the compound is described as **polyunsaturated**. Below is part of the carbon chain in **a** a saturated fatty acid, **b** an unsaturated fatty acid, and **c** a polyunsaturated fatty acid.

Fats and oils are not pure compounds; they are mixtures of esters. Lipids that contain esters of glycerol with saturated fatty acids are called **saturated fats**. Lipids which contain esters of glycerol with unsaturated fatty acids are called **unsaturated fats** or **polyunsaturated fats**, depending on the number of double bonds. Animal fats contain a large proportion of saturated esters and are solid. Plant oils contain a large proportion of unsaturated esters and are liquid at room temperature. Many scientists believe that eating a lot of saturated fats increases the risk of heart disease.

Unsaturated oils can be converted into saturated fats by catalytic hydrogenation. The vapour of the oil is passed with hydrogen over a nickel catalyst (see Section 9.17). The hydrolysis of fats and oils gives soaps and detergents (Section 9.11).

SUMMARY NOTE

Fats and oils are together called **lipids**. Essential food components, they are sources of energy and of dissolved vitamins. A layer of fat provides thermal insulation for warm-blooded animals. Delicate organs are protected by a layer of fat.

Lipids are mixtures of esters of glycerol with carboxylic acids (called fatty acids). The carboxylic acid may be saturated or unsaturated or polyunsaturated. Unsaturated fats and oils can be converted into saturated fats and oils by catalytic hydrogenation. Lipids are a source of soaps and detergents.

JUST TESTING 119

1 **a** In Fig. 22.5, which are the fats and which are the oils?
  b What is the main difference between fats and oils?
2 A label on a soft margarine carton says 'Low in saturated fats'. What is meant by this? What benefit to health do people claim for such foods? Name a product that is high in saturated fat.

Fig. 22.5

3

The above equation represents the formation of a fat.
Name the substance A, one substance which could be HB,
and the substance D.

22.4 Proteins

Muscle, skin, hair and haemoglobin are all **proteins**. Proteins are compounds of carbon, hydrogen, oxygen, nitrogen and sometimes sulphur. They are vitally important in living things for the following reasons:

1 Proteins are the compounds from which new tissues are made. When organisms need to grow in size or to repair damaged tissues, they need proteins.
2 All the reactions that take place in living organisms are catalysed by enzymes, and enzymes are proteins.
3 The activities of plants and animals are regulated by hormones, and many hormones are proteins.
4 Proteins can be used as a source of energy in respiration.

Proteins have large molecules. A protein molecule consists of a large number of amino acid groups. There are about 20 amino acids. The simplest is glycine, of formula

$$
\begin{array}{ccc}
H & H & O \\
\diagdown & | & \diagup\!\!\!\diagup \\
N\!-\!C\!-\!C \\
\diagup & | & \diagdown \\
H & H & O\!-\!H
\end{array}
$$

Fig. 22.6 Model of a glycine molecule

The general formula of an amino acid is

R is a different group in each amino acid; it can be —H, —CH_3, —CH_2OH, —SH and many other groups. An amino acid molecule contains two reactive groups: the carboxyl group (—CO_2H) which is acidic, and the amino group (—NH_2) which is basic (like ammonia, NH_3). The amino group of one amino acid molecule can react with the carboxyl group of another amino acid molecule. When this happens, the two amino acids combine to form a **peptide** and water. The two amino acid molecules may be either the same or different.

$$H_2NCHR_1CO_2H + H_2NCHR_2CO_2H \rightarrow \begin{array}{c} H_2NCHR_1CONHCHR_2CO_2H \\ + H_2O \end{array}$$

The group —CONH— has formed between the two amino acid molecules. This group is called the **peptide link** and has the structure:

$$-\overset{\overset{O}{\|}}{C}-\overset{\overset{H}{|}}{N}-$$

The peptide that has been formed has a carboxyl group at one end and an amino group at the other end, so it can combine with more amino acids. The process can be repeated as shown by the following equations. The different shapes, e.g. ∅ and □, represent different amino acids.

∅ + □ → ∅—□ + H₂O
∅—□ + ◯ + ⊗ → ◯—∅—□—⊗ + 2H₂O
◯—∅—□—⊗ + ∅ + □ → ∅—◯—∅—□—⊗—□ + 2H₂O

In this way, many amino acids can combine to form a polymer with long-chain molecules. Each link in the chain is a peptide link. **Peptides** have molecules with up to 15 amino acid groups. **Polypeptides** have molecules with 15–100 amino acid groups. **Proteins** have still larger molecules.

Proteins in the diet

Animals make the proteins they need by combining the appropriate amino acids (as shown above). Animals can make some amino acids in their bodies. The other amino acids that they need and cannot make must come from the diet. These are called **essential amino acids**. Animals digest the proteins in their food to obtain the essential amino acids, and then combine the amino acids to build the proteins they need. A protein that contains all the essential amino acids is called a **first class protein**. Meat, fish, cheese and soya beans supply first class proteins. A protein that lacks some essential amino acids is called a **second class protein**. Flour, rice and oatmeal supply second class proteins.

You will have seen news coverage of famine areas showing children with swollen abdomens. They are suffering from the disease called **kwashiorkor**. This is caused by a diet that is very low in protein. In parts of the world where rice is the staple diet, kwashiorkor is common.

Structure of proteins

The amino acid sequence in a protein is called its **primary structure**. In addition to this, the polypeptide chain coils into a three-dimensional shape called its **secondary structure**. In many proteins, the secondary structure is helical (spiral). It is kept in this shape by bonding between groups in different parts of the chain. In many proteins, the coiled polypeptide chains also fold and turn into a complex shape known as the **tertiary structure**. Myoglobin is a protein similar to haemoglobin that stores oxygen in muscle tissue. A haem group, which contains an iron(II) ion, enables it to bond oxygen. The tertiary structure of myoglobin is shown in Fig. 22.7.

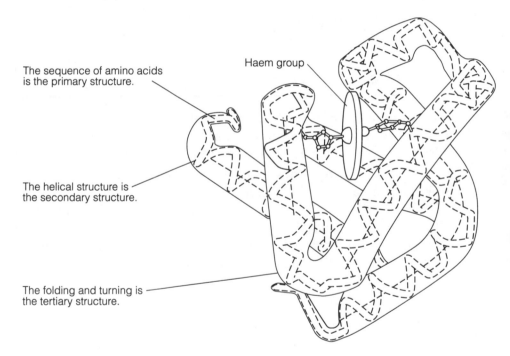

The sequence of amino acids is the primary structure.

Haem group

The helical structure is the secondary structure.

The folding and turning is the tertiary structure.

Fig. 22.7   The tertiary structure of myoglobin. The polypeptide chain is coiled into eight helical sections. The coiled chain folds and turns to produce a compact structure. In the centre is a haem group, containing an iron(II) ion, which binds oxygen

Enzymes

The reactions that take place inside the cells of living organisms are catalysed by **enzymes**. Enzymes are proteins. An enzyme is **specific** for a certain reaction or type of reaction, that is, it will catalyse only that reaction or type of reaction. For example, the enzyme pancreatic lipase catalyses the hydrolysis of lipids, but has no effect on the hydrolysis of proteins or carbohydrates. The enzyme urease catalyses only the hydrolysis of urea. The substance that the enzyme helps to react, e.g. the lipid, is called the **substrate**. The substrate has to fit into the contours of a certain region in the enzyme called the **active site**. Only a substance that will fit the active site is enabled to react; this is the reason why enzymes are specific. The fit between substrate and enzyme has been described as 'like a lock and key'. Figure 22.8 shows how an enzyme is thought to interact with its substrate.

Like other proteins, enzymes have a complex three-dimensional structure. Treatments that causes the protein to lose its tertiary structure, e.g. high pH, low pH and high temperature, are said to **denature** the protein. A denatured enzyme loses its catalytic power.

Fig. 22.8 The hydrolysis of a protein catalysed by an enzyme

The region of the enzyme called the active site. Part of the substrate molecule fits into the active site. Chemical bonds form between the substrate and the active site. These bonds weaken the peptide link.

Weakened by its bonds to the enzyme, the peptide link is hydrolysed.

The two peptide molecules that are formed leave the active site.

JUST TESTING 120

1 a What reactive groups does an amino acid possess?
b How do these groups enable amino acids to polymerise?
c What is the difference between a peptide and a protein?

2 a What is meant by the 'substrate' of an enzyme?
b What is meant by the 'active site' of an enzyme?
c What is meant by the statement that an enzyme is 'specific' for a certain substrate?
d How does the possession of an active site explain why the enzyme is specific for a certain substrate?
e How does the active site enable the enzyme to do its job?

3 Name the group of polymers formed by **a** monosaccharides, **b** amino acids.

4 a What type of substance is this?

$$H_2N-\overset{\displaystyle H}{\underset{\displaystyle CH_2-OH}{C}}-CO_2H$$

b Draw the structural formula of the compound (other than water) that is formed when two molecules of this substance react together.
c On your drawing, show the peptide link.
d What further reaction or reactions can the product in **b** undergo?

SUMMARY NOTE

Amino acids, of general formula $H_2NCHRCO_2H$, polymerise to form peptides, polypeptides and proteins. Protein molecules have a **primary structure** (the sequence of amino acids), a **secondary structure** (often helical) and a three-dimensional **tertiary structure**.

Enzymes are proteins. They catalyse reactions which take place in living organisms. An enzyme is specific for a certain reaction. If its three-dimensional structure is lost, the enzyme is **denatured** and loses its catalytic activity.

22.5 Food additives

Why use additives?

Three-quarters of the food eaten in industrialised countries is processed. The food processing industry adds many substances to food. They are called **food additives**. A food additive is defined as a substance that is not normally eaten or drunk as a food, either by itself or as a typical ingredient of food. Although salt and sugar are added to foods, they are not classified as additives. The purpose of an additive may be

1 to preserve food
2 to flavour food
3 to colour food
4 to alter the texture of food.

You will often hear additives described as 'chemicals', as though they are suspect in some way. However, proteins, vitamins and all all the other substances that occur naturally in foodstuffs are also chemicals. No substance may be used as an additive unless the food manufacturer can give a good reason for its use. In 1950, 50 additives were in general use; now 3500 additives are used in our food.

Types of food additives

Preservatives and antioxidants.   In between the time when food is harvested or slaughtered and the time when it is eaten, it is stored in the warehouse, in the shop and in the home. Without food additives, many foods would deteriorate. Chemical **preservatives** are added to stop the growth of micro-organisms. These preservatives increase the food's shelf-life, that is, the length of time the food will keep before it deteriorates. If foods have longer shelf-lives, there is less wastage on storage, and the shopkeeper should be able to charge lower prices and to stock a wider range of foods. Does the customer receive all the benefit of the lower prices? Some people believe that the savings from the widespread use of additives go to the food manufacturers rather than the customers.

When fats and oils are oxidised, unpleasant-smelling acids are formed. This is why foods that contain fats and oils can turn rancid on exposure to the air. **Antioxidants**, which are added to prevent oxidation, include BHA and BHT (butylated hydroxyanisole and butylated hydroxytoluene), sulphur dioxide and sulphites.

Sulphur dioxide destroys the vitamin thiamine, and is not used in meat, which is an important source of thiamine. It is, however, used in products such as salami which are processed at temperatures above room temperature and could otherwise become infected by bacteria. (For sulphur dioxide and sulphites as reducing agents, see Sections 14.3 and 14.4.)

Additives that alter the taste of food.   The number of **flavourings** in use is about 3000. This large number is not so surprising when you realise that a mixture of up to 50 substances is needed to produce a natural flavour such as peach.

Fig. 22.9 Foods preserved by sulphur dioxide

Many food items are sweetened with sucrose (sugar); this is a food, not an additive. However, some people want to cut down on sucrose because they are overweight, and diabetics are unable to cope with sucrose. Substitute **sweeteners** are saccharin, sorbitol and mannitol.

Flavour enhancers are not flavourings; they are substances that stimulate the tastebuds to make existing flavours seem stronger. The most common is monosodium glutamate, MSG.

Fig. 22.10   These foods contain MSG

Additives that alter the colour of food.   The techniques of food processing often cause a food to lose some of its colour. Then the manufacturer will want to restore the original colour of the food by means of a food additive. It is **food colourings** that give the most cause for concern over additives. Colourings are not added to baby foods.

Additives that alter the texture of food.   When oil and water are added, they form two layers. Some substances, called **emulsifiers**, can make oil and water mix to form an emulsion (see Section 9.11). Any substance that helps to prevent the emulsion from separating out again is called a **stabiliser**. Margarine, ice cream and salad dressings all contain emulsifiers and stabilisers.

The foods in Fig. 22.12 have **modified starch** on their labels. This is used to thicken foods, and can be a main ingredient of instant soups and puddings.

Powdery foods and crystalline foods, such as cake mixes and table salt, become lumpy if they absorb water. To prevent this, **anti-caking agents** are added. These substances can absorb water without becoming wet. Products such as bread and cakes deteriorate if they dry out. **Humectants** are added to keep these products moist.

To make jams, desserts, etc. set, a **gelling agent**, e.g. pectin, is added.

Fig. 22.11   These foods contain emulsifiers and stabilisers

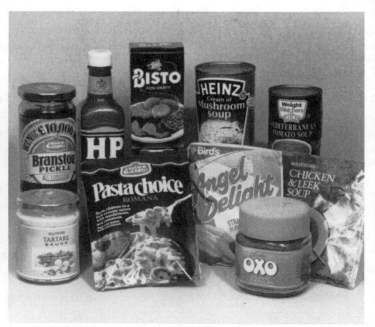

Fig. 22.12   These foods contain modified starch

Fig. 22.13 Which products contain an anti-caking ingredient? Which contain a humectant?

E numbers

Before an additive may be used, it must be approved by the Government. It is illegal to add anything harmful to food. When an additive is approved by the European Community (EC), it is given an **E number**. The EC has drawn up a list of 314 safe additives. This is the numbering system:

Colourings: E number begins with 1, e.g. E120 (cochineal)
Preservatives: E number begins with 2, e.g. E210 (benzoic acid)
Antioxidants: E numbers 310–321, e.g. E321 (butylated hydroxytoluene, BHT)
Texture controllers: E numbers 322–494, e.g. E406 (agar)
Additives that have been passed in the country of origin but not yet in the EC have a number only, e.g. 128 (red 2G); 513 (sulphuric acid); 526 (calcium hydroxide).

Are additives a danger to health?

We eat between 3 and 7 kg of additives a year. Some people think that over a long period, some additives could be a threat to health. The opinion of medical doctors is that additives do not contribute to serious illness. Although *some* additives are known to make *some* people ill, some natural foods also make people ill. When a person reacts to a food by becoming ill, the reaction is called an **intolerance reaction** or an **allergic reaction**. Allergic reactions can take the form of asthma (breathing difficulty), rhinitis (like hay fever), eczema (a skin complaint), digestive troubles, headaches, migraines, and hyperactivity. When hyperactive children are put on a diet free from additives, they often improve dramatically. Tartrazine (E102), a yellow dye, is suspected of causing hyperactivity. If you know that you are allergic to tartrazine, you can read the labels on foods such as sweets, fizzy drinks and packet desserts and reject any that list E102. Many people prefer to buy foods that contain no additives. Large supermarket chains have reduced the number of additives in their products, and some have additive-free items.

JUST TESTING 121

1 Which types of additives are present in this peach dessert?

> **Peach Dessert**
>
> Ingredients: Flour, Sugar, Peach, Animal and Vegetable fat, Dextrose, Modified starch, Sorbitol syrup, Glucose syrup, Citric acid, Preservative E202, Flavouring 107, Emulsifiers E406, E412, E466, Colours E104, E150

2 Explain the difference between a preservative and an antioxidant.

3 Explain how an emulsifier acts to stop salad dressing from separating.

4 The labels on two marmalade jars are shown below.

> **Orange and lime marmalade**
>
> Ingredients: Sugar, Oranges, Limes, Glucose syrup, Gelling agent E440, Acidity regulators E330, E331, Colours E102, E120, Preservative E220

> **Orange marmalade**
>
> Ingredients: Sugar, Oranges, Limes, Glucose syrup, Gelling agent E440, Acidity regulators E330, E334, Colours E104, E120, Preservative E220

Which marmalade would be the better choice for someone with a hyperactive child?

Explain your answer.

5 The labels on two soft drink bottles are shown below.

> **Pop**
>
> Ingredients: Carbonated water, Colour (caramel), Sugar, Phosphoric acid, Flavourings, Caffeine, Citric acid, Preservative E221
>
> BEST SERVED ICE-COLD

> **Diet Pop**
>
> Ingredients: Carbonated water, Colour (caramel), Artificial sweetener (Aspartame), Phosphoric acid, Flavourings, Caffeine, Citric acid, Preservative E211
>
> BEST SERVED ICE-COLD

a Which sweetener is present (i) in Pop, (ii) in Diet Pop?

b Which preservative is present in both drinks?

c Why do the labels recommend serving the drinks ice-cold?

d What is the difference between Pop and Diet Pop that enables Diet Pop to be described 'low calorie'?

Exercise 22

1 Why are the following described as high-energy foods?

   a potatoes, **b** rice, **c** olive oil, **d** pasta, **e** butter

2 **a** Why is starch a better food store for animals than glucose?

   b How can starch be converted into glucose?

   c Why are fats and oils better stores of energy than carbohydrates?

   d What is the chemical difference between a saturated fat and an unsaturated fat?

   e What difference with respect to health is attributed to unsaturated fats as compared with saturated fats?

3 The amino acid serine has the structural formula

$$H_2NCHCO_2H$$
$$|$$
$$CH_2OH$$

   a Draw the formula of the dipeptide formed from two molecules of serine.

   b Indicate the peptide link in the molecule.

   c Write the formula of the ion formed when serine is dissolved in an alkaline solution.

   d Write the formula of the ion formed when serine is dissolved in an acidic solution.

   e A polypeptide is hydrolysed to give the amino acids A, B, C, D and E. Partial hydrolysis gives the peptides BC, CA, CAE, ED and AE. What is the sequence of amino acids in the polypeptide?

4 **a** Explain the difference between the primary, secondary and tertiary structure of a protein.

   b Explain how denaturation causes the loss of catalytic activity of an enzyme.

   c Why is the interaction of an enzyme and its substrate described as the 'lock and key' model of enzyme activity?

5 Explain the distinction between

   a a fat and an oil

   b butter and margarine

   c an unsaturated oil and a polyunsaturated oil.

6 **a** List four types of food additives. Give the reasons why they are added to foods, and give a named example of each.

   b Which organisation gives 'E numbers' to food additives? What does the possession of an E number tell you about an additive?

Table of symbols, atomic numbers and relative atomic masses

Element	Symbol	Atomic number	Relative atomic mass	Element	Symbol	Atomic number	Relative atomic mass
Actinium	Ac	89	227	Erbium	Er	68	167
Aluminium	Al	13	27	Europium	Eu	63	152
Americium	Am	95	243	Fermium	Fm	100	253
Antimony	Sb	51	122	Fluorine	F	9	19
Argon	Ar	18	40	Francium	Fr	87	223
Arsenic	As	38	75	Gadolinium	Gd	64	157
Astatine	At	85	210	Gallium	Ga	31	70
Barium	Ba	56	137	Germanium	Ge	32	72.5
Berkelium	Bk	97	247	Gold	Au	79	197
Beryllium	Be	4	9	Hafnium	Hf	72	178
Bismuth	Bi	83	209	Helium	He	2	4
Boron	B	5	11	Holmium	Ho	67	164
Bromine	Br	35	80	Hydrogen	H	1	1
Cadmium	Cd	48	112	Indium	In	49	115
Caesium	Cs	55	133	Iodine	I	53	127
Calcium	Ca	20	40	Iridium	Ir	77	192
Californium	Cf	98	251	Iron	Fe	26	56
Carbon	C	6	12	Krypton	Kr	36	84
Cerium	Ce	58	140	Lanthanum	La	57	139
Chlorine	Cl	17	35.5	Lawrencium	Lw	103	257
Chromium	Cr	24	52	Lead	Pb	82	207
Cobalt	Co	27	59	Lithium	Li	3	7
Copper	Cu	29	63.5	Lutecium	Lu	71	175
Curium	Cm	96	247	Magnesium	Mg	12	24
Dysprosium	Dy	66	162.5	Manganese	Mn	25	55
Einsteinium	Es	99	254	Mendelevium	Md	101	256

Element	Symbol	Atomic number	Relative atomic mass	Element	Symbol	Atomic number	Relative atomic mass
Mercury	Hg	80	201	Samarium	Sm	62	150
Molybdenum	Mo	42	96	Scandium	Sc	21	45
Neodymium	Nd	60	144	Selenium	Se	34	79
Neon	Ne	10	20	Silicon	Si	14	28
Neptunium	Np	93	237	Silver	Ag	47	108
Nickel	Ni	28	59	Sodium	Na	11	23
Niobium	Nb	41	93	Strontium	Sr	38	87
Nitrogen	N	7	14	Sulphur	S	16	32
Nobelium	No	102	254	Tantalum	Ta	73	181
Osmium	Os	76	190	Technetium	Tc	43	99
Oxygen	O	8	16	Tellurium	Te	52	127
Palladium	Pd	46	106	Terbium	Tb	65	159
Phosphorus	P	15	31	Thallium	Tl	81	204
Platinum	Pt	78	195	Thorium	Th	90	232
Plutonium	Pu	94	242	Thulium	Tm	69	169
Polonium	Po	84	210	Tin	Sn	50	119
Potassium	K	19	39	Titanium	Ti	22	48
Praesodymium	Pr	59	141	Tungsten	W	74	184
Promethium	Pm	61	147	Uranium	U	92	238
Protactinium	Pa	91	231	Vanadium	V	23	51
Radium	Ra	88	226	Xenon	Xe	54	131
Radon	Rn	86	222	Ytterbium	Yb	70	173
Rhenium	Re	75	186	Yttrium	Y	39	89
Rhodium	Rh	45	103	Zinc	Zn	30	65
Rubidium	Rb	37	85	Zirconium	Zr	40	91
Ruthenium	Ru	44	101				

The Periodic Table

Group   1   2

Period 1

1
H
hydrogen

Transition metals

Period	Group 1	Group 2							
Period 2	3 Li lithium	4 Be beryllium							
Period 3	11 Na sodium	12 Mg magnesium							
Period 4	19 K potassium	20 Ca calcium	21 Sc scandium	22 Ti titanium	23 V vanadium	24 Cr chromium	25 Mn manganese	26 Fe iron	27 Co cob.
Period 5	37 Rb rubidium	38 Sr strontium	39 Y yttrium	40 Zr zirconium	41 Nb niobium	42 Mo molybdenum	43 Tc technetium	44 Ru ruthenium	45 Rh rhodi
Period 6	55 Cs caesium	56 Ba barium	57 La lanthanum	72 Hf hafnium	73 Ta tantalum	74 W tungsten	75 Rh rhenium	76 Os osmium	77 Ir iridiu
Period 7	87 Fr francium	88 Ra radium	89 Ac actinium	104* Ku kurchatovium	105* Ha hahnium				

Inner transition metals

58 Ce cerium	59 Pr praesodymium	60 Nd neodymium	61* Pm promethium	62 Sm samarium	63 Eu europi
90 Th thorium	91 Pa protactinium	92 *U uranium	93* Np neptunium	94* Pu plutonium	95* Am americ

*Artificial element. does not occur naturally.

			3	4	5	6	7	0
								2 He helium
			5 B boron	6 C carbon	7 N nitrogen	8 O oxygen	9 F fluorine	10 Ne neon
			13 Al aluminium	14 Si silicon	15 P phosphorus	16 S sulphur	17 Cl chlorine	18 Ar argon
28 Ni nickel	29 Cu copper	30 Zn zinc	31 Ga gallium	32 Ge germanium	33 As arsenic	34 Se selenium	35 Br bromine	36 Kr krypton
46 Pd palladium	47 Ag silver	48 Cd cadmium	49 In indium	50 Sn tin	51 Sb antimony	52 Te tellurium	53 I iodine	54 Xe xenon
78 Pt platinum	79 Au gold	80 Hg mercury	81 Tl thallium	82 Pb lead	83 Bi bismuth	84 Po polonium	85 At astatine	86 Rn radon

64 Gd gadolinium	65 Tb terbium	66 Dy dysprosium	67 Ho holmium	68 Er erbium	69 Tm thulium	70 Yb ytterbium	71 Lu lutetium
96* Cm curium	97* Bk berkelium	98* Cf californium	99* Es einsteinium	100* Fm fermium	101* Md mendelevium	102* No nobelium	103* Lw lawrencium

Numerical answers

Just testing 44
5a 3×10^{10} tonne
 b 1.5×10^4 square miles

Exercise 8
 7a 500 g
 8 0.73 tonne
10a 300 tonne/day
 b £30/day

Exercise 9
 6 3×10^4 tonne
 8 0.1 tonne
 9a 10 g
 b 80 drops
10a 0.35 mg/day

Just testing 65
1a 137
 b 5
 c 4
 d 9

Just testing 68
1a 23 g
 b 480 g
 c 3.5 g
 d 7.0 g
 e 16 g
 f 128 g
2a 2 mol
 b 0.025 mol
 c 1 mol
 d 2 mol
3a 64 g
 b 980 g
 c 20 g
 d 200 g
4a (i) 27 g; (ii) 1350 g
 b (1) 54 g; (ii) 9 g

Just testing 69
1 159 g
2 50 g
3 88 g
4 18.6 g
5 142 g

Just testing 70
1d $2Hg(s) + I_2(s) \rightarrow 2HgI(s)$
2d $4Cu(s) + O_2(g) \rightarrow 2Cu_2O(s)$

Just testing 71
1a Cu_2O
 b Ca_3N_2
 c PCl_3
2a $CaCO_3$
 b BeO
 c CH_3
3a HgS
 b P_2O_3
 c $FeCl_3$
4a $n = 2$
 b $n = 7$

Just testing 72
1 $C_2H_2O_4$
2 C_3H_6O

Just testing 73
1 150 cm³ O_2, 75 cm³ CO_2
2 120 l
3 6 l
4 500 g

Just testing 74
1a 0.20 mol/l
 b 0.040 mol/l
 c 0.040 mol/l
 d 0.80 mol/l
2a 0.50 mol
 b 0.020 mol
 c 0.060 mol
 d 2.5×10^{-3} mol

Just testing 75
1 0.30 mol/l
2 0.24 mol/l
3 5.0 cm³
4a 0.50 l
 b 0.125 l

Just testing 76
1 **a** 14.0 g **b** 8.0 g **c** 51.8 g
 d 40.0 g **e** 14.8 g
2 **b**
3 0.159 g
4a 24 l H_2, 24 l Cl_2 **b** 24 l H_2, 12 l O_2
5 86.4 g
6 0.655 g
7 +2
8 9650 s = 2 hours 41 minutes

Exercise 12
 1 £30 million
 2 2×10^{22}; 7.5×10^{-18} p
 3a 0.20 mol
 b 0.40 mol
 c 1.20 mol
 d 0.20 mol
 7 102 tonne
 8 0.145 mol/l
10 1.6×10^{10} km
11a £120/day
12 19 kg

Exercise 13
5a 4.6 million tonnes
 b 8.2 million tonnes

Exercise 14
8d 3.9 kg

Just testing 112
1 26 g
2 −715 kJ/mol
3 −57 kJ/mol
4a −2.85 kJ

Just testing 113
1 −124 kJ/mol
2 −484 kJ/mol
3 −56 kJ/mol
4 −95 kJ/mol

Exercise 20
8c 2260 kJ

Exercise 21
2b (i) 20 cm³; (ii) 500 cm³;
 (iii) 25 cm³
3c (i) 0.85 minute; (ii) 1.5 minute
7d (i) 1.2% per day;
 (ii) 0.55% per day

Index